Ayurvedic Garbha Sanskār

The Art and Science of Pregnancy

Dr. Shri Balaji Tambe

Ayurvedic
Garbha Sanskār

- **First Edition : 28 June, 2011**
  Languages published in Marathi (First Edition - 4 March 2007, 19 editions published), Gujarati (First Edition - 6 March 2011)

- **Publisher :** Balaji Tambe Foundation

- **Editorial Team:** Dr. Smt. Veena Tambe, Dr. Malvika Sunil Tambe, Dr. Sujata Sanjay Tambe, Dr. Bhagyashree Zhope

- **Translation Assistants :** Dr. Sujata Sanjay Tambe, Ishwari Thornton, Barry O'Reilly, Karan Makhija, Garima Goyal, Dr. Neha Goyal

- **Cover Page Design :** Shrikant Chavhan
- **Cover Page Model :** Madhurani Prabhulkar
- **Page Layout :** Vijaya Kolhe, Suhas Kadre
- **Photography :** Avdhoot Hembade, Sanjay Pethe, Sunil Tambe.
- **Calligraphy :** Jayant Bhosle, Babu Udapi

- **Printing, Sales and Distibution:** Sakal Papers Ltd.
  595, Budhwar Peth, Pune - 2. Tel: 020-24405678 / 88888 49050

- **Printed at :** Wikas Electrical & Ceramic Products Pvt. Ltd.
  Commercial Printing Division
  Plot No. 32, Trimbak Road, M.I.D.C., Satpur, Nashik - 7
  Tel: 0253-2350066 / 9881099150

- **ISBN:** 978-93-80571-85-0

- **MRP :** ₹670 (IN INDIA ONLY)

Dedicated to my parents

Respected Vedic Scholar
Late Shri Vasudev Dhundhiraj Tambeshastri

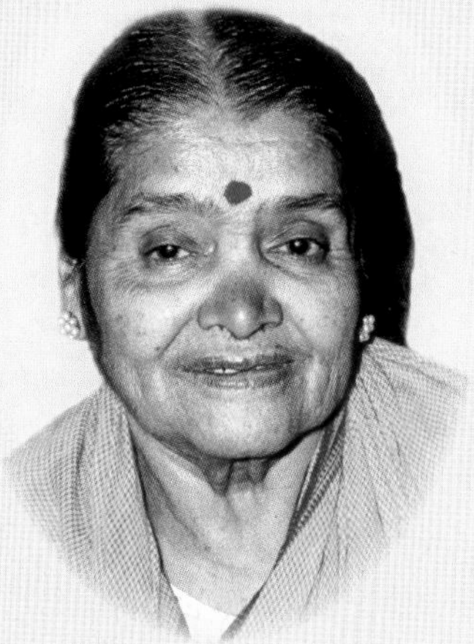

Late Smt Lakshmibai Vasudev Tambe

Dedicated to my revered parents,
who instilled in me their values and good culture!

- Balaji Tambe

An Introduction to the Author

Dr. Shri Balaji Tambe was born to Shri Vasudev Tambe Shastri and Smt. Lakshmibai Vasudev Tambe. Among those of the spiritual path, Shri Vasudev Tambe Shastri had attained a very high spiritual authority, and the child Balaji's attraction to, and intelligence in that sphere were apparent and ingrained very early. The atmosphere at home was very conducive to the study of the Vedas, Upanishads, Puranas and mantras and other spiritual techniques. At the age of five he began formal schooling as well as a formal spiritual education and completed both with degrees in engineering and Ayurveda. With the blessings of his parents and the Grace of Sadguru Shri Dattatreya he had studied both worlds - the physical, visible and rational, as well as the spiritual, subtle and omniscient. And further, he studied and researched the Indian traditions, Ayurveda and other Vedas, puranas, mantra and tantra (verbal and physical techniques), yoga, astrology and music, to understand their essence and see how they can be applied to enrich various spheres of life.

Since the year 1965, he has been writing under the pen name 'Aum Swarupa', and established a centre for meditation under that aegis. He has given diksha (spiritual initiation) to many into the Aum chanting meditation practice called 'Santulan Om Meditation' or SOM Yoga, and inspired their spiritual development. A large number of his disciples, both in India and abroad, now practice this meditation technique. This seven-fold technique's most important features include social service and group meditation. Since 1982, Dr. Tambe conducts an annual seminar in the monsoon, where he focuses on the science and rationale of spirituals subjects, and demonstrates their practical aspects as well.

Dr. Shri Balaji Tambe has, over the years, developed both SOM Yoga, for meditation, and a special yoga technique called Santulan Kriya Yoga (SKY). Numerous people, through many centres, both in India and abroad, continue to benefit from these systems.

Over the last forty years, Dr. Tambe has been untiringly lecturing on subjects from the ancient scriptures and sciences, and the Shrimad Bhagawad Geeta, the Ramayana, Mahabharata and Ayurveda. In the sphere of health, apart from practicing and spreading Ayurveda, he regularly conducts concerts on Healing Music, spreading its health effects, in India and abroad. And in following Ayurvedic instructions in an uncompromising manner, and through his research and experiments, Dr. Tambe has evolved a complete and holistic system of healing. The mastery of Yoga and Ayurveda is, it seems, embedded in his being.

To bring life in balance he has established the Atmasantulana way of life. Its purpose is not merely to cure disease, but to increase health, and enhance one's entire outlook towards life. In 1982, on the basis of the Vedic Gurukul lifestyle, he established, in the peaceful, pure and spiritual environs of Karla, the Atmasantulana Village. He has since constantly been evolving practices that help keep life in balance. Dr. Tambe's ability to present ancient and complex spiritual concepts in extremely easy terms endears him even to new generations.

To ensure that medicines are produced strictly

in accordance with Ayurvedic instructions and tradition, a pharmacy has been established at Atmasantulana Village. Dr. Tambe says that music is not merely for entertainment, and he has composed and produced several albums of healing music. And so along with physical health he has provided the elixir of psychological and spiritual health to many.

In both India and internationally, his writings on Yoga, Ayurveda, Astrology, Healing Music and Spirituality, appear in leading newspapers and magazines, on a regular basis. He has written several books over the years, including Sanyulan Kriya Yoga (SKY), Ayurvedic Home Remedies (English and Marathi), Living Meditation Through Aum Swarupa (in 4 parts), Shri Ram Vishwapanchayatan in Marathi also published as the Aatma Ramayan in Gujrati (which reveals the real meaning of the Ramayana), Chakra Sudarshan that explains the seven chakras in the body (Marathi) and Ayurveda Uvach (Marathi), among others. He has been, since its inception, the editor of the ECHO magazine that is published at the Atmasantulana Village. He is the chief consultant to the 'Family Doctor', a weekly supplement to the leading Marathi newspaper, Sakal. Dr. Shri Balaji Tambe has a daily (mon to sat) show on the Marathi TV channel, Saam, called Shri Geeta Yog – Version 2011 in which he conducts discourses on the Shrimad Bhagawad Geeta. He has recently begun writing series of books on the Bhagawad Geeta in English as well as Marathi– one book for each of its 18 chapters. The series is called Peacock Feathers and Shri Geeta Yog Shodh Brahmavidyecha in Marathi. Three books from the series in Marathi, and one from the series in English have already been published.

DR. TAMBE HAS BEEN THE RECIPIENT OF SEVERAL NATIONAL AND INTERNATIONAL AWARDS INCLUDING...

- The "Recognition of Excellence in Health Care" Trophy from IMM.
- "Priyadarshini Puraskar" for the preservation and development of Ayurved.
- His project, "Pran-Vedic Community Health Initiative," was selected for Expo 2000 held at Hanover in Germany.
- A public felicitation by the Mayor of Pune for his outstanding contribution to Ayurved.
- "Satyashodhak Samajbhushan Puraskar 2006" from the Shri Gajanan Maharaj Shikshak Prasarak Mandal.
- "Ayurved Bhushan Puraskar" from the Ayurved Research Foundation.
- Member of the Committee for the Standardisation of Ayurved Treatment Centres, Govt. of Maharashtra (2007) BCUD Member - University of pune
- The Scroll of Honour 2010 - presented by the Pimpri Chinchwad Municipal Corporation in recognition of Dr. Shri Balaji Tambe's work in various fields.
- "Dnyan-vidnyan Puraskar" form Jyeshtha Nagarik Manch, Nagar, 2011
- "Saint Shri Gulabrao Maharaj Puraskar" from the Gulabrao Maharaj Sahitya Sammelan, 2011

My Intent...

Na mantram no yantram tadapi ca na jāne stutimaho
na cāhvānam dhyānam tadapi ca na jāne stutikathāḥ
Na jāne mudrāste tadapi ca na jāne vilapanam
param jāne mātastvadanusaraṇae klēśaharaṇam

Matrudevo Bhava

When speaking of our deities in India we always talk of 'Radha-Krishna' or 'Sita-Ram', and certainly in the vernacular, always the mother before the father. A mother occupies the highest pedestal in the world.

In the above verse, the revered Shri Adi Shankaracharya says - *A mother will love her offspring even if it is not particularly intelligent, has no knowledge of the scriptures, is not attractive, or unable even to cry properly. Even merely thinking of the mother brings comfort and eases pain.*

A crying baby, when put on its mother's lap, experiences an indescribable joy and contentment from the love being powered by the mother.

There is a wonder and greatness to Motherhood. Since Woman agreed to be Mother, she is venerated. Even God almighty, it is said, sought the help of Mother Earth, without whom he could not create Nature. A fine sapling or quality seed is useless in the absence of fertile soil - or if there is no soil at all!

The woman carries the child for nine months, accepts the inconveniences and discomforts that come with pregnancy. It would be gross injustice not to give her credit for this.

We certainly do not intend to discuss the superiority of one gender over the other! It is to infer that if the prospective mother lacks in, what one may call, 'feminine balance'. i.e. if all aspects relating to childbearing are not sound, then her child will be highly affected.

I want to bring to attention that as a society we have paid very little attention to women's health. If a child is born with defects, the responsibility for this certainly lies with both parents, but it *hinges more* on the mother's health. She has a much greater effect on the child as compared to the father.

Just imagine, if children are born blind, deaf, or with any other defects, then who will enjoy the beauty of this world? If children are born with holes in their hearts, who will sit in the jet planes we've designed?

I wished to draw attention to the health of the woman and the unborn child. During the period between 1970-1972, I began to design certain health related programmes for women. They dealt with several subtle, interesting and often overlooked questions

What should a woman do to maintain her health? When and what should she eat? How should one treat, or even better, prevent menstrual and urinary disorders? What kind of relationship should man and wife share so that a husband contributes to his wife's well-being and ensures that her hormonal health remains in balance.

Since many years I started making medicines for this purpose and gave them free, as a service to humanity. I cannot stress more about the importance of care during pregnancy, care during child birth, and women's health in general. I decided to help people in these matters in what little way I could. So over the years, I developed a project called *Ayurvediya Garbha Sanskar*. While going through this book you will see how future generations could have much happier lives with the help of 'Garbha Sanskar'.

The perspective I offer people is that once a child is born with a physical or mental handicap or incapacitation, not only that individual but his entire family will go through hardship for their entire lives. Instead, it will always be better for the would-be parents to invest in some care as advised here for just 12 to 18 months prior to conception. This way they will reap the benefits for their entire lives, as well as for the lives of their children.

We believe that a child is simply born due to the union of man and woman. This is as foolish as assuming that when a seed is merely thrown onto soil, it will survive, grow, and bear fruit. We are unaware that for this process to be fully realised in human beings, 'Garbha Sanskar' is absolutely essential.

Today's youth owes its good health to healthy parents. This good health has not been achieved automatically; it is the result of Ayurvediya Garbha Sanskar, carried out over many generations (as part of their lifestyle and traditional, and perhaps not explicitly, or known by this name). This health is, by no means, to be taken for granted. Fortunately, with the advent of modern science, technology, and transportation, it has become easier to adopt 'Ayurvediya Garbha Sanskar.' If we want to do something for life long happiness and contentment, then we must follow 'Garbha Sanskar'.

It is important to understand the tenet that every human is expected to contribute something to the world. While not every family will have an exceptional child, like Vivekananda who worked to bring about social change, Shivaji Maharaj who protected his people, or Saint Dyaneshwar who helped guide us on to a spiritual path, what is true is that every child can be cultured to become a person who is peace-loving, health-conscious and contributes positively to the world. We must take up the responsibility to ensure that this happens as far as possible. Else, people's lives will be restricted to working, earning money and building homes - and doing nothing that would make us proud!

Now, although having a child is an entirely natural process, some couples experience difficulty in conception. Some precautions are recommended before conception, and a certain amount of planning is necessary. And right from conception until delivery, it is important that the foetus is well protected. These precautions will ensure that conception occurs without hinderance, and the child will, hopefully, be physically and mentally fit, make his or her mark in the world, and work positively for mankind.

This entire process should not be left to nature's cycle or chance. Appropriate care during pregnancy will ensure a happy and illness free life for the child and these effects even carry over to successive generations!

Once we have understood the importance of this idea, it should follow that utmost care is taken to maintain the health of women. And it is simple and effective to do so if one uses ayurvedic remedies and medicines.

Women are generally sensitive because their hormonal systems are quite delicate. I have carefully studied the female hormonal system, and researched the effects that music has on it. I have also referred to our ancient Indian literature, stories and sciences. With the help of this research I composed music which is now on the albums 'Feminine Balance' and 'Garbha Sanskar', compilations designed to be listened to before conception, and during pregnancy, respectively. Through evaluations of the children whose mother's had regularly used these compositions and through their responses, we realised the compositions had exremely positive results. Based on these results we decided to distribute these albums on a large scale. Times Music, a leading worldwide publisher, made them available to all, including international audiences. The basic aim of these efforts is to help people bear healthy children so we can be assured of strong future generations.

Ayurvedic literature is rigorous and detailed in its description of the physiological functioning and development of the human body. It covers a lot of related behavioural topics. Apart from the process of Garbha Sanskar itself, topics like conception, child care and other necessary details like tests before, during and after pregnancy, diet, clothing and so on, are covered in this book.

Several people have worked tirelessly on this project. Dr. Bhagyashree Zhope, and my daughters-in-law, Dr. Sujata and Dr. Malvika, who work with me, have made great contributions.

They have maintained detailed records about women who had come for treatment, seeking to have a child. They have recorded medicines prescribed to them, difficulties faced by these women during pregnancy as well as remedies, details of childbirth, and so on. Dr. Malvika kept notes of everything she experienced during her own pregnancies.

My wife, Mrs. Veena Tambe, provided guidance based on her experience in bringing up our two sons. She has also contributed immensely on lifestyle, diet, massage and yoga during and after pregnancy as well as care for the infant. Mrs. Tambe has conducted many workshops on these topics, in India and abroad, and this book has benefited greatly from her hands-on experience.

Although a male doctor, I have been able to advise and treat women during pregnancy effectively, but as a mother, Dr. Malvika has been able to make a several additional significant inputs. And both, Dr. Malvika and Dr. Bhagyashree, have worked untiringly, to find references in Ayurved and correlate them with my practical experience and insight, for articles in the weekly supplement of *Family Doctor*, a part of the *Sakal* family of newspapers. Mrs. Vijaya Kolhe's efforts, in transcribing the text of *Family Doctor* and *Ayurvediya Garbha Sanskar* have been invaluable. My son, Sunil managed the difficult task of photographing Yoga postures and treatments, such as *dhoop*, and Jana Rosenhagen demonstrated for these photographs. My personal assistant, Dr. Nameeta Parekh, has done an excellent job of coordinating my national and international tours, appointments at the clinic, and day-to-day activities, to leave me with sufficient time for writing this book.

I have received extremely positive feedback from many people who benefited from the information they discovered in the articles I have published on this subject. From this feedback, it was obvious, that society has an urgent need of such information. This was all the encouragement I needed to expand the information already published, collect it, and make it available to the general public, in this form. Mr. Abhijit Pawar, Mr. Sanjeev Latkar and Mr. Abhijit Mulye, from Sakal, carried the idea further. They suggested the book be translated into languages other than Marathi. Mr. Sanjeev Latkar and Mr. Abhijit Mulye also helped to edit the articles from the *Family Doctor* so that they could be published in the book. The book's appearance and layout is due to the efforts of Mr. Nandan Mithari, Mr. Hemant Vandekar, and Mr. Anil Redekar, all from Sakal.

This book has turned out to be like an experienced and wise older woman who passes on her expertise about conception, health and child care to younger women in her fold. I am confident that this book will serve to guide women well.

And finally, one will ask whether this information is only for women. Not at all! Topics relevant to men's health related with producing children have also been included, to make the book useful for both husband and wife.

Ayurvedic Garbha Sanskar is a publication intended to help contribute to future generations who will work to uplift humanity!

Balaji Tambe

The Garbha Sanskar Family

Dr. Shri Balaji Tambe, Dr. Mrs. Veena, Tanishka, Tanushree
Behind - Shri Sanjay, Dr. Mrs. Sujata, Dr. Mrs. Malvika and Shri Sunil

Families commonly expect news of the arrival of a new family member soon after a couple gets married. However, pregnancy without adequate preparation is not advisable. So how does one prepare for pregnancy? Where do we get reliable and experienced guidance? How should we culture new life in the womb and when should this process begin? And after the child is born, what should be done to culture the child further?

Dr. Shri Balaji Tambe provides expert guidance and answers to all of these questions!

Note from the Publisher

Rather than a translation, this book is an adaptation for the English speaking audience. We have tried to provide adequate explanations for Ayurvedic terms in the book. We expect that you will read through the entire book at least once, even if you intend to use only a certain part (for e.g. if you have already conceived). There is a glossary at the end for those who wish to expand their knowledge further.

With respect to medical formulations advised throughout the book, there are several which are prepared by Santulan Ayurveda as proprietary medicines in our own pharmacy. They are easy to identify as their names normally begin with or contain 'Santulan' or 'San'. Information on Santulan Ayurveda centres and its dealer network is available at www.santulan.in. These medicines have all been prepared with the Garbha Sanskar project in mind and have proved extremely successful. The other medicines mentioned here can all be found in the Ayurvedic Formulary of India and are manufactured by several other companies. We have put out names of medicines and their constituents in the hope that other diligent practitioners of Ayurved may be able to use them to help benefit the world at large.

In today's world it has become mandatory to safeguard oneself with a disclaimer. There are now hundreds of thousands of women and families who have shown confidence in these practices. One has only to look at the volume and quality of feedback we have received to understand the transformative nature of the Ayurvedic Garbha Sanskar. Even though the book is a fantastic guide, it is advisable to consult a physician before, during and after your pregnancy. The behavioural practices are obviously safe to follow, as are the prescribed lifestyle and food habits.

Share your experiences with others. See if you know others who may need your help or vice versa. Don't be discouraged if you don't get results overnight – it is not expected. Spend time with the book to grasp what is being said. Try and notice the effects of the measures you have taken. If you face problems, or what is more likely, get great results, or merely to satisfy your doubts or growing interest in the subject, feel free to write in to us.

You can write in your questions or experiences to response@garbhasanskar.in.

Ultimately, we want you to have the best children possible. Surely you cannot imagine that will happen without any effort on your part. But to be actively participating in creating a beautiful, radiant and happy child, and we hope, a whole generation like that, is an opportunity you should not pass up!

INDEX

Baby care...

Appendices

Ayurvedic Garbha Sanskār

1

Preparing for Pregnancy...

'Garbha Sanskar' is essential for creating intelligent and healthy children. It is also important to be aware of the proper age for child bearing, to be mentally ready for parenthood, and to have a healthy reproductive system before conceiving a child.

Values lasting through multiple lifetimes

The Universe originates from the void *(shunya)*. The terms 'void' and 'zero' do not imply that nothing is present. 'Zero' is a point from which the scope for progress is infinite, and 'zero' is complete in itself.

If one wants to understand any substance or entity, one invariably needs to inquire into, and understand, the causes and processes of its formation. In the case of human beings, the process through which we are made will obviously affect our future potential and indeed, our entire lives. *How* we come *to be*, is naturally of supreme significance, since the quality of human life depends on this process.

The common man may be unfamiliar with the following agricultural considerations. Before selecting a piece of land, the farmer examines the quality of its soil, local geographical conditions such as rainfall, the accessibility of water, and locally available manpower and electricity.

Once he selects the land, to use it, he has to plough it, and treat it with fertilizer and other necessary substances, and when the time is right, sow appropriate seeds of a good quality. He needs to be extremely careful when the seeds sprout and begin to grow. Even a fully grown crop needs a lot of attention.

A verse from the *Sushrut Sharirsthan*, one of the defining treatises of Ayurved, states

ध्रुवं चतुर्णां सान्निध्यात् गर्भः स्यात् विधिपूर्वकम् ।
ऋतुक्षेत्राम्बुबीजानां सामग्र्यात् अङ्कुरो यथा ॥
...सुश्रुत शारीरस्थान

Dhruvam caturṇām sānnidhyāt
garbhaḥ syāt vidhi-pūrvakam
ṛtukṣetrāmbu-bījānām
sāmagryāt aṅkuro yathā
...Suśruta śārīrasthāna

*In the process of bringing about a healthy crop, it is of importance that the the season be **appropriate**, the soil be **cured**, the provision of water be **optimum** and the seed be of **high quality**. Similarly, for ideal conception, it is important that the season and occasion be **suitable**, the woman and her womb be **free of all illness**, the availability of nutrition for development of the foetus be **optimum,** and the seed (sperm and ovum) be **healthy and potent**.*

Ayurved, since ancient times has presented the idea that there is an *ideal* process to creating human beings, and that it should be followed carefully and completely. For this, it has developed a complete science called *Garbha Sanskar*.

It describes a range of preparations to be undertaken by the parents-to-be to ensure physical health, treatment for ideal conception, and care during the 280 days of pregnancy - all essential for a perfectly healthy child.

The unborn child carries some

destined programmes according to its past actions, but it receives its physical nourishment from the mother and its mind is still attached to her. The mother's behaviour, diet, thoughts, speech, and actions, have a profound impact on the foetus.

The child is a combination of three phenomena - its own destiny, the qualities and defects of its parents and the treatment and care it receives during pregnancy. Ayurved and the other Vedas contain detailed descriptions of the process to help produce a healthy child, with excellent physical, mental and intellectual qualities.

When sperm meets the ovum, it is not necessary that the result be an embryo. Conception only occurs when *life force* (chetana) also enters the seed and fuses with them at the same time, giving rise to the live embryo. It is very important that we understand and realise this.

This *shloka* from *Charak Sharirsthan* elaborates:

गर्भस्तु खलु अन्तरिक्षवाय्वग्नितोयभूमिविकारश्चेतनाधिष्ठानभूतः।

... *चरक शारीरस्थान*

Garbhastu khalu antarikṣa-vāyvagni-toya-bhūmi vikāraścetanādhiṣṭhāna-bhūtaḥ

...Caraka śārīrasthāna

The five gross elements (Pancha-mahabhoot) are not enough to give life. The integration of life force with these elements is imperative. That is what happens when conception takes place. This life force is free and independent, and enters the embryo of its own will. Thus, the creation of a new life is considered to be no less than a natural miracle!

Right after this rush of life force, comes the formation of the baby's mind. This is explained in the following verse from the *Charak Sharirsthan*

तत्र पूर्वं चेतनाधातुः सत्त्वकरणो गुणग्रहणाय प्रवर्तते ।

... *चरक शारीरस्थान*

Tatra pūrvam cetanā-dhātuḥ sattva-karaṇo guṇa-grahaṇāya pravartate ....Caraka śārīrasthāna

From the moment fertilisation occurs i.e. the embryo is formed, it has an individual mind.

This mind carries imprints of good and bad actions from past lives. This mind (which has always been present) carries with it all the Sattvik, Rajasik and Tamasik impressions from actions of previous births.

Life before childbirth, including the nine months of pregnancy are considered the past life of the person. The qualities of our forefathers, in the form of our chromosomes, which account for almost all our development, constitution and behaviour, already exist in us. So we should try and understand that we already exist, much before being born into this life. That is the past life being referred to here. A bloodline continues as an unbroken chain and has a specific set of qualities and characteristics. And your qualities are the forerunners (of the qualities) of your own future generations!

In the next *shloka* we see that according to Ayurvedic philosophy the foetal mind is closely interrelated to that of its parents, especially the mother. According to Charakacharya:

सत्त्ववैशेष्यकराणि पुनस्तेषां तेषां प्राणिनां मातृपितृसत्त्वान्यन्तर्वन्त्याः श्रुतयश्चाभीक्ष्णं स्वोचितं च कर्म सत्त्वविशेषाभ्यासश्चेति ॥ ... *चरक शारीरस्थान*

Sattvavaiśeṣyakarāṇi punasteṣām teṣām prāṇinām mātṛpitṛsattvānyantarvantyāḥ śrutayaścābhīkṣṇam svocitam ca karma sattvaviśeṣābhyāsaśceti

.....Caraka śārīrasthāna

It says here - a baby's mind is not a blank slate, but neither is it a finished product. *At the stage of the embryo, the mind is deeply attached to its parents. It can* ***listen****, and is moulded by the types of stories and music the mother listens to when she is pregnant, and forms itself accordingly. Whatever she listens to with attention contributes to culturing the mind of the child.*

So it follows, for example, that if a pregnant woman wants to remove attitudes that are 'rajasik' and 'tamasik' and bear a child with a 'sattvik' nature - full of intelligence, courage, dynamism and the ability to discern between right and wrong - she should listen only to 'sattvik' stories, which leave good impressions on the mind.

The *Sharangdhar Sanhita* also describes the same idea

गर्भोपपत्तौ तु मनः स्त्रिया यं जन्तु व्रजेत् तदृशं प्रसूते । ...शारंगधर

Garbhopapattau tu manaḥ striyā yam jantu vrajet tadṛśam prasūte ....śāraṅgadhara

The child will have the kind of qualities that occupy the pregnant woman's mind.

When a pregnant woman desires a child who is courageous, clever, beautiful and healthy, she should listen to stories of people who possess such ideal qualities. She should read their biographies, and perhaps, contemplate upon their lives.

CULTURING THROUGH SOUND

The most effective medium to culture the foetus is sound. Scientifically coordinated sound combinations, such as *mantras*, or even music based on such principles, can be *understood* and imbibed directly by the mind. It is not necessary to actually comprehend the music and words. Such vibrations will act directly on the mind of both mother and child. So, healing music created especially for pregnancy can have an all-round positive effect on the health of the child and its personality.

Dr. Shri Balaji Tambe's music album *Garbha Sanskar*, healing music for pregnancy, created with exactly this purpose, is being thoroughly researched in association with the University of Pune. The effects observed until now are surprisingly positive, and have exceeded expectations.

Most of us are aware of the story of Abhimanyu in the *Mahabharata*. Abhimanyu learned the art of breaking into a special battle formation, or *chakravyuha*, when he was still in his mother Subhadra's womb, as Shri Krishna explained the procedure to her.

If you look closely into the Indian epics you will find clear references to procedures from Garbha Sanskar. The *Ramayana* describes the *Putrakameshti Yadnya* before Shri Rama was born. The deity of fire (referring to our hormonal system), emerged from the *yadnya* (even the intake of food is a *yadnya*) and gave a gift of *payasadaan* to King Dashratha. This *payas* is part of Garbha Sanskar therapy (in the form of rejuvenating preparations) taken to help produce a healthy child.

Kaushalya's (Rama's mother) desires (cravings or *dohaale* which are explained in detail in further chapters), to perform *yogasana* - such as *Vajrasana* and *Veerasan* - indicate that she was to expect a valourous and strong child.

Although all this culturing obviously reaches the womb through the woman, her husband has an equally important role to play. During pregnancy husband and wife need to take care of each other. With so many changes taking place in the woman's body, her husband should be extra attentive to her needs.

An ideal example of a relationship between husband and wife is Shri Rama and Sita. Any particular cravings (*dohaale*) that Sita had during pregnancy were taken seriously by Shri Rama. He knew that if these wishes were not fulfilled, or correctly dealt with, in accordance with Garbha Sanskar, then the child that is born may not be completely healthy. These desires come not from the mother, but from the unborn child, and she is only the medium to express the desires of the foetus she carries. Across Indian culture these cravings and desires are treated with sensitivity, as a practice that will benefit the developing child.

Husband and wife should spend enough time with each other. They should cultivate trust and have a deep bond. Shri Rama and Sita's mutual trust allowed Sita to tell Shri Rama freely of her cravings. These cravings can also give you clues, to a certain extent, about the nature, personality, ambitions and temperament of your unborn child - perhaps, you could say, an idea of the 'program' of your child. Sita wanted to go for walks in the forest; wander and sing, free as a bird. She craved the mellifluous sounds of the flute and wished to cradle a newborn calf, look into its innocent eyes and bring fodder for it. She wanted to wear natural *valkal* clothes, and carry water from a river in pots on her head and waist. It all seemed to express one idea clearly. It was Sita's desire to live a simple natural life, in an *ashram*-like environment, in the forest.

It is important to take notice of which of these desires have a physical nature and which ones have a psychological nature.

As we will see further in this book, Ayurved explains with great care the diet a woman should follow through each stage of pregnancy. Recommended foods and more importantly, foods that she should avoid, are described in great detail. Along with this, the month-by-month growth of the foetus, the nutrients and energy required for this growth, potential disorders, anatomical problems, preventive measures, and remedies, are all listed.

Ayurved also provides guidance on which deities to worship and which *mantras* to recite. Everyone wants a healthy, clever and cultured child, but is ignorant of the fact that one can actually prepare for producing such progeny. Even people who understand this idea are still unaware of what exactly can be done. With the pace of our lives increasing all the time, taking time out for yourself has become more and more difficult. *After* the child is born everyone easily accepts that it is vital to give time to your baby. But couples should give time and attention even before conception, to prepare for, and welcome their child with appropriate measures. The child born as a result of such careful preparation will benefit immensely. And these preparations, carefully put together and scrupulously researched over thousands of years, have been set down in Ayurved since ancient times.

With the world's population increasing steadily, and the furious pace of development around us, there is an increasing competitiveness in society. The next generation will have to be more spirited and intelligent to face this ably. If we want to ensure that the material development we see around us actually translates into real progress for the human being, then we need to nurture the coming generation with the values to deal with this development. Garbha Sanskar, perhaps, is the only known programme researched and designed with this purpose!

- **A child is born with the cumulative effect of the mother's lifestyle, its own Karma (destiny), the constitution of its parents, and the measures taken before and during pregnancy.**
- **The use of sound, and healing music, is vital to the process of Garbha Sanskar.**
- **Parents-to-be should devote time to prepare for their child even before conception, to ensure that they have a healthy, intelligent, and cultured child.**
- **Although Garbha Sanskar reaches the foetus through the mother, the father too plays an important role.**
- **The science of Garbha Sanskar seems to be the only solution designed to ensure that future generations are increasingly intelligent, progressive and multifaceted.**

For healthy reproductive cells

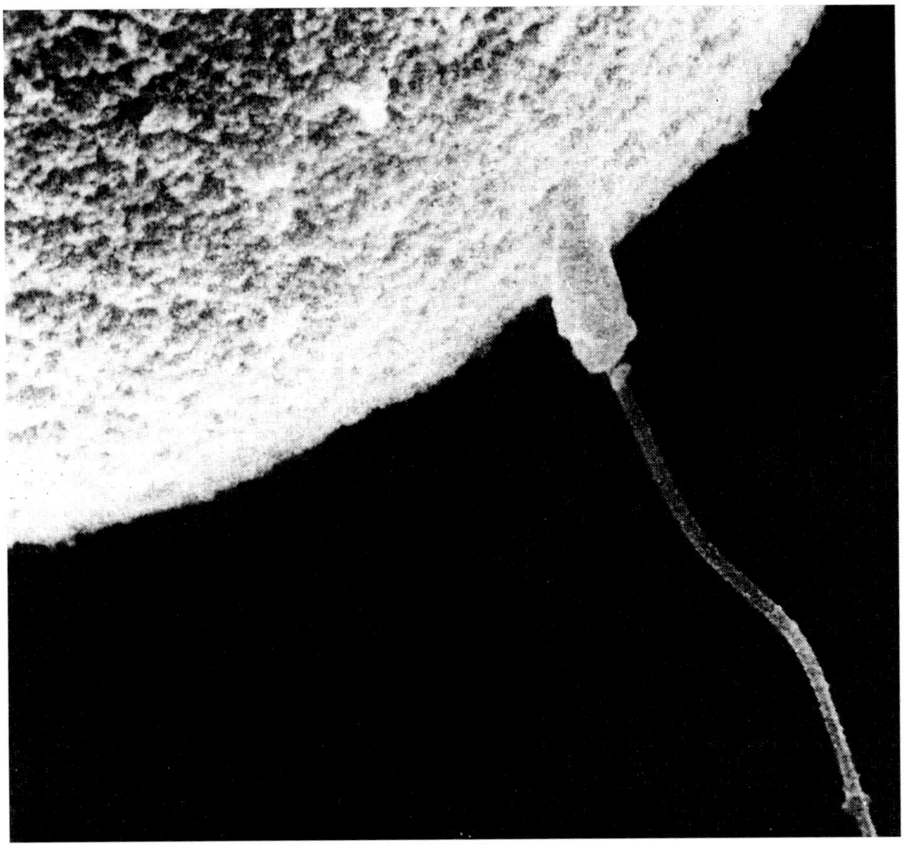

For healthy conception and a well - implanted foetus, one has to understand the importance of a healthy uterus and good male and female seeds (sperm and ova). For conception, the basic physical requirement is the coming together of a sperm and an ovum.

The male and female seeds are the essence of the man and woman. If both have worked hard to be healthy in body, mind and spirit at the time of conception, then, without doubt, their child too will enjoy these positive characteristics.

Therefore, Ayurved places special emphasis on the health of the parents in the lead-up to pregnancy, and in particular on the health of the woman.

Although the man is necessary for conception, it is the woman who holds the child for nine months in her body and nurtures it. The phrase 'blood relation' has a physical basis. The mother, via the placenta, nourishes the foetus through her blood. Also, in the early years of a child's life, the mother is a major pillar of support. Even as the child grows into an adult, the mother is always the one who plays a vital role in moulding, nurturing, imparting values and taking care of the child's food, health, education etc. She is the foundation for a person's development.

Now, if the child faces any major illness, defect or disability, the joy of parenthood is truncated. Ayurved reflects deeply on this, and prescribes in great detail, processes that will help all people have wonderful and capable children full of desirable qualities.

THE IDEAL AGE FOR CONCEPTION

The average age at which girls first experience menstrual periods is around thirteen years. The average age at which boys properly begin to produce semen is around sixteen years. At these early stages though, both boys and girls still need their tissues to become more mature. Some more time is required for their seed (reproductive cell) to become more complete and potent. Ayurved advises on the ideal age for both men and women to have children.

According to Indian culture, the first quarter of life is Brahmacharya, i.e. 'bachelorhood'. This period corresponds to the first twenty-five years of life and is called 'Brahmacharya-ashram'. It should be spent in learning and education. After this period, a person is eligible to marry and start a family. This phase of family life is called 'Ghruhasth-ashram'.

**तस्यां षोडषवर्षायां पञ्चविंशतिवर्षः पुरुषः पुत्रार्थं प्रयतेत ।
तदा हि तौ प्राप्तवीर्यौ वीर्यान्वितम् अपत्यं जनयतः ॥** ...*अष्टांगसंग्रह शारीरस्थान*

Tasyām ṣoḍaṣa-varṣāyām pañca-vimśativarṣḥ
puruṣḥ putrārtham prayateta
Tadā hi tau prāpta-vīryau vīryānvitam
apatyam janayataḥ .....Aṣṭāṅgasaṅgraha śārīrasthāna

To give birth to a healthy child, a man should be at least twenty-five, while a girl is ready at sixteen.

Nowadays, women in India usually marry when they are around twenty-two or twenty-three. The ideal time for pregnancy is one to one-and-a-half years after marriage.

It is also important to note the upper age limit for having children. If the man has taken measures to culture and protect his semen from an early age then he should be capable of having children up to the age of 65 or even 70. After the age of 75, it is recommended that he abstain from sexual intercourse. Women have to take other things into consideration. Apart from healthy ova, the flexibility and elasticity of the muscles needed for delivery, the strength of the uterus, and general physical health are all important. Ayurved advises that it may not be good for women to bear children after the age of 35. If a woman wants to have a child after this age, she should undergo suitable Ayurvedic treatments as early as possible, right from the time she has planned to have a child.

Ayurved mentions more than once that the woman should be younger than the man. ***'Visheshaat cha vayovarnavrudhaa'.*** This phrase means that for marriage and conception, it is not suitable that the woman be older than the man.

LINEAGE AND CONSTITUTION

Ayurved also insists very strongly that the Man and woman should not be from the same *gotra* (family and lineage as maintained in traditional records).

अतुल्यगोत्रस्य रजःक्षयान्ते रहोविसृष्टम् । ...*चरक शारीरस्थान*

Atulya-gotrasya rajaḥ-kṣayānte rahovisṛṣṭam

....Caraka śārīrasthāna

Acharya Charak states very early on in his discourse that the man and woman who are to come together should belong to different gotra.

The reason being, that chromosomes coming from the same lineage will have similar patterns. These chromosomes may not be able to match properly and will increase the possibility of disorders in the child.

It is not enough to only ensure that the parents are not from the same *gotra*. They should not even be from the same *pravar* (greater subdivisions of the lineage), as these conditions are highly unsuitable for having an ideal and healthy offspring.

Modern science has now backed this ancient wisdom. Studies have consistently shown that a child will have increased congenital defects if the parents are related (intermarriage between cousins etc).

The next factor, to be considered is called *anyayoni*. This means that men and women who have very dissimilar body constitutions, nature, habits and personalities, should not marry or have sexual intercourse. So it follows that two such people conceiving a child together is totally prohibited in Ayurved. If they are still determined to come together and conceive, then all the Ayurvedic cleansing measures and purifying therapies mentioned in this book should be performed before they attempt to conceive.

In short, it is important that the man and woman preparing for conception be of appropriate age, suitable lineage, a similar nature, have a loving and caring attitude towards one another and excellent health - all necessary prerequisites for ideal conception.

MENTAL PREPARATION

Ayurved advocates that both man and woman should be willing to have a child and carry out the recommended preparations before conception. Unplanned or accidental pregnancies are strongly opposed in Ayurved. Therefore, only when the man and woman are physically and mentally prepared, should they plan a baby.

शुक्रशोणित जीव संयोगे तु खलु कुक्षिगते गर्भसंज्ञा भवति ।

...चरक शारीरस्थान

śukra-śoṇita jīva samyoge tu khalu kukṣigate garbhasañjñā bhavati ....Caraka śārīrasthāna

In this verse, the word 'kukshi' refers to the uterus. *Shukra* is the male reproductive cell or sperm. *Shonit* is the female reproductive cell or ova. The third element required for conception is *jiva* (or 'the spark of life'). *It is only when all three come together that the embryo will be formed.*

The egg and sperm are capable of shaping a new life and they carry the qualities of the man and the woman. The physical, mental, and spiritual state of both the parents is represented in their eggs and sperm. These properties decide the foundational development (which Ayurved calls *prakriti*) of the embryo. In common language, we often refer to a person as having a 'strong constitution' or a 'weak constitution'. This constitution is decided at the moment of conception. The healthier and purer the sperm, ovum, and life force, the stronger the constitution of the baby resulting from their coming together.

On the other hand, if either the man or the woman is weak or suffering from any disorder or imbalance during conception, then that will affect their reproductive cell, and affect its potency, also affecting the constitution of the child.

PURE AND HEALTHY REPRODUCTIVE CELLS

A woman's ovaries produce ova, which, if unfertilized, are expelled through menstrual discharge. In men, sperm is contained in semen. It is important to understand and see what state menstrual discharge and semen should be in, for ideal conception. Their indicators are given below. Their ideal qualities and possible defects are described in Ayurvedic texts in detail. Menstrual blood, for example, should ideally be as described in *Madhavnidan*:

मासान्निष्पिच्छदाहार्ति पञ्चरात्रानुबन्धि च ।
नैवातिबहुलात्यल्पमार्तवं शुद्धमादिशेत् ॥

शशासृक् प्रतिमं यच्च यद्वा लाक्षारसोपमम् ।
तदार्तवं प्रशंसन्ति यच्चाप्सु न विरज्यते ॥ ...*माधवनिदान*

Māsānniṣpicchadāhārti pañca-rātrānubandhi ca
Naivātibahulātyalpamārtavam śuddhamādiśet

śaśāsṛk pratimam yacca yadvā lākṣārasopamam
Tadārtavam praśamsanti yaccāpsu na virajyate
.....Mādhavanidāna

Ideally a woman's period should:

- Take place every 28 days.
- Last for 4-5 days.
- Discharge blood which is not sticky in nature and is free of clots.
- Not be accompanied by a burning sensation, pain, or discomfort.
- Neither be excessive nor too scanty.
- Cleanse the uterus.
- The blood dischagred should be bright red in colour. The stains it leaves on cotton cloth should be easily washable under running water.

This kind of clean blood during menstruation indicates ideal health for conception. Even a minor deviation from the descriptions above is considered unhealthy and needs to be treated.

In many women, menstrual bleeding lasts only one to two days, is blackish or pale red, is accompanied by mucus, or contains clots. Women mostly think that this is normal and carry on with their regular lives.

In addition, sticky menstrual blood, or a white or red discharge (e.g. leucorrhoea, menorrhagia) outside of the time of menstruation, causes the loss of nutrients that would otherwise strengthen the bones, bone marrow, and *shukra dhatu*. These symptoms also need to be watched for carefully, and treated accordingly.

Imbalances in *vata*, *pitta*, and *kapha doshas*, could lead to imbalances in the menstrual process.

Signs of imbalance in menstrual blood

- **Imbalance due to *vata* -** painful, scanty menstruation, dark blood of a blackish colour.
- **Imbalance due to *pitta* -** excess bleeding, bad smelling discharge, burning sensation during discharge.
- **Imbalance due to *kapha* -** sticky and mucoid discharge.
- **Imbalance due to all three *doshas* -** scanty, painful, bad smelling discharge, accompanied by clots.

Menstruation like this is unsuitable for child bearing. If conception does occur, the foetus could be weak and there are increased chances of a miscarriage.

Healthy semen in men has been described as below:

तत्सौम्यं स्निग्धं गुरु शुक्लं मधुगन्धि मधुरं पिच्छिलं
बहु बहलं घृततैलक्षौद्रान्यतमवर्णं च शुक्रं गर्भाधानयोग्यं भवति ।
...अष्टांगसंग्रह शारीरस्थान

Tat-saumyam snigdham guru śuklam madhu-
gandhi madhuram picchilam bahu
bahalam ghṛta-taila-kṣaudrānyatamavarṇam ca
śukram garbhādhāna-yogyam bhavati
...Aṣṭāṅgasaṅgraha śārīrasthāna

Healthy semen is mild, well-lubricated, thick in nature, sweet, white in colour, smells like honey, is ample in quantity, and resembles *ghee*, oil, or honey. This kind of semen is considered perfect for conception.

Signs of imbalance in semen

- **Imbalance due to *vata* -** semen is frothy, scanty, very liquid in nature, and ejaculation is delayed and painful.
- **Imbalance due to *pitta* -** ejaculation is accompanied by a burning sensation; semen is non-viscous in nature, yellowish in colour.
- **Imbalance due to *kapha* -** semen is discharged in excessive quantity, and is very thick and heavy in nature.
- **Imbalance due to all three *doshas* -** semen is scanty and foul smelling, accompanied by pus and clots.

According to Ayurved, conception from this kind of semen is rare, and if it does occur, there could be the following complications:

शुक्रस्य दोषात् क्लैब्यमहर्षणम् ।
रोगि वा क्लीबमल्पायुः विरूपं वा अपत्यं प्रजायते।
न चास्य जायते गर्भः पतति प्रस्रवत्यपि ।
दुष्टं शुक्रं हि नरं सापत्यं सदारं बाधते नरम् ॥ ...चरक सूत्रस्थान

śukrasya doṣāt klaibyamaharṣaṇam
Rogi vā klībamalpāyuḥ
virūpam vā apatyam prajāyate
Na cāsya jāyate garbhaḥ patati prasravatyapi
Duṣṭam śukram hi naram
sāpatyam sadāram bādhatē naram .....Caraka sūtrasthāna

Poor quality sperm or semen could lead to the child having a short life span, being weak, and less good-looking than it might have been. In most cases, conception doesn't even take place, and if it does then the chances of miscarriage are high. Unhealthy semen causes problems to the man himself, to his child and to the woman as well.

So it is vital to understand that the health of your baby depends on both of you being healthy. If you find deficiencies in yourselves, correct them before you try and conceive.

Now-a-days, through techniques like sperm counts etc., at least one factor in conception i.e. the quantity of sperm can be checked.

FURTHER PRECAUTIONS FOR CONCEPTION

All too often, once a couple has decided to have a child, they want one immediately. Being in a hurry will not prove good for the resulting child. Rushing into it can have an adverse effect on both mother and child.

The woman is most important in the process of producing a child. Firstly, the future mother's menstrual cycles need to get regular. They need to come every 28-29 days, and the bleeding needs to last for four to five days each time. The symptoms mentioned earlier, such as clots and pain during menstruation, need to be dealt with, a should recurrent urinary tract and bladder infections. Signs of hormonal disturbances, for example thyroid disease, anovulatory cycles (a menstrual cycle in which no ovum has been released by the ovaries), sudden weight gain, sudden growth of facial hair, heaviness or pain in the breasts, should be treated immediately.

Many people consider themselves healthy, while in fact their disease has only been suppressed or masked by medication instead of being eradicated at the root. Even if your condition isn't causing discomfort any more, and even if you do not feel or understand this, the body may still be diseased. Even being mildly diseased is not good for anyone, and it is particularly dangerous for a couple trying to conceive since the child will be the one to suffer the consequences for its entire life. Whether man or woman, ideally, you need to treat and cure all imbalances first, and only then conceive.

And if one really follows this line of thought, it is also possible to prevent hereditary diseases. Couples with a family history of diseases such as bronchial asthma, skin ailments, mental disorders, epilepsy, or other brain conditions can take measures to see that these problems are not passed on to the child. These measures should be started and followed through, in the form of appropriate medication before conception, and throughout pregnancy, until the baby is born.

These therapies are all set down in the Ayurvedic texts, and they have been shown to have excellent results. For example, if you already have a child with asthma, the mother can take medicines that act on the respiratory system (e.g. Sitopaladi powder), during each of her following pregnancies. This will drastically reduce the likelihood of the other children suffering from asthma or any other respiratory disorders. This list can go on, and it depends on how much effort the parents want to put in for the sake of their child.

It goes without saying that such precautions and effort are nothing compared to the benefits your child will experience throughout his or her life.

- **For marriage and conception it is unsuitable that a woman be older than her partner.**
- **Men and women should ensure that they achieve optimum health and maximum vitality before they conceive.**
- **Unplanned, unwanted, or accidental pregnancy is not in accordance with Ayurvedic science.**
- **For an ideal pregnancy, it is necessary that a woman has regular menstrual cycles and produces healthy ova.**
- **Children born from unhealthy semen are likely to be weak, less good-looking, and possibly have a shorter lifespan.**

Culturing the seed

The first step towards a successful conception is purification of the body. In Ayurved, the cleansing of the body is based on the purification of the five elements that make up the body - space, air, fire, water, and earth.

Cleaning and purification of the space (*Akash*) and air (*Vayu*) elements which together form *Vata dosha*, is achieved by administering *basti*. The fire (*Agni*), air (*Vayu*) and water (*Jala*) elements form *Pitta dosha*, which is removed through *virechan*. *Kapha dosha,* made up of the water *(Jala)* and earth (*Prithvi*) elements is balanced by *vaman*.

सर्वेषु च शुक्रार्तवदोषेषु स्त्रीपुंसौ
स्नेहादिकर्मभिर्विशेषेण चोत्तरबस्तिभिः पुनः
पुनरुपाचरेत् ।

...अष्टांगसंग्रह शारीरस्थान

Sarveṣu ca śukrārtaadoṣeṣu
strīpuṁsau snehādikarmabhirviśeṣeṇa
cottarabastibhiḥ punaḥ punarupācaret

....aṣṭāṅgasaṅgraha śārīrasthāna

This shloka recommends therapies prior to conception in the following manner:

To remove all kinds of imbalances in the sperm and ova, therapies such as oleation (snehan), steam (svedan), vaman, virechan, bastis and other specially prepared uttar-bastis are highly recommended.

PANCHA KARMA

Everybody does not require all these therapies during *Pancha Karma*. The aim is to make sure that the three *doshas* (*vata*, *pitta* and *kapha)* are more or less in balance.

People who are planning for a child and suffer from any chronic or congenital disease, or those who have recently suffered a major illness, should definitely do *Pancha Karma*. For others, who are generally in good or even excellent health, *Pancha Karma* will enhance your strength and sense of well-being even further, and provide a chance to wipe out or mitigate any future possibilities of disease in you and help produce a child with excellent health. *Pancha Karma*, if done properly, cannot harm you under any circumstances, on the contrary it will provide a huge boost to your life.

An expert physician will be able to plan and administer these therapies according to your constitution and imbalances. *Virechan* and *basti* are generally the most suitable therapies that help balance all three doshas with excellent results.

Pancha Karma is not simply a bunch of therapies. *Virechan*, for example, is not merely a flushing of the intestines, and *basti* is not just an enema. The entire concept of *Pancha Karma* is to be understood and applied as a whole. It is extremely scientific and each of its steps and procedures have important roles to play in the process of purifying the body.

It begins with *svedan* (steam bath) and *snehan*. Snehan is a combination of *abhyang* (massages) and drinking specifically prepared ghee cultured with herbs. This ghee is prepared strictly according to Ayurvedic recipes. The dosage of this ghee is dependant on many factors such as age, strength and the constitution of the person. This ghee, should be consumed for at least 3 days during *snehan*. The ghee has now loosened all toxins stuck in the various areas of the body. Then massages and steam baths are administered again, to bring the toxins loosened by the ghee into the digestive tract to be expelled.

It is often found that only a small number of perfunctory therapies are performed under the pretext of *Pancha Karma* in many therapy centres - just a few massages and a *shirodhara* do not qualify as a full *Pancha Karma*. Such superficial procedures are insufficient. For any real benefit - and to properly clean the whole body - the treatment needs to be scientific, extensive, and incorporating internal and external lubrication as described above. *Snehan* and *svedan* should be followed by the appropriate combination of *virechan* and *bastis* and then finally other therapies that provide strength after the cleaning process.

Some of these therapies are as follows. The *kundalini* massage is a good therapy for the back, which improves the flexibility of the spine and strengthens it. It also enhances the flow of energy in the spinal cord. *Uttar dhoop* and *uttar basti* are therapies for strengthening the uterus, and generally very beneficial for women. They should be administered under medical spervision for best results.

The process of Pancha Karma should be followed without compromise. This should take a minimum of two to three weeks, if you really want it to be done scientifically and completely.

The idea behind Panch Karma before conception is to purify the seeds of both man and woman. When the body is cleaned like this, the ability to absorb nutrients is multiplied several-fold. Ayurved has a number of rejuvenating tonics and herbal preparations to help increase strength, memory and life-energy (*ojas*). Consequently, the quality and strength of the sperm and ova are greatly improved. After a well done Pancha Karma you will find that your complexion has improved and the senses function more efficiently. The mind is refreshed and one becomes more optimistic. Besides, couples will also find an increase in attraction towards one another.

The results of the Pancha Karma therapies will go a long way. They facilitate conception and implantation of the embryo, and have continued benefits to ensure a smooth pregnancy and good health for the child to be born.

DIET AFTER PANCHA KARMA

After *Pancha Karma*, Ayurved advises specific medicines that help increase the potency of the sperm and ovum and raise *ojas* (life energy). It also provides detailed guidance on diet.

In the Ayurvedic system of understanding the body, *shukra dhatu* is the final and deepest layer of body tissue (body constituent). It is considered one of the main repositories of strength, energy and *prana* in the body. It is, of course, present in both men and women. Semen in men and ova in women are produced from *shukra dhatu*. And when *shukra dhatu* is healthy the sperm and ova are healthy as well.

Shukra dhatu has a close affinity with *kapha dosha*. Any imbalance of *kapha*, whether related to food or life style, has a profound effect on *shukra dhatu*. Additionally, the food, lifestyle or behaviour that nourishes *kapha*, also nourishes *shukra*. The following foods nourish *kapha*

Milk	Figs
Butter	Almonds
Ghee	*Khuskhus* (poppy seeds)
Candy sugar	Black raisins
Godambi	Dry dates

These items, among foods, are potent enough that their nutrition reaches all the way to *shukra dhatu*. Therefore they are categorized as foods that rejuvenate the body. These foods are *sattvik* in nature.

Milk, among the above mentioned, is easily obtained, and most nutritious, and is therefore considered best. The writers of the ancient Ayurved texts describe milk as that which nourishes the dhatus, increases strength and potency, retains youth and provides general vigour to the body. Furthermore, it is mentioned that *shukra dhatu* is increased immediately on intake of milk.

To benefit in all these ways, both the man and woman preparing for conception should consume milk every day. It is even better to add *dhatu*-building and strengthening mixtures (they are like any other powdered/granulated milk additives and are called *kalpas*) to milk. **Santulan Shatavari Kalpa** is great for women, while **Santulan Chaitanya Kalpa** is beneficial for men, both easily available **Santulan Ayurved** products.

Another easy food to obtain and use is **almond**. Soak 3-4 almonds in water overnight, and peel them in the morning before eating. These need to be chewed really well to obtain their full benefit.

Panchamrut is a great food that should also be taken in the morning before breakfast. It is an extremely important food. Please refer to the chapter called Special Recipes towards the end of the book to see how to prepare and use *panchamrut*. Freshly prepared as suggested and taken every day, *panchamrut* works as a nectar. It boosts physical strength, intelligence, memory, grasping power, creativite abilities, improves complexion, and as such is ideal to help increase the quality of *shukra* in the body.

Ghee - Indian food culture advises that some ghee should always be taken with meals to purify food even further. So people generally put only a couple of drops. However, if one wants to increase *shukra dhatu* before conception, at least two teaspoons of ghee need to be eaten along with every meal.

Iron-providing food - Since women lose blood every month during menstruation, they should pay more attention to nutrition for creating *rakta dhatu* (blood). Dates, black raisins, pomegranate, soaked figs, and green leafy vegetables such as spinach should all be included in the woman's diet

Rejuvenating Tonics - Rejuvenating tonics are as important as food in the preparation for conception. Ayurved stresses the importance of a number of herbs that improve the quality of *shukra dhatu*. Please refer to a list of herbs at the end of this book. Some of these are listed below.

shatavari (Asparagus racemosus)
amla (Emblica officinalis)
gokshur (Tribulus terrestris)
ashwagandha (Withania somnifera)
kavachbeej (Mucuna pruriens)
vidari (Ipomoea digitata)
jyeshthamadha (Glycyrrhiza glabra)
bala (Sida cordifolia)
pimpli (Piper longum)
vanshlochan (Bambusa arundinaceae)
shingada (Trapa bispinosa)
durva (Cynodon dactylon).

For Women - The highly recommended *rasayans* we have for women are **Santulan Dhatri Rasayan**, **San Rose** and **Santulan Shatavari Kalpa**.

Santulan Dhatri Rasayan is made from *amla*, grapes among other ingredients that promote *rakta dhatu* and *shukra dhatu*. **San Rose** contains several potent ingredients like *mandur bhasma*, *suvarnamakshik bhasma* and rose petals, and also nourishes *rakta dhatu*, provides calcium and balances proteins in the body.

For Men - Men are advised to consume *rasayans* such as **Santulan Marrosan, Santulan Chaitanya and Santulan Prashant Churna.** *Jyeshtamadha churna* with ghee and honey, followed by a cup of hot milk is also effective. All of these *rasayans* enhance the quality of the semen.

In a chapter called *Jatee Sutreeya* in the *Charak Sharirsthan*, Acharya Charak describes in detail, measures to be taken to ensure a healthy progeny. These include scientific body purification, nutrition, and various medications.

**उपाचरेच्च मधुरौषधसंस्कृताभ्यां घृतक्षीराभ्यां
पुरुषं स्त्रियं तु तैलमाषाभ्याम् ।** ...*चरक शारीरस्थान*

Upācarecca madhurauṣadha-sanskṛtābhyām
ghṛta-kṣīrābhyām puruṣam striyam tu
tailamāṣābhyām ....Caraka śārīrasthāna

After having completed the process of purifiying the body, the man should consume ghee enriched with sweet-tasting herbs and milk. The woman should consume ghee or sesame oil similarly enriched, as well as black gram (udid).

Examples of ghee and milk preparations enriched with sweet herbs, from the Charak Samhita

For Men

Shatavari Ghrut - contains *jyeshthamadha* (licorice), *kakoli* (Curculigo orchioides), *kshirkakoli* (Gymnema lactiferum), *vidari* etc

Sarasvat Ghrut - contains *brahmi* (Bacopa monniera), *koshtakolinjan* (Saussurea lappa), *vavding* (Embelia ribes), and *vekhand* (Acorus calamus) etc.

Vrushyakshir - a highly recommended excellent milk preparation made with dates, black gram (*udid*), *shingada* (Trapa bispinosa) and *kavachbeej* (Mucuna pruriens), among other herbs.

Some other preparations like *gokshurpak* and *gudkushmandavleh*, may also be consumed in accordance with individual constitution.

For Women

Women should start a course of medicated ghee preparations such as, **Santulan Ashokadi Ghrut**, or *Kalyanak Ghruta*, along with the intake of *Shatavari Kalpa. Ladus* (dollops) made from green gram and black gram are great if they are suitable to her constitution as well. Black gram can also be taken in the form of *kheer* (a soup-like milk and sugar preparation), with saffron and cardamom added to enhance its nutritive values.

While all of these suggestions are very effective, for accurate results, consultation with an expert ***vaidya*** (Ayurvedic doctor) is strongly recommended.

Healing Music - Listening to musical compositions made especially for women will go a long way in helping women maintain feminine attributes, both physically and psychologically. It will help to promote hormonal balance and to produce healthy ova. Vedic chants, specific ragas, instrumental music - especially music played on the *veena* - and verses from the *Saam Veda*, are really effective. The album **Stree Santulan** composed by Dr. Shri Balaji Tambe is based on these principles. Many women have experienced its benefits. It helps normalise menstrual cycles and ovulation, and also keeps the uterus healthy.

Most Importantly...

Many functions of the body depend upon healthy *shukra*. While medication is good, we must work to reduce other factors that adversely affect *shukra*. We need to avoid anxiety, excessive grief, irritability, and if possible, even disappointment. Healing music, along with the chanting of Aum, and meditation, increase happiness and enthusiasm.

In brief, with a systematic cleansing of the body and the use of dietary and herbal preparations, the sperm and ova will be healthy. When this is accomplished, the couple should consciously try to conceive.

- **Both the man and the woman, should undergo Pancha Karma, for balancing all three doshas, prior to conception.**
- **Women should eat dates, raisins, pomegranate, soaked figs, leafy vegetables such as spinach, and similar nutrients to improve haemoglobin and nourish rakta dhatu (blood).**
- **Women should listen to specific healing music to attain mental and physical balance.**
- **Grief, irritability, depression, disappointment and stress may reduce the quality and quantity of shukra dhatu, and should be avoided.**
- **A minimum period of two to three weeks is required to perform Pancha Karma scientifically and properly.**

Creating the atmosphere

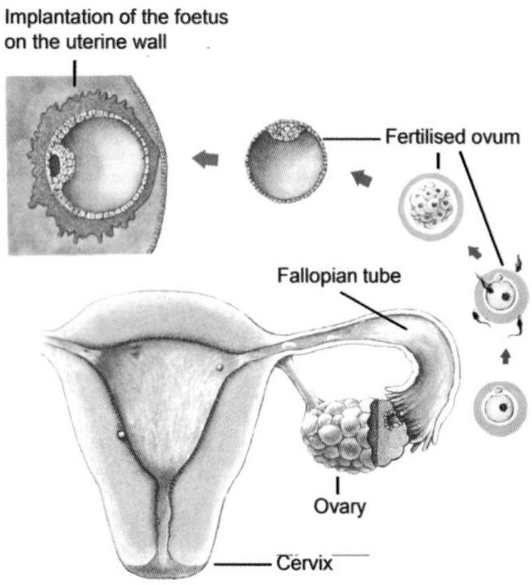

RUTUKAAL (FERTILE PERIOD) AND CONCEPTION

For conception to occur, sperm and ovum have to meet. Acharya Charak outlines other factors, besides this union, which are essential for conception, for proper growth of the foetus, and for a timely delivery.

शुक्रासृगात्माशयकाल संपद्यस्य
उपचारश्च हितैस्तथाऽन्नैः ।
गर्भश्च काले च सुखी सुखं च
संजायते संपरिपूर्णदेहः ॥ ...चरक शारीरस्थान

śukrāsṛgātmāśayakāla
sampadyasyopacāraśca hitaistathā~nnaiḥ
Garbhaśca kāle ca sukhī sukham ca
sañjāyate sampariрūrṇadehaḥ
.....Caraka śārīrasthāna

Well-formed and good quality sperm, a healthy ovum, a healthy and strong uterus, a fertile period of the woman's cycle and a cultured soul full of good deeds, should all come together. The woman should nourish herself appropriately so that conception is successful. Then, with further excellent nourishment, the foetus remains in the womb for the optimum period and develops properly, following which it will be born without deficiencies and in a comfortable manner.

Rutukaal (fertile period)

आर्तवस्रावदिवसात् ऋतुःषोडशरात्रयः ।
गर्भग्रहणयोग्यस्तु स एव समयः स्मृतः ॥ ... भावप्रकाश

ārtava-srāva-divasāt
ṛatuḥ-ṣoḍaśarātrayaḥ
Garbha-grahaṇayogyastu
sa eva samayaḥ smṛtaḥ ....Bhāvaprakāśa

Rutukaal refers to the fertile period in the woman's monthly cycle. Rutukaal remains from the first day of menstruation onwards to the sixteenth night after menstruation begins. During this period, if sexual intercourse takes place, the chances of conception are highest.

Sexual intercourse after the sixteenth night following the onset of menstruation is not favourable for conception. Just as the lotus wilts in the evening, the opening of the uterus (cervix) constricts and begins to close itself after the sixteenth day. For conception, sexual intercourse should occur during the above-mentioned *Rutukaal* (fertile period).

It is rare for conception to take place after *Rutukaal* (i.e. after the sixteenth day). Even if it occurs, there is a possibility that the resulting child will be weak, sick, have sense organs with low capacities, a diminished immune system, and diminished *Ojas* (life energy).

It is often the case that women who ovulate after the twentieth day of the menstrual cycle, or later, have difficulty in conceiving.

THE GIFT OF GARBHADHAAN

Ayurved and other ancient Indian sciences talk about the concept of the 'Sixteen *Sanskars*' to be performed during one's life. These rituals are designed to help the person achieve success, longevity and prosperity. *Garbhadhaan* is the first of these, performed for a person by one's parents. While Garbhadhaan includes conceiving the child, it is actually much more than just conception. *When a man and woman come together with the intention of producing a well-balanced, virtuous and healthy child, and imbibe the values and practices that go along with the process, it is called* **Garbhadhaan.** The suggestions made in this book about preparing for conception are all part of *Garbhadhaan*. The intentions of the parents and virtues imparted to the child are taken care of in the manner described below.

Before the actual *Garbhadhaan*, the couple should observe celibacy for one month. This conserves their *shukra dhatu* and fosters the production of healthy sperm and ovum. As mentioned earlier, fertilization occurs if the sperm and ovum meet in *rutukaal*. To conceive a strong and healthy child with the best qualities, the ideal time for sexual intercourse is a few days after menstruation, or to be more exact, from the eighth day after the onset of menstruation (counting the first appearance of bleeding as day one), up to the 15th night. During this time-span, it is best to choose days as late before the 16th night as possible. The reasons for this are as follows:

तासु उत्तरोत्तरमायुरारोग्यैश्वर्य सौभाग्यबलवर्णेन्द्रियसम्पद्
अपत्यस्य भवति । *...अष्टांगसंग्रह शारीरस्थान*

Tāsu uttarottaramāyurārogyaiśvarya saubhāgya-bala-varṇendriya-sampad apatyasya bhavati
....Aṣṭāṅgasaṅgraha śārīrasthāna

The later the ovum is fertilized, the better the chances are that the child will be healthy and prosperous, have good fortune, strength, a good complexion, and strong sense organs. Conversely, the later the ovum is fertilized after the 16th night of the cycle, the lower are the chances of such qualities flowering in the child.

Just before conception, i.e. sexual intercourse, the couple should not be thirsty, hungry, nor should they have eaten too much of food, or food that is heavy to digest. It is recommended that they have a meal of *sattvik* food, which is satisfying and good for their constitutions. The partners should have mutual respect and love for each other, as well as a genuine desire to produce a child together. They should be free of feelings such as anxiety, mourning, sadness, anger, and exasperation.

In addition to all the above, thoughts and acts that increase *vata* (late nights, thoughts that cause stress etc.), should be avoided. If they are not avoided, there could be problems during fertilization, and if conception does occur, it could result in miscarriage, *moodhgarbha* (the foetus taking an inappropriate position in the womb), or other damage to the foetus.

THE IDEAL TIME FOR CONCEPTION

According to Ayurvedic literature, sexual intercourse should take place only at night, and preferably during the first half, i.e. before 1:30 a.m. with the time before midnight being considered best. It is recommended that one should abstain from sexual intercourse during the day. Conception occurring during the day is not advisable.

The constitution of the child is also dependent on the weather and season during which conception takes place. Since, in winter (*hemant & shishir* seasons of the Indian year), physical strength is at its peak, conception should ideally occur during this time. If possible, conception should not occur on the eleventh or thirteenth day of the lunar cycle (Ekadashi and Trayodashi respectively), or on day of the black moon (amavasya). If one believes in astrology, an ideal and auspicious day should be chosen accordingly.

Calculation of the exact date of menstruation

To determine the first day of menstruation (if bleeding starts at night), divide the night into three parts from sunset to sunrise. If bleeding occurs during the first two thirds, then the previous day may be taken as the first day of menstruation. If bleeding begins during the final third, then the next day is considered to be the first day of menstruation.

For example: If the time between sunset on Monday at 7 p.m. and sunrise on Tuesday at 7a.m. is twelve hours then the first two thirds comprise eight hours. So if bleeding starts on or before 3 am during the night, then Monday is considered to be the first day of menstruation. If bleeding begins after 3 a.m. then Tuesday is considered to be day one. If a woman finds herself in a situation where she needs to make this calculation, she should surely attempt to be as accurate as possible, taking even minutes into account.

If one has further doubts about Garbhadhaan or conceiving a child, then one should immediately consult an Ayurvedic physician who is well versed in the elementary principles of the science. With regard to the above subject, Ayurvedic research offers many more very fine details which can be helpful.

THE BEDROOM

The bedroom, where conception should occur, should be peaceful, clean, and purified with *dhoop* (incense and herbal smokes). The bed should be large enough, and covered with clean white, cream, or light coloured bed-sheets. Dark, or overly bright colours, are to be avoided, since their reflected colours can dissipate the feeling of peace in the mind. Any natural fragrances used like incense, flowers, attar, should be appealing to *both* partners. The rooms cleanliness cannot be over-emphasized and there should be no thorny plants in the room. There should be no casually placed items, and certainly no sign of disorganisation in the room at all. Ideally the couple should dress in white. To some people these guidelines may appear exaggerated, but they all have subtle positive effects on the mind. This, in turn, helps promote peace, happiness, and enthusiasm.

Further, Ayurved directs that the woman should get into bed with her left foot first, and the man with his right foot. Before sexual intercourse, he should recite the following mantras:

अहिरसि आयुरसि सर्वतः प्रतिष्ठाऽसि धाता त्वा ददतु विधाता त्वा दधातु ब्रह्मवर्चसा भव ॥ *... चरक शारीरस्थान*

Ahirasi āyurasi sarvataḥ pratiṣṭhā̱si dhātā tvā
dadatu vidhātā tvā dadhātu brahma-varcasā bhava
....Caraka śārīrasthāna

This verse acknowledges the foetus, saying:

"Oh foetus, you are like the sun to me, you are my life, you are my fame, and reputation. May God protect you, and may you obtain true spiritual knowledge."

ब्रह्मा बृहस्पतिर्विष्णुः सोमः सूर्यस्तथाऽश्विनौ ।
भगोऽथ मित्रावरुणौ वीरं ददतु मे सुतम् ॥ *...चरक शारीरस्थान*

Brahmā Bṛhaspatiḥ Viṣṇuḥ
Somaḥ Sūryastathā Aśvinau
Bhago~tha Mitrāvaruṇau
vīram dadatu me sutam ....Caraka śārīrasthāna

This mantra addresses the Gods thus: *"O Brahma, Brihaspati, Vishnu, Som, Surya, Ashwinikumar, Bhag, Mitra, Varuna, and others, I request all of you to bless me with a brave, healthy and good progeny."*

After chanting both mantras like this, the couple should then engage in sexual intercourse, the woman lying on her back, to accept her partner's semen. After intercourse, a cloth soaked in cold water should be placed on the lower part of her abdomen, to help reduce the heat generated in the uterus.

Although it is not necessary that each of the above instructions be followed word to word, it is important that the underlying principles and basic aims are understood and practised, especially in today's world. Even if the mantra is not chanted in Sanskrit as it is described, its meaning should be kept in mind, and the necessary energies and attitudes to create a healthy offspring should be evoked.

During this entire ritual, attitude and mental preparedness play a very important role.

Mental Preparation

Acharya Vagbhat describes the relationship between the mindset of the parents-to-be and that of the foetus, in the following verse:

इच्छेतां यादृशं पुत्रं तद्रूपचरितांश्च तौ ।
चिन्तयेतां जनपदांस्तदाचारपरिच्छदौ ॥ *...अष्टांगहृदय शारीरस्थान*

Icchetām yādṛśam putram tadrūpacaritāmśca tau
Cintayetām janapadāmstadācāraparicchadau
...Aṣṭāṅgahṛdaya śārīrasthāna

The mind of the foetus is influenced by the thoughts of its parents prior to and during the act of conception.

The couple should have positive thoughts, an enthusiastic outlook, and a strong desire for a healthy child. Throughout the pregnancy, the environment at home should be happy, pleasant and should radiate contentment. It is important that the expectant mother remain as contented and happy as possible.

Before attempting to conceive, please consider the following points carefully.

The first and most important criterion is that the couple have a socially accepted relationship, and be prepared to accept responsibility for their child's physical, mental and emotional development and stand by the child as and when required.

Every conscientious couple must assess themselves with respect to their ability to instil their offspring with proper values and culture (*sanskar*), to nurture, love, and provide for the education of their child. Only if these criteria are met, should they proceed and plan a pregnancy.

Parents bear the responsibility of raising and taking care of the child, until he/she becomes independent, and begins a life of his/her own. The father and mother ideally should not give themselves the freedom to live apart or in separation until the child is an independent adult. They should certainly stay together during the entire period of their child's development and education. Pregnancy and parenthood are an immense responsibility, and all those desiring children should be fully aware of this.

WHERE SHOULD CONCEPTION OCCUR?

In new times we have begun to adopt new norms and create new traditions. It is important to mention here that conception should definitely not occur in a new, foreign or distant place e.g. during a honeymoon, or while getting away from hectic schedules for a 'change of scene'.

There is a reason behind these recommendations. Unfamiliar places are unlikely to have been built in accordance with *vastu shastra* principles. They may not have the highest hygiene standards even if they appear very clean superficially. If one cannot be assured of the positive energy or purity of the space then it is best not to conceive in such places. This, conversely, also means that it is good to choose a place which is untainted, filled with familiar energies, and built according to *vastu* guidelines (the obvious expectation embedded here is that your home has been built in accordance with *vastu shastra*).

In addition to all these procedures, the couple should consciously avoid mental stress, familial disagreements and any possibilities of dissatisfaction during the period when intercourse is planned with the intention to conceive. When attempting to conceive, one should not be under any untoward emotional stress related to illness or sudden death in the family, and hectic activity for any reason. All of these can adversely affect mental and physical balance, sometimes without you even realizing it. The couple should find themselves in as balanced a state as possible, physically and mentally, before conception. Even a joyful event such as a wedding can, through the stress of organisation, late nights, and irregular meals, disturb the body's equilibrium. This is not conducive for *Garbhadhaan*. It is better that all such events, emotionally or physically stressful, are over with before the attempt to conceive.

You should extend this care even to the level of thought. It is as important to be pure in thought and spiritually oriented at this time, as it is to be in good physical condition. Participating in prayers and *satsang,* reading the scriptures and spiritual books and practicing meditation are all strongly advisable. This should continue even after you have conceived. Even throughout pregnancy, all members of the family should make all effort to ensure that the environment in the house remains happy, and radiates satisfaction and serenity.

If you have not been careful before marriage or during the attempt to conceive, then you could be suffering from several mental and physical inadequacies or imbalances, and you should visit a vaidya.

Sexual overexcitement in women (leading to white discharge), or masturbation, and other sexual problems in men, need to be done away with before planning to have a child. These practices lead to deficiencies in the body, which should be treated by a vaidya. Only when the vaidya confirms that vitality has been fully recovered, should one continue the preparations for conception as suggested in this chapter.

It is not very difficult to follow the above-mentioned guidelines. Any action undertaken with total dedication always gives the best results and this applies here as well. All couples who wish to have a healthy child, should follow these guidelines.

This Garbhadhaan Sanskar will prove to be an invaluable and unsurpassable gift for your beloved child. It will not only prove beneficial for that child's future but also for society. We are sure that today's educated, conscientious, and intelligent youth will consider following these guidelines seriously.

- **The mind of the foetus is deeply influenced by the thoughts of the parents-to-be, prior to and during the act of conception (Garbhadhan).**
- **The favourable period for conception is from the eighth to the fifteenth day, after the onset of menstruation.**
- **The couple intending to have a child should have a socially acceptable relationship.**
- **Purity of thought and environment, and a positive mental attitude, play an important role in the process of conception.**
- **Conception should not occur in places which are new or unfamiliar.**

The body's reproductive infrastructure

Conception cannot be willed. One cannot just make up one's mind, and then expect that conception should be successful. It is dependent on several factors. Let us begin with the understanding of the male and female reproductive systems.

THE FEMALE REPRODUCTIVE SYSTEM

In Ayurved, the anatomical organs from the vagina to the uterus are known as *'Tryavarta Yoni'*.

शंखनाभ्याकृतिर्योनिस्त्र्यावर्ता सा प्रकीर्तिता ।
तस्यास्तृतीये त्वावर्ते गर्भशय्या प्रतिष्ठिता ॥

...*सुश्रुत शारीरस्थान*

śaṅkhanābhyākṛtir-yosni
stryāvartā sā prakīrtitā
Tasyāstṛtīye tvāvarte
garbhaśayyā pratiṣṭhitā ...Suśruta sārīrasthāna

The first of these three parts is the vagina. The cervix, which is the entrance to the uterus, is the second. The third part, where the foetus will be implanted and nourished, is the uterus, known in Sanskrit as the 'Garbhashaya'. 'Ashaya' = empty space, 'garbha' = embryo, i.e. the hollow space where the embryo will reside.

The uterus is, quite simply, the most important organ in a woman's body. It is normally approximately 8x5 cm in size. It weighs between 50-80g, has an internal volume of approximately 3 ml, and its walls are about 1.25 cm thick. The muscles of the uterus are extremely flexible and stretchable. The uterus can expand to 4-5 times its normal size, and weigh up to one kilogram during pregnancy. After delivery the uterus gradually returns to its normal size and weight within forty-five days.

During pregnancy, the opening to the uterus (the cervix) remains closed, and its re-opening signals the start of the process of childbirth. If, for some reason, the cervix opens up during the course of the pregnancy, this poses an increased risk of miscarriage. In fact, if there is a possibility that the cervix may open during pregnancy, or if it is observed to be dilating, it can be sewn closed to prevent the chances of a spontaneous abortion.

During pregnancy, i.e. before delivery, the cervix is circular in shape, whereas after childbirth it takes the shape of a slit. Cervical tissues are not sensitive to touch, temperature or pain.

Emerging from the uterus to the right and left are the fallopian tubes, which terminate at the ovaries. At the ovarian end these tubes broaden like a half - open hibiscus flower.They are designed like this so that the egg (ovum) released from the ovary is caught by the broad, hibiscus-like end and transported to the uterus. Infections in the fallopian tubes can cause obstacles to this transportation process. In such cases, the egg cannot pass through the fallopian tubes normally, and so conception cannot occur.

There are two ovaries. Each is approximately 3 x 2 x 1 cm in size. The right and left ovaries release one egg each (these eggs are also called oocytes) every alternate month i.e. only one ovary is active at a time. As soon as the egg emerges from the ovary, it is drawn into the fallopian tube. When a girl child is born the total number of ova present in her ovaries is already determined and cannot be increased or changed during her life.

In a normal twenty-eight day cycle the ovum is released from the ovary between the twelfth and the fourteenth day, as calculated from the first day of menstruation. This procedure is called **ovulation**. In every monthly cycle, for 12 to 14 days, the uterus prepares itself for pregnancy. If conception does not occur in that cycle, the preparatory proliferated tissue in the uterine walls is sloughed off and expelled gradually during menstruation. It is to be noted, however, that even if menstruation is regular, this does not necessarily mean that ovulation has occurred. In cases of anovulatory or non-ovulatory cycles, no ovum is released, though menstrual discharge will be present. In such cases conception of course is not possible.

During a normal menstrual cycle, bleeding lasts for four to five days. The flow of blood is heavier during the first two days, and gradually tapers down in the following three days. The average blood lost during menstruation is around 50-100 ml.

THE MALE REPRODUCTIVE SYSTEM

The male reproductive cell is known as *shukranu* (sperm). According to Ayurved, *shukra dhatu* resides all over the body and semen, which is its essence, is discharged during sexual intercourse. A healthy male ejaculates around 3.5 ml semen at a time. One ml semen contains approximately 60 to 120 million sperm, and each sperm is around 1/500 of an inch in size. Sperm are produced in the testicles, transmitted through the testicular canals (vas deferens), and released with the semen. In spite of a large number of sperm being present in the seminal fluid, only around 300 to 500 healthy sperm reach the ovum. The time required for the sperm to travel from the cervix to the fallopian tubes is around one hour. Only one sperm can enter the ovum, after which penetration by another sperm is not possible.

According to Ayurved, the characteristic quality of sperm is 'mild and cooling' *(soumya)*, and one must take care to protect it against high temperatures. Sperm can only be produced at temperatures lower than regular body temperature. Accordingly, nature has devised a special way to keep the temperature in the testes lower than in the rest of the body, by placing them in a sac outside the main body.

Even though the quantities of semen and menstrual blood mentioned here are considered normal for the general population, there are variations according to individual constitution and other external factors.

CONCEPTION

For conception to occur, sperm and ovum must meet. The mature ovum is released from the ovary, and enters the fallopian tube, where it remains for some time. The ovum stays alive for approximately 24 hours. If the fusion of ovum and sperm occurs during this time, conception has taken place. The fertilised ovum then slowly makes its way to the uterus and implants itself in the uterine wall, from where it receives its nourishment until it develops its own nutritional system (through the placenta).

TWINS AND MULTIPLE PREGNANCIES

Single birth (i.e. the birth of one child in every pregnancy) is generally the norm. However, if the sperm and ovum are not healthy, or are imbalanced or diseased, the uterus may become implanted with two or more zygotes (fertilized eggs). This is called *yamal garbha* in Sanskrit.

Ayurved says the following in relation to multiple pregnancies:

बीजेऽन्तर्वायुना भिन्ने द्वौ जीवौ कुक्षिमागतौ ।
यमावित्यभिधीयेते धर्मेतरपुरःसरौ ॥ *...सुश्रुत शारीरस्थान*

Bīje~ntarvāyunā bhinne dvau jīvau kukṣimāgatau
Yamāvityabhidhīyete dharmetarapuraḥsarau
...Suśruta śārīrasthāna

When, due to vata dosha, the fertilised ovum gets divided into two parts, and both parts get implanted in the uterine wall, leading to the formation of two zygotes, these zygotes are known as 'twins'.

If the resulting division is into more than two, and each part becomes implanted separately, then it results in a multiple pregnancy.

Two types of twins

- When the fertilised egg divides into two parts, then the two zygotes formed are identical in each and every respect (monozygotic or identical twins). They have the same sex. After birth these twins look exactly alike, and exhibit similar behaviour.

- When two eggs are accidentally fertilised by two different sperm, then two separate zygotes are formed. These two zygotes are completely different from each other (fraternal, dizygotic or non-identical twins). Here their gender may or may not turn out to be the same; they may both be male, both female or one female and one male.

The ratio worldwide of single childbirths: twins: triplets is 10000:1000:1.

The uterus is actually designed to support only one embryo at a time. A single embryo ensures adequate space for the baby, and adequate nourishment for both, the mother and the child.

If the sperm or ovum have an inherent imbalance, this may cause *vata* to divide the cell (zygote) into two or more parts, resulting in twin or multiple pregnancies. It has been observed that the occurrence of twins is often genetic, that is, the birth of twins is more common in certain families. However, it has been observed that women who have undergone hormone treatments prior to conception are also likely to give birth to twins or triplets, even if there is no family history of multiple pregnancies. According to Ayurved, unsuitable eating habits, unnatural behaviour, and an inappropriate lifestyle cause the *yamal garbha*.

Now that you understand the basics of the apparatus of the body's reproductive system, the next couple of chapters will inform you on the various kinds of obstacles both a man or woman might face while trying to conceive. The solutions to these problems as well as preventive measures are also provided. The most important aspect for women, though, is how they can take good care of themselves so they can completely avoid any chance of even encountering such problems.

- **The ovum stays alive for 24 hours after release, and conception occurs if it is fertilised by a sperm during this time frame.**
- **The number of ova a woman is going to produce in life is pre-programmed from birth and this number cannot be increased or changed during one's lifetime.**
- **Sperm is cooling and mild in nature, and exposure to excessive heat is therefore not advisable. Tight-fitting clothes are also to be avoided.**

Feminine balance

Women have some specific aspects in their physical structure and hormonal cycle that constantly undergo changes. If this hormonal cycle works efficiently, they are less likely to fall ill.

Ayurved describes a few simple but effective guidelines to ensure that a woman's health remains balanced.

- 7-8 hours of peaceful sleep.
- Strict rest, physically and mentally, during menstruation.
- Regular use of oils cultured with herbs, such as **Santulan Femisan Oil**. *'Pichu'* - keeping a swab soaked in **Santulan Femisan Oil** in the vagina overnight - is simple and very effective.
- *Dhoop* or smoke therapy - an effective way to prevent or cure infections in the reproductive tract
- Taking care of the breasts. Apply specific oils and pastes on the

breasts to help maintain hormonal balance.

- Listen daily to scientifically composed music for women's health e.g. the **Stree Santulan** album (its contents are explained later in this chapter).
- As far as possible eat only *sattvik* and easily digestible food according to your constitution.
- Practice suitable yoga asanas daily.

Apart from all the above, if women understand the idea that taking extreme care of themselves during menstruation is the cornerstone of their health, then they will benefit immensely.

DHOOP, PASTES, OILS ETC.

Dhoop is a very highly recommended form of therapy in Ayurved. Many Indian households will be familiar with using *dhoop* for spiritual or religious rituals, or to keep insects away. It is essentially a therapeutic methodology which can be applied to different uses. *Dhoop* is extremely helpful for women for e.g. **Santulan Shakti Dhoop**, helps medicinal herbs enter the vagina in the form of smoke particles. This helps regulate the menstrual cycle and maintain hormonal balance. It also prevents infections and vaginal discharge. In Ayurvedic practice, after childbirth, smoke therapy is normally administered on the new mother's entire body. Smoke therapy is highly recommended once or twice a week even for general good health. How you can administer *dhoop* to yourself is explained in later chapters.

From a very early age in women, their breasts and uterus require attention. The application of therapeutic pastes and oils is a simple and effective method of keeping them healthy. Ayurved has several preparations of pastes or *lep* that can be regularly applied on the breasts. Oils infused with herbs, like *Dadimadhya* oil, or **Santulan Suhrud Oil**, should be lightly massaged on to the breasts, at least twice or thrice a week. This will keep the breasts healthy and firm. It also helps prevent lumps, cyst formations and tumours in the breasts.

After childbirth the breasts undergo changes for lactation. It is important to take care of the breasts at this point so that there is no possibility of any hormonal imbalance.

HERBS, MEDICINES AND TREATMENTS

Santulan Femisan Oil

1. Helps maintain hormonal balance.
2. Detoxifies and strengthens the vagina, cervix, and uterus.
3. Enhances the capacity of the uterus to allow implantation of the fertilised ovum.
4. Helps ovaries and fallopian tubes remain healthy.
5. Prevents dryness in the vagina; provides required lubrication.
6. Prevents looseness of the vaginal muscles, both after childbirth, and due to advanced age.
7. Prevents infections and inflammations of the vagina and bladder.
8. Prevents vaginal discharge.

Santulan Femisan Oil also helps to dissipate excessive heat in the body and fosters sound, peaceful, and deep sleep. Since it provides so many benefits, it can indirectly, and to a large extent, alleviate feelings of frustration and mental distress. Many women have reported the experience of these benefits after using **Santulan Femisan Oil**.

In addition to everything mentioned above many women may require special medication. Please consult a *vaidya* on these matters and therapies. For general information, some effective treatments are mentioned below:

- **Herbal preparations:** *Shatavari*, aloe vera, *ashoka* (Saraca indica) and *manjishtha* (Rubia cordifolia), are excellent for women. *Shatavari Kalpa* should be mixed with milk and had everyday. It strengthens the reproductory organs, promotes a proportionate feminine figure, and a glowing complexion. A teaspoon of fresh aloe vera gel is great for women in general (except during pregnancy, when it is to be avoided completely). *Kumari Asav*, *Ashokarishtha* or **Santulan Feminine Balance Asav**, made from herbs such as aloe vera, *ashoka*, and *anantmool* (Hemidesmus indicus) are even more effective. Regular intakle helps regulate the menstrual cycle, ensures adequate and normal flow of blood during menstruation, helps keep the reproductive organs healthy, and assists in maintaining hormonal balance. **ManjishthaSan** and **San Rose** help to purify *rakta dhatu* (blood) and improve haemoglobin content.

Ayurved has several more medicines for women. Depending on individual constitution, and the severity of the problem, as well as causes and symptoms, medicines such as *Chandraprabha*, *Gokshuradi Churna*, **Santulan Ashokadi Ghruta**, and *Phalaghruta* may be prescribed for hormonal imbalances.

Other therapies possible under medical supervision are:

- **Vaginal Douche :** A specific herbal decoction is used to cleanse the vagina. The herbs used for this process, such as *dhayati*, *trifala* and *ashoka*, help to heal abrasions and small lesions in the mucus membrane of the vagina, prevent vaginal infections and inflammations, and reduce vaginal discharge. *Dhoop* should follow a vaginal douche for additional benefits.

- **Uttar Basti :** *Uttar Basti* is a very effective therapy following vaginal douche. A specially prepared oil or herbal ghee is inserted into the uterus through the vagina and cervix. *Uttar Basti*, promotes proper ovulation and stabilises the fallopian tubes to allow them to propel the ovum in the right direction at the right time. It strengthens the uterus in preparation for a normal and healthy conception.

MUSIC

Hormonal levels or secretions are easily affected by physical and mental health. A woman's psychological condition is an important contributing factor for the maintenance of hormonal stability. It should come as no surprise that music, as a therapy, achieves miraculous results for hormonal health. **Stree Santulan** is a musical compilation created with exactly this intention. It contains specific Vedic mantras, primarily from the Saam Veda and Rig Veda *ruchas*, composed in specially selected *raga* (melody systems). It also has some mantras from the Atharva Veda that are recommended specifically for the protection of women. Among the several tracks on the CD, *Achyutashatakam*, a composition thousands of years old, by Shri Adi Shankaracharya, is played and sung in *Raga Sarang*. *Raga Bibhas* too aids feminine balance. Instrumental music played on the *veena* is also very beneficial. The traditional *Suryakavach* is important as it aids the individual organs of the body to work to full capacity, and helps keep the body full of energy. A composition of the *Yamunashtak* helps eliminate depression, fear, and anxiety, and promotes peace of mind and cheerfulness. It also promotes beauty, health and renews vitality in the body.

A lot of research study, practical application,

and feedback from users, have all shown that these compositions have a very positive effect on hormonal balance and women's physiological processes.

DIET AND YOGA

A balanced diet and yoga are absolutely essential. The following suggestions are very important:

1. Eat sattvik and nourishing food.
2. Eat meals at regular times
3. As far as possible, abstain from foods, such as cabbage, cauliflower, kidney beans (*rajma*), dried peas, chick peas (*chole*), capsicum, gawar beans, aubergine (eggplant), raw tomatoes, and eggs.
4. Avoid having milk and fruit together (i.e. in a fruit salad or a milk shake).
5. Reduce the intake of extremely sour, spicy, salty and fermented foods, as well as deep fried foods.
6. Cut down on the intake of fast food and aerated drinks, especially late at night.

Yoga asanas chosen in accordance with one's constitution and more importantly, performed regularly, have really great results! Certain asanas such as *yogmudra*, *pavan muktasana*, *katichakrasana*, S**antulan Kriya Samarpan**, and **Santulan Kriya Butterfly**, are useful in general. Regular walks, *pranayam* and deep breathing techniques help as well. *Pranayam bhasrika* should be practiced under professional supervision.

Hormonal balance is important not only for conception but also for overall physical health, mental satisfaction, vitality and the maintenance of youth.

So, healing music, herbal supplements, special applications and therapies, regular yoga and the recommended diet, all help a woman to maintain her femininity and attain equilibrium at all levels, at all times.

Sometimes, the positive results of following all these guidelines and undergoing therapy may not be apparent for a while. There is an unseen force governing every deed (fate or karma), which is beyond our control. So, while one must follow everything as far as possible, it is essential also to keep faith in the Supreme Energy.

- **In addition to looking after the uterus, taking care of the breasts from an early age helps maintain feminine balance.**
- **Miraculous results are possible when medication is supplemented by music therapy.**
- **Women can benefit greatly by eating a teaspoon of fresh Aloe vera gel every morning.**
- **Feminine balance is essential for glowing health, happiness, vitality, mental satisfaction, youthfulness, and beauty.**
- **Proper diet and yogasanas are a must for maintaining feminine health.**

Difficulties during conception...

According to Ayurved, there are many reasons for the inability to conceive. These have been described as follows:

योनिप्रदोषान्मनसोऽभितापात्
शुक्रासृगाहारविहारदोषात् ।
अकालयोगात् बलसंक्षय्याच्च
गर्भं चिराद्विन्दति सप्रजाऽपि ॥ ...चरक शारीरस्थान

Yonipradoṣān-manaso~bhitāpāt
śukrāsṛgāhāravihāradoṣāt
Akāla-yogāt balasaṅkṣayyācca
garbham cirād-vindati saprajā~pi
.....Caraka śārīrasthāna

Anatomical or physiological disorders in the yoni (female genital tract), mental imbalance, diseased or unhealthy eggs or sperm, inappropriate food or daily activities (i.e. those which are contradictory to the constitution), sexual intercourse at times other than fertile days, lack of vitality or strength caused by disease - all of these can lead to failed or delayed conception.

Our society is generally conditioned to think that if a couple is unable to have a child, the woman is at fault. Men do not usually undergo examination until the results of tests conducted on their partners prove normal. Whether the problem lies with the man or the woman, both should be treated. The reasons for abnormalities occurring in the male may be fewer, but the result is the same - infertility.

REASONS FOR MALE INFERTILITY

The main causes of male infertility are - low sperm count, deformed sperm, or the total absence of sperm in the semen (azoospermia). Malfunction of the male reproductive organs, and congenital or hereditary defects in the production of sperm, may also cause infertility in men.

Lifestyle Issues

As mentioned earlier, the lack of nutrition for *shukra dhatu* and lack of foods required for the nourishment of sperm could lead to sperm disorders, which could result in infertility. Habitually staying up late at night and severe mental stress will take their toll as well. Regular or constant intake of junk food or excessively spicy and oily food may also damage *shukra dhatu*.

Encourage a diet that nourishes *shukra dhatu* right from childhood. During adolescence and youth, soaked chickpeas are excellent for this purpose. Eating *dink ladu* (balls made from edible gum) during winter, having milk everyday, and home-made ghee and butter on a regular basis, are all highly recommended. The intake of appropriate *rasayans*, such as **Santulan Chyavanprash**, **Santulan Dhatri Rasayan**, and **Santulan Suryaprash**, as suitable to individual constitution, is very helpful.

Behavioural Issues

As mentioned earlier, Ayurved describes the properties of sperm as mild and cooling, and advises that excessive heat to the genital area should be avoided. Men should not use very hot water while bathing and avoid working in heated environments or indulge in excessive steam or sauna therapies. Tight clothes, for example tight jeans, although fashionable, may cause heat and pressure in the genital area, and have a detrimental effect on the production and the quality of sperm. Placing a laptop directly on the lap is quite harmful as well, since it generates heat. Smoking and too much alcohol is definitely harmful to the production of sperm.

Taking Care Of Shukra

Inappropriate influences during puberty in the form of pornographic magazines and visuals create improper impressions on the young mind, and usually lead to an increased tendency for masturbation. Ayurvedic philosophy strongly advocates the maximum retention and protection of *shukra dhatu*. However, because we are ignorant about this, it is not uncommon for young men to be addicted to masturbation This causes loss of *shukra dhatu* from a very young age. The widely prevalent belief that this is 'normal' and 'natural' may support the conviction that there is nothing wrong in what they are doing. Far from being natural, it only causes the destruction of semen and *shukra*.

Excess *shukra dhatu* in the body may spontaneously and involuntarily ejaculate at certain times, due to wet dreams etc. This can be considered normal and can be compared to overflow in a water tank. Even so, it should occur only at the right time and only if all the other proper functions of *shukra* in the body have been fulfilled, and there is excess *shukra dhatu* left over. If the release of *shukra dhatu* like this results in its depletion in the body, it will create obstacles to body function and can be quite harmful. So, for all these reasons *shukra* must be saved and protected until the right age has been reached (its quantities must be kept up). There is a lot we can understand about it, and do, to increase its quality as well.

The loss of *shukra* goes hand in hand with obesity, and the increase of fat *(meda dhatu)* in the body. In obesity, on one hand, the body becomes weaker due to the loss of *shukra*, and on the other hand food is only converted into fat tissue. So the nutrient from food does not reach *shukra* (which is the deepest or last level of tissue in the body) at all, causing even further *shukra* depletion. This is a vicious cycle. Obesity also leads to weakness and diminished energy during sexual intercourse.

Infections and Chronic Illness

Infertility could have other causes as well, like imbalances or infections either in the urinary or reproductive tracts, or blockage in the vas deferens. Sometimes during examination of semen, doctors may only consider sperm count and motility. The presence of pus (inflammatory cells) or blood, should not be ignored because it is an important factor. Ayurved describes such semen that has pus or blood as incompetent and of no use for conception. These cases should be treated immediately. If the egg is fertilised by such sperm it increases the chances of producing a handicapped or otherwise diseased child.

In addition to all these causes, the quality and quantity of sperm is also adversely affected by any chronic illness. Sexually transmitted diseases, such as syphilis and gonorhea also affect sperm and cause difficulty during sexual intercourse. The disease is also likely to be transmitted to the partner, causing her serious problems as well.

Psychological Issues

Many men have erectile problems during sexual intercourse, or are unable to have sex. They could also be fearful due to ignorance. These could also be psychological in nature. The cause of these can be treated. A change of food habits and lifestyle would normally help. Foods and rasayans that nourish *shukra dhatu*, as mentioned earlier, are essential.

Often, in these cases, due to embarrassment or the fear of humiliation, men do not seek help in time. This could lead to the problem becoming chronic and severe, and even cause an inferiority complex. Ayurved has specified special medicines for such problems. **Santulan Purusham Oil**, cultured with specific Ayurvedic herbs, which is very effective in these cases.

One large change in human beings in our times is the tremendous increase in our expectations in all aspects of life. Most people are well - educated, have stressful jobs, work overtime, and try to earn as much money as possible. This leads to fatigue, mental disturbance, agitation, loss of peace of mind, stress and anxiety, all of which are usually ignored and taken as part of life. Often, this results in physical weakness and the depletion of *shukra dhatu*. Many patients who are young businessmen, complain of a reduced desire for sex and diminished sexual energy in their thirties.

Vitality

Whatever be the reason for infertility, the

physician will need to work on helping the patient strengthen and vitalize *shukra dhatu*. Medicines which may be beneficial here are - *Shatavaryadi churna*, *Gokshuradi churna* (to be taken with ghee and sugar), *Suvarnamalini vasant*, *Vasantkusumakar*, and *Makardhwaj rasa*. All these should be taken after medical consultation. These mixtures help to purify semen, and increase shukra dhatu.

It is very important to deal with stress effectively. Music therapy is extremely effective in dealing with mental tensions. A good diet (as already described), sleeping and rising early, and yoga asanas according to one's constitution are imperative for a life full of vitality.

REASONS FOR FEMALE INFERTILITY

Anatomical Reasons

As mentioned before, *yoni* refers to the female genital tract, which is comprised of 3 parts *viz* the vagina, cervix, and uterus. Anatomical anomalies of any of these parts, e.g. a small and contracted vagina, lack of aperture in the hymen, a narrow cervical opening, anatomical irregularities in the uterus, or a weak uterus, blocked fallopian tubes, polycystic ovaries, and other ovarian disorders, could all result in the failure to conceive. In addition, physiological disorders, such as anovulatory cycles, could also prevent conception.

Excess Heat

A functional imbalance during menstruation, and an excess of *pitta dosha*, lead to excess heat in the vagina. In this increased temperature the sperm entering the vagina may be destroyed, and conception does not take place.

Psychological Issues

In rare cases, where the woman is fearful of, or apprehensive about sexual intercourse, or cannot endure sex, of course, conception becomes difficult.

These problems should be treated promptly and correctly. Superficial or temporary therapies will not lead to complete treatment.

Family Relations

Another extremely important aspect to keep in mind is the relationship between the woman and her husband's family. The woman especially, should have good relations with her husband's side of the family. Since the child-to-be also receives certain 'programmes' from the father, it is imperative that the woman has the support of his family. If they do not support her, it could block the chances of conception for the couple.

Hormonal Imbalance

This is the most important part of the subject of women's health. You will find that disorders due to hormonal imbalance overlap with, and are related to, several other problems that women may encounter. When talking about hormonal imbalance for women, the most important aspect, and the most neglected one, are the activities and behaviour of women during menstruation.

Ayurvedic science has clearly given menstruation a lot of thought. There are detailed descriptions about this issue in the texts. Behaviour and lifestyle that needs to be adhered to during these days is outlined explicitly.

Behavior During Menstruation

Menstruation constitutes the first three days of the monthly cycle, and a special regime is prescribed for these special days. During this time the woman loses a certain amount of blood and is therefore more sensitive and emotional. Women should take extra care to avoid all kinds of mental and physical stress during menstruation. It is recommended that she should not exercise too much, lift any weights, or even work too much. During menses a woman should avoid crowded places, late nights, sleeping in the day, trimming nails and hair or taking a full bath. Not taking a bath does not mean that physical cleanliness and washing should be neglected; it merely means that she should not wash her hair, stand under the shower or bathe in a tub, as would be normally done.

Menstruating women should not watch scenes or movies which excite her or elicit fear (such as horror movies) or read such books. They should certainly avoid disputes with family members or at work. Food should be light, nutritious, and *sattvik.* She should make sure that she has proper and regular bowel movements. It is highly recommended that she contemplates on good and positive thoughts during this period.

During these three days the flow is directed downward in the body, and physical energy is low. So contact with places and things of high energy, should be avoided e.g. temples and kitchens (food and water, except that which is meant for her own consumption). More importantly, she should abstain from sexual intercourse during these three to four days.

After observing all the necessary guidelines during the three days of menstruation, she should wash her hair on the fourth day and dress in clean clothes. Sexual intercourse after the seventh day of menstruation is considered problem-free.

All of these guidelines have been set out to protect the health of the woman and her future child. Couples who want to have a healthy offspring should pay heed to these rules and follow them very strictly. All women should adhere to these guidelines throughout their years of menstruation to maintain good health, hormonal balance, and femininity in general.

In modern times the life of women has changed dramatically. They are equal to men in terms of work and household chores. Women have assumed responsibility for their careers, along with caring for and nurturing their families. Modern women have advanced into every possible field, made their mark in almost all walks of life, and have reached new heights.

And consequently, the woman has also been driven further away from her nature. Her innate tendencies, such as delicateness, sensitivity, tenderness, and her emotional life, have been compromised. She may have to pursue a job or career that may clash with her basic nature, health, or constitution.

Since every job requires a specific physical and mental constitution, it follows that all jobs are not suitable for all people. In addition to taking care of the home, a career-woman may have work-related stress, tension with her superiors etc which could cause her general health to deteriorate.

Not so long ago, women would want to sit for meals with their husbands and families, but today, after working at home as well as the workplace, women regularly say, "Let's go out for dinner." This habit harms everybody's health.

We have learned, rather too easily, to say that we

do not have the time to follow things that are good for us. And so the simple rules of behaviour during menstruation are ignored, along with much needed rest during these days. All this will result in hormonal imbalances and several related disorders.

It is difficult to prove 'scientifically' the negative effects of not following these guidelines during menstruation, but it is easily seen that general health is adversely affected. None of the processes of child birth, from conception, to implantation of the embryo, pregnancy, and delivery, will ensue in a planned and desirable manner if these practices are ignored. They will be fraught with difficulty. Hormonal imbalances in young women mean that their health is poor at an early age, causing several unexplainable illnesses. Cases of children being born with diseases which seem to have no cause are also on the rise. The causes for such seemingly unexplained diseases in both, young women, as well as newly born children, will be rooted in the woman's behaviour during menstruation, and her overall lifestyle that has disturbed her hormonal balance. In order to prevent these potentially tragic problems please consider the above mentioned guidelines very carefully and act on them!

There are more serious instructions as well. Like as follows.

अज्ञानाद्वा प्रमादाद्वा लोभाद्वा दैवतश्चवा ॥
सा चेत्कुर्यात् निषिद्धानि गर्भो दोषांस्तदाप्नुयात् ॥ ... *भावप्रकाश*

Ajñānād-vā pramādād-vā
lōbhād-vā daivataśca-vā
Sā cet-kuryāt niṣiddhāni
garbho doṣānstaāpnuyāt ....Bhāvaprakāśa

The child will pay the price of the woman's ignorance, weaknesses, greed (for unhealthy things) *and in general, the mistakes she makes.*

Ayurved sets out, very clearly, the possible consequences to the child if menstruation guidelines are not followed by its mother, before conception. Therefore Ayurved says that a woman should habituate herself to be careful during menstruation from an early age. Obviously, she should be doubly careful in the months before she conceives. If she behaves in a manner that will disturb her hormonal balance during this preparatory period, the chances of adverse effects on her child increase dramatically. Ayurved gives examples such as, if a woman cries during the first three days of her menstruation it is possible that her child will be born with disorders of the eye. If she sleeps in the day, the child could be over-active or fidgety; if she works in excess, the child could be mentally retarded or psychotic; if she has a full body 'Abhyang' massage, the child could be born with skin disorders; if she applies kajal (kohl) to her eyes, the child could be born blind.

Several of these cause and effect relationships will provide answers to the question "Why did this happen?" when there appears to be no obvious cause for a particular disease in a child.

Even if a woman is not planning for a baby, such actions during menstruation may adversely affect her own health. A regular menstrual cycle is an indicator of hormonal balance. Changes in the hormonal system could cause not only irregular menstruation, but also may bring on symptoms such as depression, sudden increase in weight, pimples and rashes on the face, and premenstrual bloating (especially heaviness of the breasts and oedema).

It is obviously extremely desirable to have healthy conception, proper growth of the foetus, nourishment in the uterus for the foetus, smooth delivery in the normal period of nine months, and adequate lactation. They are all dependent on optimal hormonal balance.

Inappropriate food and lifestyle habits are already responsible for disturbing the hormonal system. Nowadays women ignore that they need to rest and care for themselves during menstruation, causing further unnecessary strain. Then, fixes like contraceptive pills, especially immediately after marriage, to prevent pregnancy, and the rampant use of other hormonal pills to try and control menstrual cycles according to one's convenience, really puts pressure on the body causing cases of severe hormonal imbalance.

Scanty Menstrual Discharge

A delayed menstruation, reduced bleeding, or a short menstruation is called *rajakshaya*. This could be accompanied by pain during menstruation, and could also include blood flowing in the form of clots.

The two main causes for this are a diet lacking in proper nutrition, and low haemoglobin (anaemia). Anaemia could also result from long, chronic illnesses such as typhoid or jaundice. Factors that lead to imbalance in vata dosha can also cause *rajakshaya.* According to Ayurved, menstrual blood originates from *rasa dhatu*. Any factor which causes this *dhatu* to diminish e.g. excessive thinking or stress, can also lead to *rajakshaya*.

If this condition prevails for an extended period of time, it could lead to an increase in weight - primarily in the back and waist region - excessive hair loss, darkening of the skin, increased body heat or general weakness.

In general, women will take only problems like weight gain and hair loss seriously! However, if the root cause of *rajakshaya* is treated, then all other related problems will disappear along with it. Aloe vera is beneficial in such cases, and medications such as *Kumari Asav*, *Ashokarishta*, or **Santulan Feminine Balance Asav**, which are prepared from aloe vera and other herbs, are useful in the treatment of *rajakshaya*.

Milk, according to Ayurved, should be consumed everyday. In cases of hormonal imbalance, **Santulan Shatavari Kalpa**, and **Santulan Shatanant Kalpa** are very useful to help nourish *rasa dhatu* and are to be taken with milk. To nourish *rakta dhatu* (blood) and increase haemoglobin, **San Rose** is recommended for everyday consumption.

Excess Menstrual Discharge

The opposite of *rajakshaya* is excessive menstrual bleeding (menorrhoea). Many women are under the false impression that the heavier the menstrual flow, and the longer the bleeding lasts, the deeper and more intense the cleaning and purification process will be. Actually heavy and prolonged bleeding does nothing more than deplete strength. The loss of blood also leads to dullness and loss of lustre on the skin, dizziness, and hair loss. There could also be recurring bouts of irritation, psychological turmoil, and a general loss of peace of mind. The most serious resulting problem, however, is the weakening of the uterus, and if this is not rectified, it could lead to the inability to conceive.

Depending on the cause of the excess blood loss the treatment is aimed towards the following 4 points:

1. Stopping blood loss
2. Recovery of blood lost
3. Cleansing and strengthening of the uterus
4. Restoration of hormonal balance.

The remedies recommended for this include: *Pushyanug churna, Lodhrasav,* roasted and puffed alum, **San Rose**, vaginal douches with special herbal decoctions (*kadha*), inserting medicated oils into the vagina (i.e. a cotton swab soaked in oil such as **Santulan Femisan Oil**), and herbal ghee preparations such as **Santulan Ashokadi Ghruta** and *Phalaghruta*, to strengthen the uterus.

The main cause of this condition, is an imbalance in *vata* and *pitta doshas*. The following foods are to be avoided in this condition.

Very oily or spicy, fermented products.

Tamarind, sour yoghurt, dried peas, chickpeas, dried beans and legumes, and kidney beans, should be excluded from diet.

Vaginal Discharge and Infections

The appearance of a white and sticky or watery discharge, is considered normal only if it occurs one or two days prior to the onset of menstruation, or at the time of ovulation. A discharge occurring at any other time is not considered normal. It could lead to back ache, pain in the legs, weakness, and fatigue. This requires attention, even if the quantity of discharge is very negligible. Ayurvedic physicians call this condition *Som Rog* (*Som* means elixir, *Rog* means disease). In such cases, the woman loses *shukra* and other vital *dhatus* important for 'life' (i.e. which are equivalent to an elixir), in the form of vaginal discharge. This causes the uterus to become weak thereby making it difficult for the woman to conceive.

In many cases, women ignore abnormal or heavy vaginal discharge, and are completely unaware that the appearance of even small amounts of discharge, whether regular or sporadic, is an alarming development. As a result, this serious symptom may be ignored for years.

At the Atmasantulana Village, in Karla, many couples have been treated for infertility. Even though most of their tests showed normal results, they were still unable to conceive. After many questions and a deeper probe into their medical histories, it often is discovered that one or both partners have neglected urinary or genital tract infections in the past.

Women often take hurried, haphazard treatment for these disorders and since such infections are difficult to treat they are often not cured completely. Certain medications often treat the problem superficially, and relieve only the troublesome symptoms, leaving a dormant internal infection which continues to surface in any number of situations. After such prolonged and recurrent infections, the chances of conception are obviously reduced.

A large part of the therapy for such problems is the use of **Santulan Femisan Oil**. In a later chapter the complete recommendations for the care of the gynaecological system have been described. They include placing cotton swabs doused in **Santulan Femisan Oil** in the vagina, cleaning the vagina with herbal douches and smoke therapy. This should be accompanied with the intake of **Santulan Uricool Satulan Prashant Churna.**

Try to avoid very spicy, sour or dry foods and restrict the intake of sour curd, cauliflower, cabbage, capsicum, green beans, eggs, dried legumes, dried peas, meat, pork and other non-vegetarian foods. By following this, it will help you recover hormonal balance and then sustain it for good health.

According to Acharya Charak, one of the main reason for infertility is *yoni-vyapad*. This refers to disturbances that are generated in the female reproductive system due to inappropriate food habits, lifestyle and behaviour.

The 4 main disorders of the *yoni*, as described are: *up-pluta*, *pari-pluta*, *shuska*, and *vamini*.

UP-PLUTA YONI-VYAPAD

**पाण्डुं सतोदमास्रावं श्वेतं स्रवति वा कफम् ।
कफवातामय व्याप्ता सा स्यात् योनिरुपप्लुता ॥**

... चरक चिकित्सास्थान

Pāṇḍum satodamāsrāvam
śvetam sravati vā kapham
Kaphavātāmaya vyāptā
sā syāt yonirupaplutā ...Caraka cikitsāsthāna

In this condition women have a discharge that is faint, light-coloured, or mucus-like (kapha), accompanied by sharp pain like needles (pricking sensation) in the vagina. This disorder is caused by an imbalance of kapha and vata dosha.

PARI-PLUTA YONI-VYAPAD

**शूना स्पर्शाक्षमा सार्तिर्नीलपीतमसृक् स्रवेत् ।
श्रोणि वंक्षणपृष्ठार्तिज्वरार्ताया परिप्लुता ॥** *... चरक चिकित्सास्थान*

śūnā sparśā-kṣamā sārtirnīlapītamasṛk sravet
śroṇi vaṅkṣaṇa-pṛṣṭhārtijvarārtāyā pariplutā
...Caraka cikitsāsthāna

In this disorder, the mucus membrane of the vagina becomes inflamed and very sensitive. There is a yellowish vaginal discharge, accompanied by backache. This disorder is caused by an imbalance of pitta and vata dosha.

SHUSKA YONI

**व्यवायकाले रुन्धन्त्या वेगान् प्रकुपितोऽनिलः ।
कुर्यात् विण्मूत्रसङ्गार्तिं शोषं योनिमुखस्य च ॥** *... चरक चिकित्सास्थान*

Vyavāya-kāle rundhantyā
vegān prakupito~nilaḥ
Kuryāt viṇmūtrasaṅgārti
śoṣam yonimukhasya ca ...Caraka cikitsāsthāna

Some women tend to ignore their bladder or bowel movement urges while engaging in sexual intercourse. This causes a gross imbalance in vata dosha resulting in dryness in the vagina. The woman experiences pain during intercourse and this could lead to problems in conception.

VAMINI YONI

**शुक्रं गर्भाशयं गतम् ।
सरुजं नीरुजं वाऽपि या स्रवेत् सा तु वामिनी ॥** *... चरक चिकित्सास्थान*

śukram garbhāśayam gatam
Sarujam nīrujam vā~pi yā sravet sā tu vāminī
....Caraka cikitsāsthāna

In many cases, due to a vata - pitta disorders, the semen is not accepted, and merely flows out of the vagina after sexual intercourse. This could result in infertility. Sometimes in these cases, the woman may experience pain when the semen flows out of the vagina.

The treatment for these disorders includes a mix of specific herbal preparations in addition to *uttar dhoop*, *uttar basti*, and vaginal oil-swabs to cleanse the gynaecological system. These should be combined with the requisite diet and lifestyle changes.

Anovulatory Cycles

Anovulation (a menstrual cycle without the release of an egg from an ovary) is yet another cause of infertility. Again, because of hormonal imbalances, many women have anovulatory cycles, even though the menstrual cycles themselves may be regular. The absence of an ovum obviously leads to infertility.

Blocked Fallopian Tubes

More and more causes of infertility today lie in inappropriate food and lifestyle habits because they tend to increase *vata dosha*. *Vata* imbalance in turn leads to obstruction of the fallopian tubes. Here, in spite of normal ovulation, there is no possibility of conception, since the sperm cannot reach the ovum to fertilize it. Several issues like tuberculosis, chronic blood loss, deficiency in *rakta dhatu*, and even frequent miscarriages are some of the other reasons for *vata* imbalance. In some cases, subtle or dormant vaginal infections may travel upwards and affect the fallopian tubes and ovaries.

Ovarian Cysts

Then there is the possibility of either internal or external ovarian cysts causing infertility. According to Ayurved this disorder occurs due to an imbalance in *vata-pitta*.

There are many types of cysts. If the cysts are small and asymptomatic they may remain undetected for quite some time. Some cysts produce symptoms which vary in their intensity and only occur at specific times. In many cases, the only symptom may be abdominal pain during menstruation or ovulation. Such cysts disappear completely after some time, either on their own or after being treated.

Other types of cysts may interfere with ovulation, and this could cause infertility. These cyst will have the above symptoms in addtion to more severe symptoms like excess facial and body hair growth and weight gain. These cases are generally quite difficult to treat.

Thyroid Dysfunction

In addition to all of the above menstruation-related problems, another increasingly common disorder is thyroid dysfunction. This can be caused by careless behaviour during menstruation, or a disturbed menstrual cycle. The symptoms could range from swelling of the body, weight gain, to an increase in blood pressure.

Uterine Fibroids

Further causes of infertility are localized growths in the uterus, known as *arbud* in Ayurved. This term refers to a superfluous growth anywhere in the body due to the imbalance of a *dosha.* Such growths in the uterus are called fibroids. Until a few years ago, this disorder was mainly detected in women of around fifty years of age. However, fibroids are now common even in young women. They are mainly caused by a *vata* imbalance, which could then influence either *pitta* or *kapha doshas*. If the fibroid is large, it will obstruct conception and implantation; if small, it could be the cause of frequent miscarriages. It can lead to pre-term or premature delivery, and if the pregnancy goes to full term, it is possible that the child will be born handicapped or diseased.

Fibroids should not be neglected, irrespective of whether one wants to have a child or not. They should be treated because of the many problems they may cause. Women with fibroids tend to have shorter menstrual cycles, excess bleeding, heaviness in the lower abdomen, severe pain during menstruation, backache, sciatica, a 'pulling' type of pain in the legs, accumulation of fat around the waist and abdomen, and frequent urination.

With proper treatment, the fibroid can be reduced in size, or may disappear completely. If made smaller it can remain in the uterine cavity without causing any complications whatsoever. While treating the fibroid it is imperative to also stop the excessive flow of blood that it is causing. If the fibroid is found to be of an unusually large size, surgery may be the only alternative. But surgery should be the last resort. It should be considered only if all other conservative efforts have failed. As far as possible, only the fibroid should be surgically removed, while preserving the uterus.

In spite of an increasing incidence of fibroids among women, the presence of cancer in such growths is negligible. On detection of fibroids women should not assume that it is cancerous and start to panic. It warrants emphasizing again that a hysterectomy (removal of the uterus) should not be performed without careful consideration, or under any pressure. A hysterectomy causes severe hormonal imbalance, which when added to the original imbalance (that prompted the hysterectomy in the first place) will prove extremely difficult to treat. The after-effects arising from such a major step will have to be borne throughout life.

After a hysterectomy, the increased levels of male hormones in the woman's body pose a serious threat to her femininity. A similar increase is seen after menopause. It has also been seen that within six months to two years after a hysterectomy, many women suffer from a variety of problems due to the imbalance in the reproductive tract. Only rarely are there no side-effects.

Hormone Replacement Therapy (HRT) too is gaining acceptance and popularity. However, many ongoing studies have shown that HRT can produce severe side-effects. It is, therefore, only recommended as a last resort, under unavoidable circumstances.

Over the years, we have observed many cases where women suffer from disorders, such as sudden weight gain, fat accumulation at the waist and hips, hormonal imbalance, severe arthritis, and other types of *vata*-related ailments. Illnesses such as hypertension, diabetes and heart disease mostly found in men so far, have also arisen in women who have undergone a hysterectomy.

The fear of infertility should not be the only cause to be attentive to diseases of the reproductive tract. The overall health of a woman is also dependent on this. Of course, the best way forward is prevention rather than cure. But should these problems still occur, the best way to treat them is in accordance with Ayurvedic guidelines. Other methods of treatment, such as surgery, should be considered only in certain cases, depending on the gravity and seriousness of the disease.

The incidence of female infertility is on the rise. In the past such cases were not so often seen. Rare or uncommon causes of infertility are becoming increasingly frequent and newspapers and magazines often report on the 'increasing infertility in the world' as one of today's most important issues.

With modern medicine and testing methods, many ailments can be detected and diagnosed at an early stage and treatment can begin promptly. The root cause of all of the above-mentioned problems is basically hormonal imbalance. And this imbalance should be treated immediately and certainly prevented from recurring.

The remedy you opt for should remove the cause and origin of the imbalance without causing other side-effects.

If one delays treatment for any reason or if the appropriate therapies are administered improperly, it could lead to many more problems. *Pitta* in the woman's body may increase, causing heat, or she may gain a lot of weight, both of which will lead to complications in future. So it is essential that appropriate therapy is taken under expert medical supervision.

- According to Ayurved, stress and mental agitation is a major cause of infertility.
- Late nights, mental stress, too much spicy and oily food, smoking, drinking alcohol, and eating junk food, is harmful for shukra dhatu.
- It is essential that shukra be protected and conserved, not only until the appropriate age for conception is attained, but it should be carefully used, and increased throughout life.
- A regular menstrual cycle is indicative of hormonal balance.
- As a result of menstrual problems, or an unnatural lifestyle, some women may suffer from thyroid problems, swelling of the body, weight gain, and hypertension.
- A hysterectomy should not be carried out without very careful consideration and unless there is no other way out.
- Women should take appropriate measures to bring a disturbed hormonal system into equilibrium.

2

Care of the Pregnant woman...

Pregnancy and delivery is almost like a second birth for a woman. She and her family have the responsibility of maintaining her health as well as that of the life growing inside her. It is essential to have comprehensive knowledge about diet, yogasanas, and several other 'Do's and Don'ts'.

Early days of pregnancy

The onset of pregnancy is one of the most unforgettable moments in a woman's life. Your heart is sure to miss a beat when you realize that you are pregnant!

That which was a secret, deep inside her, is confirmed and finally revealed. Her happiness, and the joy of communicating the news to her family, know no bounds. But women also generally feel a little shy during this whole process, and anxious at the same time, as a hundred questions start going through their minds: Is everything ok? Will the pregnancy proceed without problems or unforeseen events? Is the baby alright? Is it a boy or a girl or perhaps even twins?

An especially intuitive woman may immediately sense that she has conceived. But most women only begin to suspect that they may be pregnant when they miss a period. By then, 14 -15 days have already passed since conception. It is now possible to conduct a pregnancy test at home (the H.C.G. hormone test), and once confirmed, the pregnant woman should immediately start following the guidelines in this book. After the second period is missed it is necessary to be checked once by a gynaecologist. However, avoid internal examination as far as possible. To help with this process the symptoms of pregnancy at this stage are provided below.

निष्ठीविका गौरवमङ्गसादः
तन्द्राप्रहर्षौ हृदये व्यथा च ।
तृप्तिश्च बीजग्रहणं च योन्यां
गर्भस्य सद्योऽनुगतस्य लिङ्गम् ॥ *...चरक शारीरस्थान*

Niṣṭhīvikā gauravamaṅgasādaḥ
tandrāpraharṣau hṛdaye vyathā ca
Tṛptiśca bīja-grahaṇam ca yonyām
garbhasya sadyo~nugatasya liṅgam

....Caraka śārīrasthāna

- *Nausea, cravings, vomiting, bouts of dizziness or giddiness*
- *Poor concentration, combined with a feeling of deep inner satisfaction*
- *Fatigue and weakness*
- *The appearance of goose pimples all over the body for no apparent reason*
- *Palpitations*
- *Heartburn*
- *Aversion to strong smells*

It is not necessary that all these symptoms will appear in all women. The symptoms are highly pronounced in the first pregnancy. In following pregnancies they become less pronounced. And there are always a few fortunate women who do not experience any of these symptoms at all.

The first two to three months of pregnancy bring nausea and loss of appetite. This can be alleviated with herbal preparations such as *sutshekhar* or *drakshadi vati*.

Quick Remedy for morning sickness: Soak half a tea spoon (tsp) of coriander seeds in water for 30 mins, then grind to a paste. Mix with an equal amount of sugar. Take 2-3 teaspoons of raw rice (without boric powder or any other insecticides) in half a cup of water. Let it soak for ten minutes. Squeeze the rice in the water. Sieve the water to remove the rice. Eat the above mentioned paste with this water.

Please understand that each pregnancy is unique. Two successive pregnancies may give rise to different symptoms in the same woman. These experiences are dependent on the constitutions of both mother and baby.

It is not uncommon for older women, when observing a young woman who is pregnant, to ask, "Why is she suffering so much? We never had so much trouble." Situations and times have changed, and the prevailing health and strength of each individual elicits different reactions. Avoid comparing one pregnancy with another.

To calculate the expected date of delivery (EDD) please refer to the table given towards the end of the book.

Pregnancy is an important and sensitive period for the mother and child. A new living being is taking shape in a woman's body, and it is crucial that she takes extreme care of her diet, lifestyle, and even thinking patterns.

Acharya Charak has described this condition as follows.

पूर्णमिव तैलपात्रं असंक्षोभयताऽन्तर्वत्नि भवत्युपचर्या ।

... चरक शारीरस्थान

Pūrṇamiva taila-pātram asaṅkṣobhayatā~ntarvatni bhavatyupacaryā ...Caraka śārīrasthāna

A pregnant woman is like a pot full to the brim with oil which requires an absolutely steady hand to take it from one place to another. The pregnant woman must pay attention to this new life that is as dear to her as her own life, as well as herself, with great care.

Family and relatives need to contribute by extending all manner of support. During this period, it is absolutely necessary that the woman be protected on the physical, as well as the psychological levels. This all-round alertness is very important for her well - being.

DO'S AND DON'TS DURING PREGNANCY

The pregnant woman always needs to act with caution. Let us see what Ayurved recommends for her at this time. Please make a concerted effort to follow these recommendations as far as possible during pregnancy.

उत्कटविषमकठिनासनसेविन्या वातमूत्रपुरीषवेगानुपरुन्धत्या दारुण अनुचितव्यायामसेविन्याः तीक्ष्णोष्णातिमात्रसेविन्याः प्रमिताशनसेविन्या गर्भो म्रियतेऽन्तः तथा अभिघातप्रपीडनैः श्वभ्रकूपप्रपातदेशावलोकनैर्वाऽभीक्ष्णं मातुः प्रपतत्यकाले गर्भाः तथाऽतिमात्रसंक्षोभिभिर्यानैर्यानेन अप्रियातिमात्रश्रवणैर्वा ।

... चरक शारीरस्थान

Utkaṭa-viṣamakaṭhināsana-sevinyā vāta-mūtra-purīṣa-vegānuparundhatyā dāruṇa anucita-vyāyāma-sevinyāḥ tīkṣṇoṣṇātimātra-sevinyāḥ pramitāśana-sevinyā garbho mriyate~ntaḥ tathā abhighātaprapīḍanaiḥ śvabhra-kūpa-prapātadeśāvalokanairvā~bhīkṣṇam mātuḥ prapatatyakāle garbhāḥ tathā~timātra-saṅkṣobhibhiryānairyānena apriyātimātraśravaṇairvā ....Caraka śārīrasthāna vāta-mūtra-purīṣa egānuparundha -

Natural urges such as urination, bowel movement or flatulence should never be suppressed, since it could result in an imbalance in *vata dosha*, which could, over a period of time, cause a variety of problems. If the urge to urinate is suppressed, there is an increased risk of urinary tract infection. It also unnecessarily increases pressure on the uterus. The holding back of intestinal gases, could lead to symptoms such as nausea, heartburn and belching. Suppression of natural bowel movement can lead to loss of appetite and anorexia. It is imperative that bowel movements be regular, to forestall the formation of intestinal gases. This also prevents the need to exert pressure during bowel evacuation, which could have an adverse effect on the uterus.

utkaṭa-viṣama-kaṭhināsana-sevinyā -

The mother-to-be should not sit on surfaces that are too hard, irregular, or uncomfortable, or on chairs that are not flat. Such sitting positions could cause her to sit in a slanted or oblique posture, or with her legs apart. She should develop the habit to sit with her spine straight at all times. This will help the foetus take an appropriate position in the womb. She should consciously try to prevent hunching over.

pratatottānaśāyinyāḥ punargarbhasya nābhyāśrayā nāḍīkaṇṭhamanuveṣṭayati -

She should sleep on her side as far as possible. Ayurved informs us that if she sleeps on her back, there are chances that the umbilical cord could twine itself around the neck of the foetus.

anucara-parirakṣaṇārtham na raktāni vāsāmsi -

Bright red clothes may attract negative energies, so are best avoided. And it is generally advisable to avoid wearing bright colours during pregnancy.

na garbhiṇīm kūpamavalokayat -

She should not look into the depths of a well, or down from the top of a steep cliff, or into a valley. These could cause fear, or a physical jolt, which could harm the baby.

apriyātimātraśravaṇairvā -

A pregnant woman should certainly not be subjected to loud or disturbing noises. Unwanted and obnoxious sounds should be reduced to a minimum in her environment. Avoid music at high volumes, discordant sounds, noise made by fireworks or any sounds that can unsettle you.

dāruṇa anucitavyāyāma -

Unnecessary physical work or inappropriate exercises that involve too much twisting and turning will impede the growth of the foetus. Gym exercises, vigourous aerobics or strenuous swimming, or lifting heavy weights can harm the foetus.

tīkṣṇauṣṇātimātrasevinyāḥ -

Food in general should not be too spicy. It should not be too hot or pungent either. If the pregnant woman eats much less than required, eats unhealthy food, or the constituents of her food do not provide enough vitality, the foetus will not receive adequate nourishment. Diet is explained in detail later on in the book.

ati mātra-saṅkṣobhibhir-yānaiḥ -

During pregnancy, travelling on potholed roads, or vehicles that vibrate a lot, should be avoided. Jerks and bumps of all kinds should be avoided.

It is important to make sure that pregnant woman suffers minimum bumps and jerks while traveling.

Women should not travel long distances during the first trimester of pregnancy. This is also true of the critical last two months of pregnancy, during which the foetus has grown very much in size. In the remaining four months in between, a pregnant woman should only travel when it is necessary and only in conditions that will be very comfortable for her.

abhighāta -

Direct injury or impact of any kind to the abdomen can injure the foetus.

prapīḍanaiḥ -

She should wear loose and comfortable garments, not tight fitting clothes that will impede circulation. Jeans, skirts and petticoats that tend to tighten around the abdomen should be avoided.

Although very much in vogue, high-heeled shoes or sandals may cause backaches, and hence should be avoided. As the foetus grows in size, it becomes more difficult for the mother-to-be to maintain a straight posture; high-heeled shoes aggravate the situation, and she could lose balance easily while wearing them.

Smoking should be given up entirely. It is a scientifically proven fact that smoking during pregnancy can have a devastating effect, hampering the mental, physical, and intellectual development of the baby.

Staying up late at night and sleeping during the day, especially in the afternoon, should be completely avoided during pregnancy. Late nights increase *vata* and *pitta*, and sleeping during the day increases *kapha* in the body. Resting in the afternoon is acceptable, but it is certainly not advisable to sleep deeply at that time.

It is not good for the pregnant woman to roam about without reason. The most ancient Ayurvedic texts note that this may have undesirable psychological effects on the child, and specifically increase the possibility of epilepsy in the child.

The expecting mother should not pay attention to things that are unpleasant, irksome, and disturbing to her. Discord and resentment in the family, and discussing disagreeable topics should be avoided in her presence. She should refrain from involving herself in such discussions.

It is important that she does not read books meant to excite or thrill, or watch horror films, which could generate fear. The unborn child is very sensitive and could easily be affected by these. She should also avoid watching television programmes that show deceit, stressful situations, unhappiness and immorality. Books and films have a deep impact on the mind, and are able to affect people both negatively as well as positively. Such influences on the unborn baby could result in the child being weak or fainthearted. In extreme cases, the excitement caused may even lead to miscarriage.

The pregnant woman should not stay in or even visit, unprotected places or deserted areas for the entire duration of the pregnancy.

It is best to avoid sexual intercourse throughout pregnancy. It is strictly prohibited by Ayurved during the first three months, when the embryo is not yet stable and miscarriage could be brought on quite easily. And in the final trimester, when the foetus has grown in size, sexual intercourse should also definitely to be avoided. During the entire pregnancy the vagina and uterus are extra-sensitive and susceptible to injury. These organs need to remain intact and protected from injury or imbalance. The sexual act is unnecessary exertion and could impair the growth of the child.

- It is important that the mother-to-be should remain happy and joyful. Feelings of grief or anxiety could cause her child to be fearful or apprehensive by nature, have a narrow outlook on life, or even a short life span. Anxiety and grief are undesirable in any case, but more so during pregnancy. Some women are more anxious or apprehensive and hence more easily disturbed than others. Thinking too much or worrying does not improve things. For the habitually anxious, it is important to break out of this vicious cycle. Music, meditation and reading spiritual and inspirational literature is sure to help.

Listening to healing and vocal music helps noticeably. Albums by **Santulan Music** such as *Spirit of Harmony*, *Yoga Nidra - for Peace and Meditation*, *Santulan Meditation*, *Aumkar Gunjan*, and *Garbha Sanskar*, have been composed for these purposes and each has a specific effect. Such music soothes and restores peace to the mind on the whole, and the mental capacities of the unborn child are improved.

- If the mother becomes jealous, angry or entertains negative thoughts it could cause the child to develop corrupt or unethical tendencies or an envious and scheming nature. So it is best to avoid the possibility of the mother even getting into such a situation.

- Sleeping too much (i.e. more than eight or nine hours), causes laziness, listlessness and even mental retardation in the child. It also slows the child's metabolism.

- The environment around the pregnant woman should be perfectly clean and tidy, and she should avoid places where there are obnoxious or unsavoury smells. She should not come in contact with menstruating women as far as possible.

- Some trees, such as the Banyan and Tamarind, are to be avoided, especially at twilight. She should not visit areas unknown to her.

- And of course, apart from all these external factors, she should not harm herself by shouting or raising her voice, getting angry or irritated.

In Indian culture, it is custom that a pregnant woman should not look at snakes. Whether it is harmful, or if the snake 'casts a shadow' on the woman, is not known, but the sight certainly instils fear and makes one temporarily mentally weak, and this is definitely harmful to the foetus growing inside.

After going through this chapter you might feel that there are too many things to do and remember if one wants to follow the entire process. But once you start actually doing these things, you will find that not only are they not so difficult, but also that they come naturally and easily to you. In fact, if you try and remain aware of the results in your body and mind when doing all these things, you will realize how much they are beginning to help you and the child growing inside you!

- All measures for care during pregnancy should be initiated once conception is confirmed.
- Each pregnancy is different, and no comparisons should be made with respect to symptoms.
- Pregnant women should not suppress natural urges, such as urination, or have sexual intercourse.
- Tight clothes, loud noises, and strenuous physical activities, are to be avoided.
- The mother-to-be should stay away from smoking, alcohol consumption, late nights, and unnecessary travelling.

Diet during pregnancy

During pregnancy the foetus obviously needs nourishment in every way possible. If the pregnant woman is extremely careful about her diet at this time, both she and her baby will reap the benefits throughout their lives. It is the 'sap' or essence - *ahar-ras* - of whatever the pregnant woman eats, and is able to digest, that nourishes the foetus inside her.

Let's see how we can provide an optimum of this *ahar-ras*. The following lines by Acharya Charak provide good advice

स्त्रिया ह्यापन्नगर्भायास्त्रिधा रसः प्रतिपद्यते स्वशरीरपुष्टये, स्तन्याय, गर्भवृद्धये च ।

...चरक शारीरस्थान

Striyā hyāpannagarbhāyāstridhā rasaḥ pratipadyate svaśarīrapuṣṭaye, stanyāya, garbhavṛddhaye ca

...Caraka śārīrasthāna

The ahar-ras of the expecting mother must fulfill 3 important functions:

- It should nourish the mother's body properly.
- It should help improve both quality and quantity of breast-milk.

- It should help nourish and develop the embryo.

All these three functions are to be separately understood and taken care of when planning the pregnant woman's diet. A lack of any of the essential nutrients will result in deficiencies in the foetus. This could retard its development, and even have extreme consequences like a sudden miscarriage, premature delivery, low weight at birth, or a weak constitution. A correctly planned diet will contribute towards preventing these problems.

ESSENTIAL FOODS

Water

Water consumed during pregnancy should be boiled for at least fifteen to twenty minutes to render it as germ-free as possible. Microorganisms ingested along with water that has not been boiled may deprive the body of important nutrients. They prevent the absorption of nutrients, especially iron. The consequences could be indigestion, loss of weight, or malnutrition. A case of worms or any intestinal infection (mainly caused due to impure drinking water) is difficult to treat in a pregnant woman because she cannot be administered any anti-parasitical medicines. So prevention is really the only solution and the best preventive measure is to thoroughly boil drinking water. Ayurved says that a specific mixture of herbs called *jala santulana churna* is really good to add to water while boiling. It purifies the water further and increases the general benefits of water.

Another important drinking-water culture recommended by Ayurved is *Suvarnabharit Jala* - or water infused with gold. It promotes the development of the brain and nervous system in the foetus. To prepare *Suvarnabharit Jala*, immerse a small piece of 24-carat gold, attached to a silver chain, into water that has been kept to boil. The piece of gold used should be reserved solely for this purpose. Jewelry that is otherwise worn should not be used. The gold can be removed after the water has been boiled completely. This water can then be used like normal drinking water. The effects of processes such as these are hard to see immediately or even over short or moderate periods. Over time, and sometimes several years later, their astonishingly positive effects become apparent and the benefits are much appreciated.

Milk

Milk is the best source of naturally available protein and calcium. It helps develop the *dhatus* of the foetus and provides a strong foundation for its bones. Many women complain of back aches and joint pains after delivery. One of the commonest causes of this is low intake of calcium during and after pregnancy. Again, the only preventive measure is a cup of milk every morning and evening throughout pregnancy. According to Ayurved, milk is best to help increase life energy and *Ojas*; it naturally facilitates the proper physical, mental, and intellectual development of the baby. It is also an important source of vitamin B-complex and vitamin A.

It is important that the milk be pure and fresh; In commercially packed milk, pasteurization is the only processing that can be considered safe. Homogenised, skimmed, vitamin-enriched, or ultra-heated milk are not recommended at all.

Milk should be boiled properly before use. It should be consumed either hot or at room temperature. Cold milk should be avoided. Try and consume milk that has its natural amount of cream. It should certainly not be too thin. Full-cream milk is best, but if this is too rich to consume, a little water may be added to it while boiling. Some people develop symptoms such as flatulence, heaviness in the abdomen, or diarrhoea after drinking milk. The following remedy will help you consume milk without such effects.

Quick Remedy to help digest milk: Add a piece [1 cm long] of crushed dry ginger (Zingiber officinale), ten to twelve pieces of *vavding* (Embelia ribes), and half a cup of water, to three quarters of a cup of milk. Heat this mixture over a low flame, until it is reduced by approximately 20% (half the added water should have evaporated) then strain it. You should end up with one full cup of milk. This type of infused milk is very easy to digest.

Many women avoid drinking milk because they are afraid of gaining weight (while it is a myth that milk makes you fat) or because they dislike it. The deficiencies arising from this for both the pregnant woman and her child, will be severe, since there is no substitute at all for the nutrition of milk.

Milk with Shatavari Kalpa: Adding 1½ to 2 teaspoons of *Shatavari Kalpa* to a cup of milk is extremely beneficial. Make sure that the *kalpa* has been produced strictly in accordance with Ayurvedic processes, and that the *shatavari* used is of good quality. *Shatavari Kalpa* is very nourishing for the expectant mother; it helps the foetus grow in a healthy manner and helps develop breast milk. It also helps to maintain the mother's figure by preventing untoward weight gain. It should be continued even during lactation.

Butter, Buttermilk, Ghee

Home-made butter (made from the cream obtained from boiled milk), fresh buttermilk (not sour), and pure ghee, are essential components of a balanced diet, not only for the expectant mother, but for everyone at all times. All of these should be part of daily intake from the onset of pregnancy. Some of their benefits are explained here.

नवनीतं नवं वृष्यं शीतं वर्णबलाग्निकृत् । *...वाग्भट सूत्रस्थान*

Navanītam navam vṛṣyam śītam varṇa-balāgni-kṛt
....Vāgbhaṭa sūtrasthāna

Fresh butter has a cooling effect, increases vitality, energy and enthusiasm, improves skin complexion and digestive fire.

The occurrence of haemorrhoids is not uncommon during pregnancy, especially in the last three or four months. Ayurved says homemade butter is an excellent medicine in such cases. One to two teaspoons of homemade butter, mixed with a little sugar eaten on a daily basis from the onset of pregnancy will help forestall the development of haemorrhoids.

A cup of fresh buttermilk, taken after lunch, aids digestion, and is beneficial for overall health. Ayurved describes buttermilk as a *vata-kapha* pacifier, easy to digest, and favoured as a dietary item for any form of gastro-intestinal disorder. Buttermilk proves helpful for several conditions like loss of taste and appetite, anaemia, and flatulence. It can be taken regularly for such symptoms occurring during pregnancy.

Many women develop oedema (water retention) during the last trimester of pregnancy. Buttermilk helps reduce swelling. The thick, sweetened or salted *lassi* available in the market is not a substitute for buttermilk.

Making Buttermilk: Add some water to curd and churn this mixture thoroughly. Churn until the butter in curd rises out. Separate this butter. What is left, is called buttermilk. The amount of water to be added to curd in the beginning depends on the thickness and consistency of the curd. Ideally, the buttermilk resulting from churning and separation of butter should end up thinner than milk. The addition of a little (1/4 tsp.) *jeera* (cumin) powder and two pinches of black salt (a particular Indian volcanic rock salt) to a glass or cup of buttermilk enhances its taste as well as medicinal properties.

As for ghee, Ayurvedic medicine describes ghee as having immensely beneficial properties, and compares it to a nectar.

शस्तं धीस्मृतिमेधाग्निबलायुःशुक्रचक्षुषाम् ।
स्नेहानां उत्तमं शीतं वयसः स्थापनं परम् ।
सहस्रवीर्यं विधिभिर्घृतं कर्मसहस्रकृत् । ...*वाग्भट सूत्रस्थान*

śastam dhī-smṛti-medhāgni-balāyuḥ-śukra-cakṣuṣām Snehānām uttamam śītam vayasaḥ sthāpanam param Sahasra-vīryam vidhibhir-ghṛtam karma-sahasrakṛt ....Vāgbhaṭa sūtrasthāna

Ghee is the best of all the oily and lubricating nutrients. It balances all three doshas, increases life energy and immunity, as well as strengthens the entire organism in general. Ghee also strengthens the sense organs such as the eyes and ears. It increases memory, intellect, and grasping power.

The regular intake of ghee benefits the expectant mother and these benefits are passed on to the developing baby as well. Regular intake during pregnancy is known to help increase the baby's intelligence.

A common question about ghee is about the manner and quantity in which it should be consumed. In general, everyone should eat about four or five teaspoons of ghee everyday. During pregnancy, it is recommended that three to four tsp of ghee be taken with lunch, and another three to four tsp with the evening meal. While it is fine to use it for *fodni*, instead of oil, during cooking, it is essential to add ghee to food - rice and dal, or chappatis - while eating.

Ghee made at home, from cow's milk, is best. If adequate cow's milk is not available for this then home-made ghee from buffalo's milk is acceptable.

Calcium and Iron

During pregnancy the mother's body demands more calcium and iron. *Rakta dhatu* (blood) is dependent on iron for its functioning. The deficiency of iron can cause weakness, fatigue, palpitations, loss of lustre and leave you without enthusiasm. More serious complications include the incomplete development of the embryo leading to complications during childbirth, or weakness, or low weight of the child at birth, among other problems.

To increase the intake of iron, leafy vegetables such as spinach (palak), fenugreek (methi), *math* (Amaranthus gangaticus), *chakwat* (Chenopodium album) and *chawli* (Vinga catiang), should be part of regular diet. The occasional intake of *ambat chuka* (Rumex vesicarius), *mula* leaves (Raphanus sativus), *alu* leaves (a kind of leafy vegetable - Alocasia indica), and *sarson* (mustard leaves - Brassica sp.) is also fine.

A few drops of lemon juice, sprinkled on leafy vegetables provide a good dose of Vitamin C, which is essential for the optimal absorption of iron. Black raisins, dates, beetroot, pomegranate, apples, *amla* and saffron also help to boost iron content. Jaggery is a good source of natural iron and may be used in small quantities during cooking.

Other useful sources of calcium and iron are wheat, *nachani* (Eleusine coracana), easily digestible pulses (such as *mung* dal and *toor* dal - sometimes along with their husks), coconut, dry dates, poppy seeds, and dollops (*ladus*) made from edible gum (Acacia arabica).

Cookware

The use of iron pots is preferable to stainless steel or non-stick cookware. Serving utensils should also ideally be made of iron. All this helps supply iron to the body and should be favoured entirely during pregnancy.

Natural vs Processed or Synthesized Foods

The following point about food is extremely important. Both food and medicine are best in their natural and pure states. The body accepts and absorbs such natural foods and medicines easily, and their benefits are greater. For example, the benefit and satisfaction derived from drinking fresh sweet lime juice cannot be replaced by a sweet lime *flavoured* drink.

This principle also applies to iron and calcium supplements. Commercial iron and calcium preparations made by mixing various chemicals, may not be easily accepted and absorbed by the body. They may also have side-effects such as constipation and even bleeding piles. In addition, such artificial preparations increase heat in the body which could have a harmful effect on the mother and her unborn child. Iron and calcium obtained through food are best so that they can be digested and assimilated optimally by all the body's systems.

Ayurved suggests many natural preparations that help to increase iron and calcium in the body without causing side-effects. *Praval bhasma*, *mouktik bhasma*, among others, are cooling in nature, and also increase calcium in the body naturally. Hence **Santulan Pittashanti, Santulan Calcisan** and *praval panchamrut* and can be taken throughout the period of pregnancy without hesitation or apprehension for this purpose. To increase *rakta dhatu* (blood), products such as *Navayas Loh*, *Mandur bhasma*, and *Suvarnamakshik bhasma*, are extremely useful. **Santulan Ayurved** products for the same purpose like **Rudhira** and **Lohit Plus**, not only nourish *rakta dhatu*, but have an additional positive effect on the overall health as well, resulting in radiant and unblemished skin. One need not take all such preparations and medicines. Please consult our expert Ayurvedic physicians to find out which are most suitable for you.

It is really important that you take natural iron and calcium preparations like these regularly to avoid hair loss, back ache, and weakness in joints and bones, which are common after childbirth.

Cereals, Pulses and Legumes

Lunch and dinner should include at least one cup of plain cooked pulses and one cup of spiced pulses. Tur and mung dal (yellow gram and green gram), are excellent for daily consumption, as they are nourishing, easy to digest and suitable for most constitutions.

Proteins are basic nutrients and should be consumed in adequate quantities. The entire development of the foetus is dependent on proteins, which are the very essence of its existence. *Mung dal* is excellent for the pregnant woman, and preparations of *matki* beans (Phaseolus aconitifolius), horse gram (kulith - Dolichos biflorus), and *masur* (red gram - Lens esculenta), could also be consumed occasionally. Fresh peas can be eaten once in a way, when in season.

Some legumes and pulses that are very heavy to digest and may be eaten only occasionally, if at all. This list includes *udid* (Phaseolus roxburghii), chick peas (harbara - Cicer arietinum), *chhole* (another type of chick pea), kidney beans, *chawli*, *pavata* (Dolichos lablab), *vatana* (dried green peas). Soya bean (Soja hispida) is best completely avoided.

Sprouts of the lighter pulses like *mung, matki* etc should be included in the diet at least once a day, preferably with the midday meal. These should be steamed or cooked before eating. A popular but mistaken trend nowadays, is to eat salads made from raw sprouts. These, when tested in a lab may show very high vitamin or mineral content, and are assumed to be nutritious. But they are very heavy to digest and will have an adverse effect on the digestive system. It is therefore better to cook sprouts before eating

Another common misconception is that a vegetarian diet lacks in protein. However, in a balanced vegetarian diet, which includes milk, pulses, legumes, and dry fruits in adequate quantities, there is no question of a lack of proteins. Another point to note is that eating either soyabeans, a non-vegetarian diet, or raw sprouts, to obtain proteins, may not be helpful, since these are difficult to digest, and therefore not absorbed easily into the body anyway. It is better to get your proteins from easily digestible foods which suit your constitution.

Grains

Grains are the main bulk of our diet. With the unfounded fear that eating rice and wheat causes one to gain weight, many people make salads and vegetables the major portion of their meals. Far from being beneficial, this imbalanced kind of diet will cause other problems. Pregnant women should certainly stay away from such fads.

Among the grains, rice, wheat and jowar (Sorghum vulgare - a type of millet) should be part of daily intake. Ayurved considers rice and wheat to be easily digestible and suitable to all constitutions.

Aged rice (rice which is more than a year old) is easy to digest, nutritious, and imparts a feeling of satisfaction. Moreover, it helps to neutralize *vata* and *pitta*, and nourish *kapha* and therefore should surely be eaten everyday.

Hot, steaming rice, topped with *varan* (unspiced *mung* or *tur* dal), a few drops of lemon juice, and pure ghee, is not only easy on the digestive system, but also tasty and very nutritious. *Khichadi* prepared with rice and mung or tur dal and eaten with pure ghee also has the same benefits.

Dal when consumed with rice or with any other cooked grain, becomes easier to digest.

Wheat is very nutritious, pacifies *pitta* and strengthens the bones. While making chapatis out of wheat, or *bhakri* (rolled and flattened bread made of coarsely ground *jowar* or *bajri* cooked on a pan and puffed on an open flame) it would be even better if the dough was soaked in milk and then prepared. This makes the dough more healthy and automatically increases intake of milk. *Fulka* and *chapati* (thinly rolled wheat breads) should be eaten everyday. *Parathas* should only be an occasional treat. Adding rice flour and bhajani (a flour made out of a mixture of grains and pulses after they have been roasted) to the dough for *parathas* can be a healthy as well as tasty option.

Since *jowar*, has cooling properties, and *bajri* (Pennisetum typhoideum), another millet variety, is hot in nature, a mixture of these flours turns out very healthy. In other grains *Jav* (Hordeum vulgare) improves the digestive capacity and pacifies *pitta-kapha dosha,* and *nachani* (Eleusine coracana) is very easy to digest. Mixing *nachani*, rice or *jav* flours, with the above mentioned jowari-bajri flour for *bhakri* will create variety.

Instead of using commercial flours, it is better to

buy grains of a good quality, and have them ground in a mill, or even better, have them ground at home. After being ground like this, the grain should not be sieved.

Ayurvedic literature recommends that the grains to be used should be about a year old, and should be roasted before grinding, as this makes them easy to digest.

OTHER ESSENTIAL FOODS

Honey

The expectant mother should ideally consume one to two teaspoons of honey every day. Honey is sweet in taste and slightly astringent. Ayurved says that it improves intelligence, balances *pitta* and *kapha dosha*, lends a glow to the skin, and enhances complexion. Honey is nourishing and beneficial for the eyes and helps to purify the blood. A spoonful of honey may be taken in the morning before breakfast, in *panchamrut* (see chapter on Special Recipes) or in milk. One should make sure that the honey is pure and of good quality. Honey is nowadays commonly adulterated with sugar syrup or jaggery, and such honey does not provide the above benefits. Honey should never be heated, so if it is added to milk, the milk should be at room temperature or lukewarm.

Panchamrut

Panchamrut, if taken every morning, works in the body as a nectar. This tonic improves physical strength, enthusiasm, energy and memory, nourishes the important organs such as the heart and brain, enhances the complexion, and balances all three *doshas*. It also helps to reduce morning sickness and dry retching, and many of these positive effects are passed on to the baby as well. Please see the recipe for *panchamrut* in the chapter on Special Recipes. A pinch of saffron added to *panchamrut* enhances its benefits even further. Saffron is hot and lubricating in nature; it strengthens and purifies *rakta dhatu* (blood). The regular ingestion of saffron during pregnancy helps to strengthen the baby's heart, enhances the baby's looks, and helps ensure proper uterine contractions during labour. Adding **Santulan Amrutshatkara** (that contains large quantities of saffron) to *panchamrut*, instead of sugar, multiplies its benefits severalfold.

Dink Ladus

The tradition of eating *dink ladus* (see Special Recipes) after delivery, should ideally be incorporated in the diet throughout the nine months of pregnancy. *Lahi* made by frying *dink* (Gum acacia) in pure ghee, if eaten regularly during pregnancy, prevents back ache and joint pain, and helps to strengthen the baby's bones. For convenience, **Santulan Marrosan** is a great replacement for dink ladus. It contains all the same ingredients, except for coconut and sugar.

Stone Sugar

Khadi sakhar, (a form of candy sugar), is cooling in nature, pacifies *pitta*, and is highly nutritious. It also improves the voice. Allowing a piece of it to slowly dissolve in the mouth can help relieve morning sickness and nausea occurring during the first trimester. Candy sugar is also a great accompaniment to homemade butter. Homemade butter with a little candy sugar should be taken everyday during pregnancy. It is generally recommended to substitute normal sugar with this type of sugar for regular consumption. Please ensure that the sugar you use for all general purposes is only sugarcane based, and not made from any other product.

Lahya

Shashti Shali Lahya (a special form of puffed rice)

is easy to digest, increases strength and improves digestion. Chewing dry *lahya* is helpful for nausea, vomiting and diarrhoea.

Quick Remedy for a burning sensation in the eyes, hands and feet: Soak a handful of lahya for three to four hours in drinking water. Strain through a seive. Drink the water.

Fasting should be avoided as much as possible during pregnancy. If you must fast, then there are certain foods permissible during fasts (i.e. eating these foods is not considered 'breaking' your fast). Among those, *bhagar* (a type of millet - Panicum milliaceum) and *rajgeera* (another type of millet - Amarantus paniculatus) are easy to digest. Potatoes and *sago kheer* (made from *sabudana* - Sagus laevus), are also considered good during fasts.

It goes without saying that it is not enough to eat just what is on the regular menu at home, even if it is varied. Please ensure that you consciously provide each and every one of these nutrients to your body and the foetus growing inside.

- **The expectant mother's diet must fulfil three important functions: it should nourish her body, help form breast milk in quantity and quality, and help nourish and develop the embryo.**
- **When considering diet, one should also focus on clean and pure drinking water.**
- **Being a natural source of protein and calcium, milk is very important during this period. It also increases strength and 'ojas'.**
- **Using iron utensils for cooking improves iron content in the body.**
- **Vegetarian diet (pulses and legumes) can fully satisfy protein requirements. The use of pulses which are difficult to digest, such as soyabeans, chhole (chickpeas), rajma (kidney beans), etc, should be avoided.**
- **Panchamrut in the morning is beneficial for both, the mother and the unborn child.**

Fruits and vegetables for the pregnant woman

During pregnancy, vegetables, fruits, grains, pulses and beans should all be part of diet in appropriate quantities and in the right form. Therefore, one needs to know which vegetables, fruits and other food should be used at what time. Several such questions have been dealt with in this chapter.

VEGETABLES

Vegetables are an integral part of a balanced diet which should include all kinds of vegetables including leafy ones. According to Ayurvedic literature the following vegetables are easily digestible and suitable for most constitutions.

1. Bottle gourd (*dudhi* - Lagenaria vulgaris)
2. Ridge gourd (*dodka* - Luffa acutangula)
3. Smooth gourd (*ghosali* - Luffa aegyptiaca)
4. Ash gourd (*kohala* - Benincasa cerifera)
5. Ladyfingers (*okra* - Abelmoschus esculentus)
6. Red pumpkin (Cucurbita maxima)
7. Potatoes (Solanum turerosum)
8. Bitter gourd (Momordica charantia)
9. Gherkins (*tondli* - Cephalandra indica)

And leafy vegetables, such as

10. Spinach (Spinacia oleracea)
11. Fenugreek (*methi* - Trigonella

foenum-graeceum)
12. Amaranth (*math* - Amaranthus gangaticus)
13. Chavalai (Amarantus polygamus)
14. Tandulja (Amarantus oleraceus)
15. Chakavat (Chenopodium album)

Cucumber, tomatoes, carrots, and beetroot, may be eaten daily in small quantities as a salad.

The specific benefits of some of these vegetables are provided below.

Bottle gourd is nutritious, strengthening, and easy to digest. Ayurved explains it as follows:

मिष्टतुम्बीफलं हृद्यं पित्तश्लेष्मापहं गुरु ।
वृष्यं रुचिकरं प्रोक्तं धातुपुष्टिविवर्धनम् ॥ ...*भावप्रकाश*

Miṣṭa-tumbī-phalam hṛdyam
pitta-śleṣmāpaham guru
Vṛṣyam rucikaram proktam
dhātu-puṣṭi-vivardhanam ....Bhāvaprakāśa

Bottle gourd nourishes the heart, balances pitta – kapha dosha, increases virya (life energy)*, is appetizing, and nourishes all seven dhatus.*

It also contains vitamin B, calcium and iron, and can be prepared in various forms such as soup, salad, vegetable, or as a sweet *(halwa)*. Using bottle gourd in such different forms not only provides variety in taste, but also ensures that all of nutritional advantages are obtained.

Carrots and pumpkin contain large amounts of Vitamin A (carotene). Okra and ridge gourd contain calcium, iron, and the Vitamins A, B, and C. Bitter gourd (*karela*) is rich in Vitamin C, as are Fenugreek leaves and *chavalai*. All of these vegetables are rich sources of essential vitamins and minerals and should be eaten regularly.

Spinach is an excellent source of iron. It can be taken in a soup form or as a vegetable. Due to its astringent taste, gherkin (*tondli*) has a positive effect on bowel movement. It helps to produce well-formed stools. It is best cooked in ghee with cumin seeds, and garnished with coriander leaves.

Bottle gourd, gherkins, and ashgourd help reduce acidity, and are thus very helpful in the first trimester of pregnancy, when morning sickness is a common complaint.

Spinach, bottle gourd, ridge gourd and *ghosali* are helpful for those who tend to suffer from constipation and hard stools.

Organic Veggies

One should try and eat vegetables which have been grown with clean and plentiful water. Organically grown vegetables (non-Genetically Modified, without insecticides, pesticides and chemical fertilizers) are best and most beneficial. Fresh vegetables should be thoroughly cleaned and washed with warm water and should always be cooked before eating. Carrot and beetroot should be steamed even if they are to be used in salads.

During the monsoon, water tends to contain a lot of impurities, and this increases the risk of bacterial and microbial contamination in vegetables. So during the monsoon, leafy vegetables should be used with caution.

Try and Avoid...

Vegetables such as sweet potatoes (Ipomoea batatas), mushrooms, corn, elephant yam (*suran* - Amorphophallus campanulatus), are difficult to digest, and should be avoided as far as possible. Capsicum, eggplant, spring onions, cluster beans (gawar - Cyamopsis psoralioides), should also be used rarely, as they increase *pitta* in the body. Carrot or tomato juice (another popular trend) also increase *pitta* and are not advisable. Tomato soup may be consumed occasionally.

On Preparation

Vegetables should not be strongly spiced or made in rich gravies. To enhance the flavour of vegetables while cooking, ingredients such as freshly grated coconut, grated ginger, sesame seeds, poppy seeds *(khus khus)*, coriander powder, and cumin powder, are fine. Fresh coriander leaves in the diet or as a garnish, are very beneficial. Coriander leaves may be served as an independent preparation as a paste or tiny cutlets when mixed with mung dal flour. They could also be added to *parathas*.

Chutnies (a chutney is a paste made from herbs, normally used as a condiment) made from several spices and herb can be good additions to one's diet.

A Simple Chutney - Mix freshly grated coconut, ginger, coriander leaves, lemon, mint, green chilly and cumin. Grind to a paste. This mixture aids digestion, and helps to stimulate the appetite, which is often diminished during pregnancy.

Try and avoid using too much chili in vegetable or soup preparations. Ginger could be used as a substitute.

Preparing food in pure ghee (as a *fodni* base) is especially recommended for the pregnant woman (and even in general). Cooking vegetables with oil (as a *fodni* base), should be kept to a minimum. The use of too much oil can cause weight-gain and indigestion. Out of the wide variety of oils available commercially, peanut oil is best for daily use.

FRUITS AND FRUIT DRINKS

It is recommended that at least one seasonal fruit be eaten every day during pregnancy. The list can include apples, grapes, pomegranates, sweet oranges, sweet tangerines, figs and *amla*. Figs, pomegranates and apples nourish the blood directly. Sour fruits such as oranges, sweet limes, tangerines, and amla, are rich in Vitamin C, and indirectly also help the development of blood.

The mother-to-be should regularly drink half a glass of undiluted orange, sweet lime or tangerine juice. The juice should have no additives. It will help nourish *rasa dhatu*, encourage the proper development of the foetus, and promote the production of breast milk after delivery.

According to Ayurvedic literature, grapes are the best of all fruits. When in season, they are highly recommended. They should be washed thoroughly and soaked in salted water for a few hours before eating. In other seasons raisins can be consumed instead. Ten to twelve raisins at a time is ideal. They should be soaked in water for a few hours as well. They nourish blood, and ensure proper bowel movements.

Fresh coconut water is another healthy drink during pregnancy. Besides benefits similar to the other juices mentioned, it also ensures that the womb has adequate amniotic fluid. It is quite common to see that amniotic fluid suddenly decreases in the seventh or eighth month of pregnancy. Coconut water is both prevention and cure in such cases. The coconut's tender pulp *(malai)* is easy to digest, nutritious and pacifies *pitta*. In general, ripe and tender coconut nourishes *mansa dhatu* (flesh and muscle), and so helps keep skin, which also develops from *mansa dhatu*, healthy and glowing. As mentioned earlier, grated coconut, fresh or dried, can be used in the preparation of vegetables, lentils or chutney.

Kokam (Garcinia purpurea) *sherbat* (concentrate with water) is good for the pregnant woman if it suits her constitution. To this the addition of cumin powder, a pinch of freshly ground black pepper, sugar and black salt, will help to pacify *pitta*, and improve digestive capacity. *Kokam sherbat* taken in slowly, in small sips at a time, is very helpful especially during the first trimester, when there may be nausea, dry retching, and a general loss of appetite and taste.

Mango is one of the most well-liked and nutritious fruits but eaten in excess it can lead to digestive imbalance and loose motions. It is best eaten as pulp, with 2-3 teaspoons of pure, home-made ghee, and a pinch of dry ginger powder (*soonth*), per cup of pulp. Ideally, mangoes should be soaked in water for two to three hours before consumption. Mango milk shakes should be strictly avoided.

Raw green mangoes, if taken regularly, increase *pitta* in the body, and should be avoided. Instead, they may be added, occasionally, to spicy *dal* (*amti*) or used in chutney. Tamarind should also be used sparingly during pregnancy. *Kokam* or lemon can be used instead, for a tangy flavour in food. Even if the pregnant woman craves tamarind or raw mangoes, their consumption should be kept to a minimum (just enough to satisfy the taste buds).

Sour fruits such as pineapple, strawberry, wood apple (kavath - Feronia elephantum), *bor* (Zizyphus jujuba), should only be consumed occasionally, and non-seasonal fruits should be avoided (one finds nowadays that markets are filled with fruit from all over the world, most of which are out of season). Custard apple, guava (Psidium guyava), pear (Pyrus communis), chikoo (Achras sapota), rose apple (jambhul - Eugenia jambolana) and watermelon, may all be eaten occasionally during pregnancy.

Papaya, which is known to cause uterine contractions, and which could induce miscarriage, should never be eaten by pregnant women.

Fresh fruit which has been cut, and freshly-squeezed fruit juice, should both be consumed immediately, as the nutritive quality of cut fruit diminishes very quickly. Fruit should be eaten during the day and not after sunset. Commercially available canned juices are best avoided, as they are stale, and may contain chemical preservatives. Often, these canned juices contain only artificial flavouring, instead of real fruit juice.

Milk shakes are yet another popular beverage, but Ayurvedic philosophy does not advocate consuming milk and fruit together and certainly not during pregnancy. The excessive intake of fruit salads and milk shakes during pregnancy, could be one of the reasons for the increased occurrences of allergies, weak lungs, or skin ailments, now common among newborn babies.

Out of all dry fruits, almonds are a must for the expecting woman. Three or four almonds soaked overnight, peeled, and eaten in the morning help to improve and maintain health and also nourish the brain of the developing foetus.

One dried date (kharik - Phoenix dactylifera) should be chewed and eaten properly everyday. Alternatively a teaspoonful of dried date powder, added to a glass of milk, should be taken every day. Fresh dates are also permissible during pregnancy. One or two fresh dates eaten daily, with two teaspoons of pure, home-made Ayurvedic ghee, help the foetus gain weight properly. Dry figs, consumed directly, or after being soaked in water, are good for the body. Apricots provide nourishment to the growing baby's brain, and may be eaten from time to time. Walnuts are heavy to digest, but are nourishing, and may be eaten occasionally. Cashew nuts, pistachios, and *charoli* (Buchanania latifolia) tend to increase *pitta* and should, therefore, be a rare treat.

- **Easily digestible and nourishing vegetables, such as bottle gourd, spinach, carrot, potato, kohala, should be included in the diet.**
- **Use ghee as a medium for cooking vegetables and spicy lentils (Amti) during pregnancy.**
- **Eating fresh fruit or drinking fresh juice of sweet, seasonal fruits is advised.**
- **Avoid eating fruit after sunset.**

What and when should an expectant mother eat?

A COMPLETE DIET FOR EACH MONTH

At each stage of the foetus' growth, its needs change. We must make sure that it receives everything required at the appropriate time. Acharya Charak recommends that milk and milk products be consumed, on their own, or cultured with medicinal herbs, on a daily basis throughout pregnancy. The various organs and dhatus of the child in the womb develop at different times, so a specific diet has been planned as required by the foetus. These guidelines will help maintain the pregnant woman's health as well.

FIRST MONTH

प्रथमे मासे शङ्किता चेत्, गर्भमापन्ना क्षीरमनुस्कृतं
मात्रावत् शीतं काले काले पिबेत्।
सात्म्यमेव च पुनर्भोजनं सायंप्रातश्च भुञ्जीत।

Prathame māse śaṅkitā cet,
garbhamāpannā kṣīramanuskṛtam
mātrāvat śītam kāle kāle pibet

Sātmyameva ca punarbhojanam sāyam-prātaśca bhuñjīta

During this time, when pregnancy is first suspected, small quantities of milk at room temperature (but boiled earlier) should be sipped throughout the day. Eat that which is suitable and can be digested easily.

(As most women do not suspect that they are pregnant until a period is missed, it is a good idea to follow this regimen from the time the woman starts trying to conceive.)

SECOND MONTH

द्वितीये मासे क्षीरमेव च मधुरौषधसिद्धम् ।

Dvitīye māse kṣīrameva ca madhurauṣadha-siddham

The woman should consume milk boiled with water and sweet-tasting herbs, such as shatavari, gokshur, bala, and vidari. The addition of **Santulan Shatavari Kalpa** to milk is an easy alternative.

THIRD MONTH

तृतीये मासे क्षीरं मधुसर्पिर्भ्यामुपसंसृज्य ।

Tṛtīye māse kṣīram madhu-sarpirbhyāmupasamsṛjya

Milk with ghee and honey should be taken every morning (one teaspoon of honey and two teaspoons of ghee in a cup of warm milk).

FOURTH MONTH

चतुर्थे मासे क्षीरनवनीतमक्षमात्रमश्नीयात् ।

Caturthe māse kṣīra-navanītamakṣamātramaśnīyāt

1 tablespoon (10 grams) of homemade butter should be consumed every morning with candy sugar.

FIFTH MONTH

पञ्चमे मासे क्षीरसर्पिः ।

Pañcame māse kṣīra-sarpiḥ

From the fifth month onwards, it is imperative that the normal meal be supplemented with seven to eight teaspoons of ghee daily.

SIXTH AND SEVENTH MONTH

षष्ठे मासे क्षीरसर्पिः मधुरौषधसिद्धं, तदेव सप्तमे मासे ।

ṣaṣṭhe māse kṣīrasarpiḥ
madhurauṣadhasiddham, tadeva saptame māse

During these months, the consumption of ghee infused with sweet herbs is recommended, ideally on an empty stomach. For example, *Shatavari ghrut*, or *Yashtimadhu ghrut*.

EIGHTH MONTH

अष्टमे तु मासे क्षीरयवागुं सर्पिष्मतीं काले काले पिबेत् ।
...चरक शारीरस्थान

Aṣṭame tu māse kṣīra-yavāgum sarpiṣmatīm kāle kāle pibet ....Caraka śārīrasthāna

From the eighth month onwards, kheer, a special soup-like preparation made with milk and sugar and various types of grains, i.e. semolina, rice or wheat, *should be eaten daily.*

NINTH MONTH

From the beginning of the ninth month, a cotton swab dipped in **Santulan Femisan Oil**, should be placed in the vagina overnight, and be removed in the morning. This should be a regular practice until the baby is born.

During this time the pregnant woman can also be administered an Ayurvedic enema of medicinal oil cultured with sweet-tasting herbs. All these measures help to balance the *apanavata,* ensuring a smooth and easy delivery.

यदिदं कर्म प्रथमं मासं समुपादायोपदिष्टमानवमान् मासात्तेन गर्भिण्या गर्भसमये गर्भधारिणीकुक्षिकटीपार्श्वपृष्ठं मृदु भवति, वातश्चानुलोमः संपद्यते मूत्रपुरीषे च प्रकृतिभूते सुखेन मार्गमनुपद्येते, चर्मनखानि च मार्दमुपयान्ति, बलवर्णौ चोपक्षीयेते, पुत्रं चेष्टं सपदुपेतं सुखिनं सुखेनैषा काले प्रजायत इति ।

... चरक शारीरस्थान

yadidam karma prathamam māsam samupādāyopadiṣṭamānavamān māsāttena garbhiṇyā garbhasamaye garbhadhāriṇī-kukṣi-kaṭī-pārśva-pṛṣṭham mṛdu bhavati, vātaścānulomaḥ sampadyate mūtrapurīṣe ca prakṛtibhūte sukhena mārgamanupadyete, carma-nakhāni ca mārdamupayānti, balavarṇau copakṣīyete, putram ceṣṭam sapadupetam sukhinam sukhenaiṣā kāle prajāyata iti ....Caraka śārīrasthāna

Following these monthly guidelines throughout pregnancy ensures that the woman's waist, back, pelvic region, hips and thighs, remain lubricated, soft and flexible. In this way, vata, especially apanavata (required for delivery), is balanced, so that labour starts at the appropriate time, and the birth of the child is easy, safe and uneventful.

If followed throughout pregnancy, the diet and herbal remedies advised above, benefit both mother and child. This helps labour occur on schedule and without complications. These guidelines also ensure that the baby is born healthy and robust, with an excellent complexion, a strong voice, and an optimal physical structure. If the expectant mother takes care of her diet, then the pregnancy will progress smoothly, and the delivery is easy.

WHAT IS BEST AVOIDED DURING PREGNANCY?

Once the pregnancy is confirmed, Aloe vera should not be eaten in any form, and medicines containing Aloe vera (such as *Kumari Asav*) should be discontinued.

Foods that are difficult to digest should be omitted from the diet. Cheese, which is very popular and considered to be a rich source of calcium, is commonly recommended during pregnancy. It is, however, difficult to digest, and often does more harm than good. Although cheese should be avoided as much as possible, a permissible alternative is fresh, soft cheese which has not been processed. It can be occasionally eaten in small quantities at lunchtime. Paneer (a type of cottage cheese), even though not as heavy as regular cheese, should not be eaten very often.

Avoid noodles, biscuits, cake and other foods made from refined flour (*maida*) as much as possible. If present in the diet at all, varieties made from whole-wheat flour are better. Make sure that the products come from a reputable and hygienic source, and are of good quality. Chemicals used in icing and decoration, and in baking powder (used to make cake soft and spongy), could be harmful.

Snacks such as *bhelpuri*, *dahi puri*, or *pani puri*, are made from refined flour, and contain large amounts of uncooked salt (i.e. salt which is added after cooking). They have almost no nutritive value and should be a rare treat.

Soda and other carbonated drinks contain a lot of pressured gas. The gas in the drink weakens the digestive fire in the human body and also causes *vata* disturbance. These drinks can also cause your throat to become sore. Such beverages are best avoided, and may be replaced by *sherbats* made from freshly squeezed lime or *kokam*.

Fermented foods are heavy on the digestive system and can lead to an imbalance in *pitta*. Snacks such as *idli*, *dosa* and *dhokla* may be eaten in limited quantities, if home-made, but the batter they are made from should not be fermented for too long, or refrigerated and used repeatedly.

Similarly, bakery products prepared with yeast, baking soda and baking powder, should be consumed only occasionally. Bread can be eaten once in a way if it is made from coarse wheat-flour, very fresh and toasted before consumption. Home-made butter and jams are preferable to their commercial counterparts.

There is an increasing use of various artificial colours in ready-made foods, to make them more attractive to the eye. This applies to cakes, tinned juices, soft drinks, as well as to some vegetable dishes served in restaurants. These added colours produce gases in the body and can cause a variety of problems to the digestive system. In addition, the artificial chemicals tend to accumulate in the body, and can have a negative effect on the kidneys, spleen, ovaries and liver. It goes without saying, that they can also have a negative effect on the development of the foetus. Foods with added food colouring should be rigorously avoided during pregnancy.

Pregnant women are usually advised to include eggs in their diet. This is not in keeping with Ayurvedic guidelines. Eggs are difficult to digest and are not easily assimilated in the body. Moreover, they increase the accumulation of *aam* (material that the body can neither absorb nor throw out). If consumed during pregnancy, the baby may be born with allergies or skin rashes. It is recommended that eggs be strictly avoided.

In fact, it is best to stay away from all non-vegetarian food, including the lighter meats such as chicken and fish. Ayurved includes them in the list of foods to be avoided during pregnancy. The reasons being that not only are they *tamasik* in nature, but often cause disturbances in the digestive system. *Pitta* problems are common during pregnancy, and as the uterus increases in size, the resulting pressure placed on the intestines slows down the digestive process. In these circumstances, it is difficult to digest any food that increases *pitta* and hence, such food is best avoided.

There is a common misunderstanding that eggs and non-vegetarian foods are necessary to meet increased protein requirements during pregnancy. However, a vegetarian diet can cater to all of the body's nutritional needs, especially proteins, in an easily digestible form and in adequate quantities.

Ayurved cautions that there should be no extremes when planning the diet for the expectant mother. It is important that all of the six tastes, namely sweet, sour, spicy, salty, bitter and astringent, be included in meals in balanced proportions. According to Acharya Charak, the excess of any of these can lead to the following side-effects in the child.

मधुरनित्या प्रमेहिणं मूकमतिस्थूलं वा ।

Madhura-nityā pramehiṇam mūkamati-sthūlam vā

If during pregnancy the mother continuously eats sweets then the child may be susceptible to a number of problems. *The child may grow up to be diabetic, or may be born mute or have the tendency to become extremely obese.*

अम्लनित्या रक्तपित्तिनं त्वगक्षिरोगिणं वा ।

Amlanityā rakta-pittinam tvagakṣi-rogiṇam vā

The excess intake of sour items, such as tamarind, tomatoes, sour yoghurt or fermented foods, *may cause the child to suffer from skin diseases, eye ailments, or nose bleeds.*

लवणनित्या शीघ्रवलीपलितं खलित्यरोगिणं वा ।

Lavaṇa-nityā śīghra-valī-palitam
khalitya-rogiṇam vā

Excess salty foods or the addition of extra salt to food, *can result in premature graying or hair loss, and may even cause early wrinkling of the child's skin.*

कटुकनित्या दुर्बलमल्पशुक्रमनपत्यं वा ।

Kaṭuka-nityā durbalam-alpaśukram-anapatyam vā

Eating lots of spicy food can weaken the baby's constitution and strength, reduce shukra dhatu, and may even cause reproductory disorders later in life.

तिक्तनित्या शोषिणमबलमनुपचितं वा ।

Tikta-nityā śoṣiṇam-abalam-anupacitam vā

An excess of bitter foods, can result in stunted growth, dryness, low weight or weakness.

कषायनित्या श्यावम् आनाहिनमुदावर्तिनं वा। *...चरक शारीरस्थान*

Kaṣāya-nityā śyāvam ānāhinam-udāvartinam vā
...Caraka śārīrasthāna

Astringent foods can cause darkening of the skin, produce gases, flatulence or induce vomiting in the baby.

In short, make sure all tastes are included in meals, and do not give in too much to individual likes. Take the pregnant woman's constitution into consideration and plan the whole range of tastes into her diet.

THE DAILY MEAL PLAN

The daily meal plan guidelines should be followed taking the constitution and digestive capacity of the expectant mother. Women are pampered during pregnancy, and they usually exhibit a desire for certain favourite foods. Do remember that repeating the same foods over and over can deprive the mother and baby of other essential nutrients. The mother-to-be should realize that she is also eating for the baby, and she may, at times have to eat things that she may not necessarily like because it is good for the child.

We have found that traditional Indian diet planning for pregnant women is extremely effective and adheres to Ayurvedic guidelines. It will also help to rule out common problems arising for mothers after childbirth, such as loss of hair, darkening and pigmentation of skin, back aches, weight gain and fat collection at the waist.

Breakfast

At approximately 8-8.30 AM - Eat just enough, so that a healthy appetite for lunch is retained. Make sure that breakfast is fresh, hot, and nutritious, and preferably grain based. Good breakfast grains are rice (in the form of flakes or puffed), semolina *upma* or *sheera*.

Along with breakfast - Panchamrut; 3-4 almonds which have been soaked in water overnight and then peeled; one fig, soaked in water overnight; 5-7 raisins; 1 glass of hot milk with 2 teaspoons of **Santulan Shatavari Kalpa**; and herbal preparations such as **San Rose, Santulan Brahmaleen Ghrut, Santulan Chyavanprash.**

At about 10-10.30 : a freshly cut fruit or glass of fresh fruit juice.

Lunch

12.30-1 PM : the food should be freshly made, easy to digest and sattvik in nature. It should meet all physical requirements of the mother-to-be, and be just enough, so that there is no feeling of heaviness after eating. Lunch should include *dal* (lentils in a soup form) and rice, one leafy vegetable or legume, one non-leafy vegetable, rolled bread in the form of chapatti, bhakri or fulka, spiced *dal*, salad and fresh buttermilk.

Afternoon Snack

5-5.30 PM: A glass of milk with two teaspoons of **Santulan Shatavari Kalpa** and one teaspoon of **San Rose**. A slice of buttered toast / rice flakes / a handful of Shashti Shali lahya / rice flour preparations such as *ukad* (a spiced rice flour preparation) / or a chapatti with ghee and sugar can be added, if the expectant mother is hungry.

Dinner

It should be hot, freshly cooked and in accordance with the individual constitution. Dinner should include soups, khichadi, rice, dal, vegetables and preferably bhakri rather than chappatis.

In addition to correct diet planning, it is important that the food be consumed in an appropriate manner.

'Udar bharan nohe janeeje yadnya karma.' This means that food is not intended solely to fill the stomach, but should be eaten with purity and respect, as an offering to the digestive fire, *jaathar agni*, in the body.

We can only offer the best possible food to the fire within us, and then pray that it is accepted and serves to help us. This is the reason for prayer before food.

An important point to note is that a woman can be given the food she craves (*dohaale*), at any time. This food should be *in addition* to the normal diet, which she should eat anyway.

The pregnant woman should never slouch while eating. There may be a tendency to do so due to the increasing size of the foetus, and consequent stress on the spine. Incorrect posture is not conducive for good digestion.

Be disciplined with timings of meals. Like other body functions, the digestive system is very sensitive during pregnancy. The body grows accustomed to certain rhythms, and so digestive juices are released at certain times. Food eaten at these times, is easily digested and absorbed, and digestive fire remains in balance. It will affect the mother and child adversely to have irregular meal times or to make sudden and drastic changes in them. It is acceptable to occasionally change the timing of a meal, if the expectant mother is not hungry. Food at inappropriate times or when one is not hungry can also be harmful. One should not be compelled to eat if there is no appetite. Many women experience a diminished appetite during pregnancy. Do not eat less food at this time as it will affect the baby. You can eat light food instead when you feel less hungry.

Dinner is best eaten early in the evening. At night, digestion is weak and physical activity is low. Therefore, the evening meal should be lighter and smaller. Especially during pregnancy, heavy evening meals will be difficult to digest, and this will cause pressure on the uterus and chest, and consequent discomfort. All other Ayurvedic guidelines given in this book pertaining to food should be followed as strictly as possible.

- **The monthly diet regime as suggested here should be strictly followed for the proper development of the foetus.**
- **Eating outside the house and eating processed foods should be avoided.**
- **A balanced diet for the mother-to-be should include all of the 6 tastes, and be freshly prepared, sattvik and nutritious.**
- **During pregnancy, it is important to have all meals on time.**
- **Food is not only intended to fill the stomach, but should be eaten with purity and respect, as an offering to the digestive fire of the body.**

Some essential activities

As the foetus grows it begins to effect certain changes in the mother-to-be as well. Ayurved has studied these changes and developments and suggests several activities for the mother, to help her respond to them effectively. These activities can all be made part of the pregnant woman's daily routine.

Although the pregnant woman will not have too many visible changes in the first trimester (first three months), her body is obviously undergoing a lot. The expanding uterus, for one, puts extra pressure on the bladder causing the urge to urinate frequently. Do not suppress this urge. Relieve yourself as soon as possible, else it may lead to disturbance in *vata dosha*. The pregnant woman should avoid any kind of strenuous activity in the first trimester. Since the foetus is still not fully stable, any exertion poses the risk of miscarriage.

CARE OF THE BREASTS

During the first trimester, the breasts and nipples undergo a lot of changes, and require special care and attention.

These changes take place so that the mother produces adequate breast milk, and so that breast-feeding is easy for the baby.

During the first trimester the pregnant woman should massage her breasts lightly with **Santulan Suhrud Oil** for 5-6 minutes everyday. After the first trimester this can be done twice or thrice a week during the whole pregnancy. This helps reduce sagging of the breasts after the baby has been weaned.

STRETCH MARKS

As the foetus grows in size, the skin around the abdomen becomes taut, and stretch-marks begin to appear. The skin in that area also tends to become dry and itchy, and stretch-marks may increase if you give into the urge to scratch. Take care that you don't let your nails damage your skin. If the itching is unbearable, you could use a soft muslin cloth to lightly massage the area, to bring relief.

From around the beginning of the third month of pregnancy it is advisable to start using oils infused with herbs that help the skin and check the development of stretch marks. E.g. Use **Santulan Rose Beauty Oil**, or a *kumkumadhya* oil to gently massage the abdomen, thighs and buttock. If you add **San Massage Powder** to the oil, it will further enhance the benefits, reduce itchiness and prevent looseness of the skin. This should be done everyday in the second trimester. From the sixth month onwards (third trimester) you should do this twice or thrice a day for best results.

Ayurvedic literature has several suggestions to help minimize stretch marks.

चन्दनमृणालकल्कैश्चास्याः स्तनोदरं विमृद्गीयात् । *...चरक शारीरस्थान*

Candana-mṛṇālakalkaiścāsyāḥ stanodaram vimṛdgīyāt ...Caraka śārīrasthāna

Gently massage the breasts and abdomen with a paste made of sandalwood (Santalum album) and lotus stem (Nelumbium speciosum).

शिरीषधातकीसर्षपमधुकचूर्णैर्वा । *...चरक शारीरस्थान*

śirīṣa-dhātakī-sarṣapa-madhuka-cūrṇairvā...Caraka

A paste prepared by mixing equal parts of the bark of the shirish tree (Acacia speciosa), the flower of the dhayati plant, mustard seeds, and jyeshthamadha (licorice), should be massaged gently onto the breasts and abdomen.

परिषेकः पुनर्मालतीमधुकसिद्धेनाम्भसाः । *...चरक शारीरस्थान*

Pariṣekaḥ punarmālatī-madhuka-siddhenāmbhasāḥ

...Caraka śārīrasthāna

A decoction prepared from leaves of the jai (a kind of jasmine - Jasminum grandiflorum) and jyeshthamadha, should be dripped steadily onto the abdomen. The liquid should be warm or lukewarm to the touch.

ABHYANG (MASSAGE)

From the fourth month onwards the pregnant woman should begin the practice of massaging her entire body gently with oil. One should use an oil like **Santulan Abhyang Sesame Oil**. Applying this oil every now and then all over the body will help prevent unnecessary weight gain and maintain your figure. During the last three months, this massage becomes imperative and should be supplemented with another oil specifically prepared for the back and spine, like **Santulan Kundalini Oil**. This oil should be massaged into the waist and back, and upto the shoulder everyday without fail in the last trimester. This keeps the joints in the back supple and lubricated, which, in turn, facilitates the process of labour.

From the ninth month onwards, a cotton swab soaked in **Santulan Femisan Oil**, should be placed in the vagina, as explained earlier.

All of these measures balance *vata*, help to maintain good health and a trim figure. They also aid in conserving strength, and preparing the body for timely and easy labour.

THE ATMOSPHERE AT HOME

The foetus is affected not only by the physical and mental state of being of its parents, but also by the atmosphere at home, and the surrounding environment. The entire family and especially the father should be alert at all times and behave accordingly.

Ayurved has advised the following traditional regime to take care of the environment around the pregnant woman.

धूपितार्चितसंमृष्टं मषकाद्यपवर्जितम् ।

ब्रह्मघोषैः सवादित्रैर्वादितम् वेश्म शस्यते ॥ *...काश्यपसंहिता*

Dhūpitārcitasammṛṣṭam
maṣakādyapavarjitam
Brahmaghoṣaiḥ savāditrairvāditam
veśma śasyate .....Kāśyapasamhitā

The pregnant woman's house should be purified with dhoop (herbal smoke) every morning and evening. Regularly perform pujas, and offer prayers in the house. The home should be absolutely free of pests like lizards, mosquitoes, spiders and other insects and rodents. The house should resound with the chanting of mantras, healing music or any other positive music.

A pregnant woman should rise early, bathe with warm water and carry out her morning rituals. She should wear plain light coloured or white clothes. She should ask for the blessings of the elders of the house and the Gods everyday. She should pray to the Sun using vermilion, *dhoop*, offerings of food and chants. In addition, it would be good if she performs *pujas* or chants as per her own beliefs and faith as well. All this will contribute towards keeping the environment in the house pleasant. It will also build a sense of peace and contentment in the woman. If possible, the woman should look at the rising sun. From all this we can infer the following. The house should have adequate sunlight to receive the sun's energy and should be well ventilated for fresh air.

The entire family should ensure there are no bitter words or arguments at home. The atmosphere should be happy, loving and enthusiastic.

Avoid watching movies and TV serials that are frightening or thrilling. For leisure, it is recommended that the expectant mother read books which speak of ethics and morals and those which improve the mind. E.g. *Shivcharitra*, *Ramanyan*, *Krishnaleela*, patriotic stories and the biographies of great personalities. Otherwise, reading material and movies should be light and humourous.

Books such as Shri Ram Vishwa-panchayatan, which bring Indian history, mythology and philosophy, into an accessible form for modern life, are also recommended.

At twilight, the pregnant woman should prepare *dhoop*, light a lamp and chant *Ramraksha*. The sound 'Ra' strengthens digestive fire and imparts a feeling of courage. It protects the mother and foetus from negative energies. If she is familiar with the *Sankatnashanastotra*, this should also be recited. The home and bedroom should be adorned with inspiring pictures, paintings and photographs.

HEALING MUSIC AND MEDITATION

Music is an integral part of Ayurvedic Garbhsanskar. Ayurved emphasizes that harmonious music should be played at home at all times. Like its mother's voice, the foetus can hear other music as well. It is possible to instil certain values *(sanskar)* into the growing foetus through certain types of music, and especially through specific mantras taken from the traditional musical system of India.

The story of Abhimanyu, who learned how to break through a complicated battle formation *(chakravyuha)*, while still in his mother's womb, is well known in Indian mythology.

Listening to specific types of healing music, mantras, and instrumental music, especially featuring the instrument *veena*, is recommended in the scriptures, to ensure good maternal and foetal health.

The Garbha Sanskar Music Album

The Garbha Sanskar music album, based on these traditional Vedic principles, has proved to give excellent results. Babies who have been exposed to this music prenatally are found to be markedly different from other children, and have excellent physical, intellectual and mental responses. This music should be heard every day, from conception until the child is born.

Since the music is familiar to them, children continue to enjoy it after they are born, and many parents have reported that their crying child calms down immediately on listening to this music.

The album begins with *Bramhaghosh*, a special Vedic *mantra* from the *Kashyapsamhita*, and verses from the *Atharva Veda*, which focus on the all-round development of the foetus to lay the foundation for a successful and peaceful life. Verses and *mantras* from the Yajur Veda and Rig Veda help the baby to attain excellent eyesight and hearing, a well-endowed and cultured voice and a long and happy life. The album also includes *Garbha Rakshak Stotra* which, by calling on all powers and deities, protects the foetus from the moment of conception until a safe birth. This special mantra also shields the mother-to-be from negative energies.

It is very important that *mantras* be pronounced specifically and be sung in the correct *raga* etc. if we want to avail of their benefits. In this album, special attention has been paid to precise pronunciation, musical notation, pressure and accent and modulation to ensure maximum benefit to the listener. Musical ragas and notes have been specifically chosen to benefit the mother, and, in particular, to instill positive values in the unborn child. For example, verses of the *Veer-rasa* from the Shrimad Bhagawad Geeta, have been chosen and performed in *Raga Shankara*. This composition helps to make the child bold-hearted, courageous and a good leader.

We will see later the importance of the *Panchamahabhoot* (five elements) in the development of the foetus. To ensure that the Five Elements, the *Panchamahabhoot*, are balanced and functioning properly in the foetus to create a complete and healthy child, the album includes *Aumkar* and *Panchatatva beejmantra*. A *veena* recital in *Raga Asavari* has also been included to increase *ojas* and *virya* (life energy) in the baby.

The newborn child is not just a physical body; it has a soul that requires values, such as truth, purity and love. The stotra *Atmasanskarshatkam-*

shivoham-shivoham has been included on the album specifically to promote these values.

The album also includes compositions from the holy *Gurbani*, to ensure that the child receives blessings from its parents, God and guide (Guru), thus helping it to lead a successful, joyful, contented and healthy life.

- **Regular massage with 'Santulan Suhrud Oil' helps the breasts remain healthy.**
- **Santulan Rose Beauty, massaged on the abdomen and thighs reduces stretch marks.**
- **'Santulan Abhyang Oil' and 'Santulan Kundalini Oil' should be massaged on the waist and back respectively, to maintain flexibility of the joints, which helps ensure an easy delivery.**
- **The atmosphere in a pregnant woman's home should be happy and contented. All family members should actively contribute to this.**
- **Healing music, such as 'Garbha Sanskar', should be listened to daily.**

Remedies for minor problems

A pregnant woman could be highly susceptible to several minor illnesses. Apart from care in diet and lifestyle, she may require medication occasionally, and this too should be done with utmost caution.

Ayurved has outlined its philosophy in this regard as follows.

व्याधींश्चास्या मृदु-मधुर-शिशिर-सुखसुकुमारप्रायैः औषधोपचारैः उपचरेत्। ...चरक शारीरस्थान

Vyādhīmścāsyā mṛdu-madhura-śiśira-sukha-sukumāra-prāyaiḥ auṣadhopacāraiḥ upacaret

...Caraka śārīrasthāna

In case of minor illnesses, the medicines prescribed should be mild, natural, easy to administer, devoid of side-effects and should not cause heat in the body.

Even simple, everyday medicines should only be given to the pregnant woman after consultation with an expert. This applies even in the case of medicines such as painkillers, many of which are contra-indicated during pregnancy. Antibiotics should be avoided as far as possible, as the mother-to-be and the unborn child are very susceptible to their side-effects. Health related complaints or symptoms should be referred to an expert immediately and suitable remedies provided without delay. It will be useful to know about some simple Ayurvedic remedies for minor complaints during pregnancy. They can be followed without problems in addition to any remedies suggested by your *vaidya*.

DIARRHEA / DYSENTERY

As soon as diarrhea or dysentery is discovered, take a mixture of lemon juice, ginger juice and honey. Ayurvedic preparations such as *Kutajaghana vati* or *Sanjeevani Vati* are simple and effective remedies, and can be taken after medical consultation.

As long as diarrhea or dysentery lasts, food should be easy on the digestion. Foods like puffed rice (*Shashti Shali lahya*), *mung-dal khichadi*, and softened rice with buttermilk are best.

If stool is watery, frequent, or contains blood or mucus, a doctor must be consulted immediately.

HAEMORRHOIDS AND FISSURES

Eating home-made butter with candy sugar is recommended for such conditions. Medical preparations like **Sancool** and **Santulan Avipattikar Churna** ensure regular bowel movements and the proper cleansing of the intestines. Homemade butter mixed with *nagkeshar* (Mesua ferrea) is also helpful. *Shatadhaut ghrut* (Ayurvedic ghee washed a hundred times under running water) or aloe vera pulp can be applied to the anal area. Every drop of blood is precious during pregnancy, and you should take care that none of it is needlessly lost.

CONSTIPATION

Santulan Avipattikar Churna or **Sancool**, after meals, is very helpful in case of constipation. A glass of hot water, with 1½ to 2 teaspoons of ghee, taken at bedtime, is also recommended.

COLD, COUGH, SORE THROAT

Add salt and a pinch of turmeric powder to hot water, and use it for gargling. **Santulan Sitopaladi Churna**, taken with hot water or honey is extremely effective.

Decoction - Add one piece of *behada*, one inch of *jyeshthamadha* (licorice), one ripe leaf of *adulsa*, to four cups of water, and boil until the liquid has reduced to one cup. Strain and sweeten with a little sugar before drinking.

GASES, FLATULENCE, ABDOMINAL PAIN, HEAVINESS IN THE ABDOMEN AFTER MEALS

A small piece of ginger, eaten with *saindhav* (rock salt) before meals is helpful. Herbal powders, such as **Santulan Annayog**, or *Lavana Bhaskar Churna*, taken after meals, are very helpful against many abdominal complaints.

FEVER

At the first sign of fever, uneasiness and body ache, drink warm water which has been boiled with coriander seeds, sandalwood and *vala* (khus). *Sanshmani vati* or *mustadi churna* are medical preparations that will help. Eat light food like *mung dal* soup or *mung dal khichadi*, depending on the appetite. Gently massaging the soles of the feet with *pad Abhyang ghrut*, using a special metal bowl (this remedy has been explained later), helps to reduce the fever. However, if the temperature is very high, no time should be wasted before medical help is sought.

URINARY INFECTIONS

For the treatment of all kinds of urinary infections, smoke therapy with **Santulan Shakti Dhoop** is excellent. If possible, a vaginal douche with herbal decoctions (of *dhayati* and *triphala*) should be administered by trained Ayurvedic therapists. **Santulan Prashant Churna** and **Santulan Uricool** are extremely helpful in these conditions. Common Ayurvedic medicines in these cases are *Chandraprabha*, *Gokshuradi churna*, *Punarnava ghanavati*. Please consult a doctor before taking any of these medicines.

SWELLING (OEDEMA)

A slight swelling of the feet is a common occurrence during the eighth or ninth month. Oedema occurring before this time, or that which occurs all over the body, is not a good sign. Puffiness of the face could be an indication of increased blood pressure. After consultation with a doctor, one may need to start taking medicines, such as *Chandraprabha*, *Gokshuradi Vati*, *Punarnava Mandur* or *Punarnavasav*.

PRE-ECLAMPSIA

From the fifth month onwards, many women suffer from swelling of the feet, high blood pressure (about 150/90), a loss of protein in the urine, and a rapid increase in weight. These symptoms are indicative of pre-eclampsia, and, if ignored, can have a disastrous effect on the mother and the unborn baby, apart from causing difficulties during delivery. When such symptoms are observed, immediate precautions must be taken to ensure that the diastolic (lower) blood pressure does not rise above 90-95 mm of Hg.

Pregnancy at an advanced age, obesity from the outset, a family history of diabetes, or improper care during pregnancy, are some of the pre-disposing factors of pre-eclampsia. Although the incidence of pre-eclampsia has been on the increase recently, a balanced diet as recommended here from the beginning of pregnancy, combined with appropriate Ayurvedic treatment, can help to prevent this condition. If the mother has a history of pre-eclampsia, you need to take extra care in subsequent pregnancies.

OTHER ISSUES

Besides these complaints, the expectant mother should be on the alert for the appearance of a white or watery discharge. Another common complaint is 'spotting' during the first few months. Both these have an adverse effect on the growth, development and nourishment of the foetus, as well as on the health of the mother, and should be treated promptly.

To alleviate the above problems:

1. Drink water that has been used to soak and wash rice.
2. Eat *nagkeshar* powder with buttermilk
3. Medcial preparations that will help are, *Pushyanug Churna* and *Shatavaryadi Churna*
4. Dhoop for the genital area.

Consult your vaidya if the symptoms persist.

No health complaints or problems, however minor, should be ignored during pregnancy, since any imbalance can affect the mother, the child and the process of childbirth. The expectant mother is in a delicate and sensitive state, and the intake of any strong medication is contra indicated. The timely treatment of any health problems, with natural and simple remedies, before they escalate, is therefore of the utmost importance.

- **During pregnancy, precautions should be taken to avoid illness.**
- **If illness does occur, strong medication should be avoided.**
- **Preventative measures should be taken, if there is a family history of a specific medical problem.**
- **An important adjuvant therapy for all minor complaints, is the intake of light and easily digestible food.**
- **Swelling anywhere on the body, or urinary infections, should be treated promptly.**

3

Nurturing the foetus…

Advances in modern medicine, coupled with technological progress, give us a detailed picture of the growing foetus. This knowledge, combined with ancient wisdom, helps us to know exactly what needs to be done during pregnancy, what is best avoided, and why…

Growth of the foetus and its nourishment

The progressive growth of the foetus has been explained in detail in Ayurved. This growth can now be seen through modern techniques. It is amazing how this ancient Indian medical science was able to describe the growth of the foetus so accurately even thousands of years ago.

FIRST MONTH

स सर्व गुणवान् गर्भत्वमापन्नः प्रथमे मासि
संमूर्च्छितः सर्वधातुकललिकृतः खेटभूतो
भवत्यव्यक्तविग्रहः सदसद्भूताङ्गावयवः ।

...चरक शारीरस्थान

Sa sarva guṇavān garbhatvamāpannaḥ
prathame māsi sammūrcchitaḥ

sarva-dhātu-kalalikṛtaḥ kheṭabhūto bhavatyavyaktavigrahaḥ sadasad-bhūtāṅgāvayavaḥ
...Caraka śārīrasthāna

During the first month, the embryo resembles a ball of kapha, and is shapeless.

SECOND MONTH

द्वितीये मासि घनः संपद्यते पिण्डः पेश्यर्बुदं वा । ...चरक शारीरस्थान

Ditīye māsi ghanaḥ sampadyate piṇḍḥ peśyarbudam vā ...Caraka śārīrasthāna

In the second month, the embryo increases in density, and slowly becomes round, oval, or shaped like a tear drop.

THIRD MONTH

तृतीये हस्तपादशिरसां पंचपिण्डका निर्वर्तन्ते
अंगप्रत्यंग विभागश्च सूक्ष्मो भवति । ...सुश्रुत शारीरस्थान

Tṛtīye hasta-pāda-śirasām pañca-piṇḍakā nirvartante aṅga-pratyaṅga vibhāgaśca sūkṣmo bhavati ...Suśruta śārīrasthāna

The tiny round foetus develops a tail, two arms, two legs and a head, and appears to have five different parts. Other organs and senses develop at a microscopic level at this time.

FOURTH MONTH

चतुर्थे सर्वांगप्रत्यंगविभागः प्रव्यक्तो भवति,
गर्भहृदयप्रव्यक्तिभावात् चेतनाधातुरभिव्यक्तो भवति। तस्मात्
गर्भश्चतुर्थे मासि
अभिप्रायमिन्द्रियार्थेषु करोति। द्विहृदया च नारी दौहृदिनीं आचक्षते।
...सुश्रुत शारीरस्थान

चतुर्थे मासि स्थिरत्वं आपद्यते गर्भः, तस्मात्तदा गर्भिणी गुरुगात्रत्वं
अधिकं आपद्यते विशेषेण । ...चरक शारीरस्थान

Caturthe sarvāṅga-pratyaṅga-vibhāgaḥ pravyakto bhavati, garbha-hṛdaya-pravyaktibhāvāt cetanā-dhāturabhivyakto bhavati Tasmāt garbhaścaturthe māsi abhiprāyamindriyārtheṣu karoti
Dvi-hṛdayā ca nārī dauhṛdinīm ācakṣate
....Suśruta śārīrasthāna

Caturthe māsi sthiratvam āpadyate garbhaḥ, tasmāt-tadā garbhiṇī gurugātratvam adhikam āpadyate viśeṣeṇa ...Caraka śārīrasthāna

The foetus becomes stable, and as it grows in size, the expectant mother experiences a feeling of heaviness. All the parts of the body become better defined, and the heart, in particular, can now be experienced.

In the fourth month, the pregnant woman is referred to as *dauhrudini* i.e. one having two

Development of the foetus

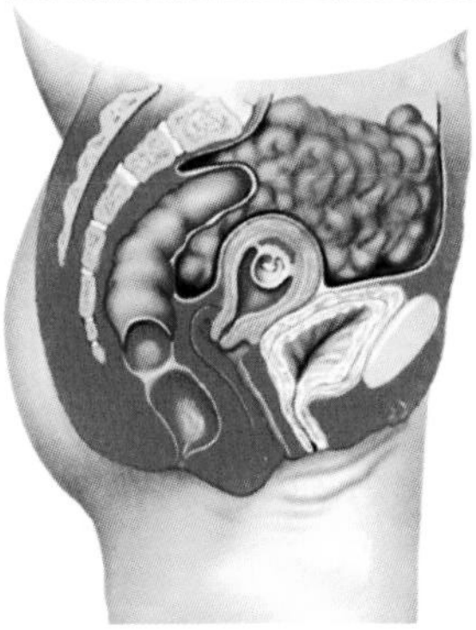

First month

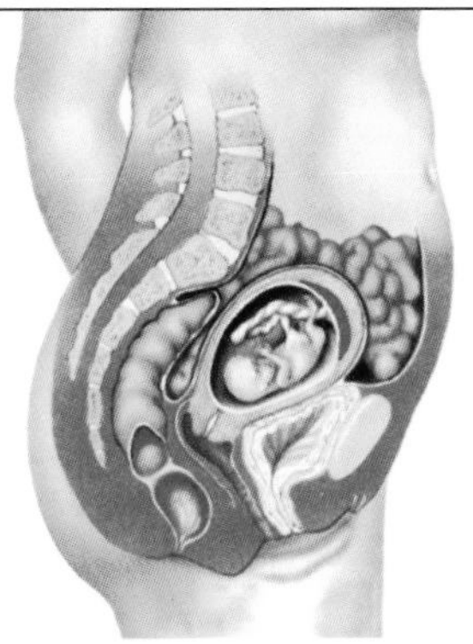

Second month

hearts - hers and that of her baby-beating inside her body. The desires of the developing foetus, described in Ayurved as *dauhrud*, or commonly known in Marathi as *dohaale*, become evident at this stage.

Ayurved says that the baby is able to voice its wishes through its heart from now on, and these are experienced by the mother as *dohaale*. It is important that these wishes be fulfilled. If not, this may lead to an increase in *vata*, which could, in turn, have an adverse effect on the foetus, and become visible after birth, as a physical disability, mental discontentment or sorrow, in the child.

Although these desires should be fulfilled, when they are related to food, one should not be over-indulgent. Excessive intake of any one kind of food can also lead to undesirable effects already described earlier. There may be a craving for things that are difficult or impossible to obtain, and in such cases, a compromise has to be worked out, so that these cravings do not go unfulfilled. For example, the desire for chalk, or mud or earth, can be met by eating *praval bhasma*, which has a similar taste. The desire for extremely sour food such as tamarind, can be satisfied with amla or *aamsool* (Garcinia purpurea).

If these desires are properly attended to, the child to-be-born will be healthy, with a happy and contented constitution, and have a long life. The favourable intellectual and physical growth of the child is also ensured.

For the above reasons, the *Seemanttonnayan sanskar* (explained in the chapter on Sanskars), has been suggested as one of the sixteen important rituals to be performed in a person's life.

FIFTH MONTH

पञ्चमे मनः प्रतिबुद्धतरं भवति । ...*सुश्रुत शारीरस्थान*

पञ्चमे मासि गर्भस्य मांसशोणितपचयो
भवति अधिकं अन्येभ्यो मासेभ्यः । ...*चरक शारीरस्थान*

Pañcame manaḥ pratibuddhataram bhavati
....Suśruta śārīrasthāna

Pañcame māsi garbhasya mānsa-śoṇitapacayo
bhavati adhikam anyebhyo māsebhyaḥ
...Caraka śārīrasthāna

From this month onwards, the child's mind becomes sensitized to various feelings and events, as well as to its surroundings. During this period, the maximum development of mansa (muscle tissue) and rakta (blood) dhatus occurs. According to the *Garbhopanishad*, the vertebral column also

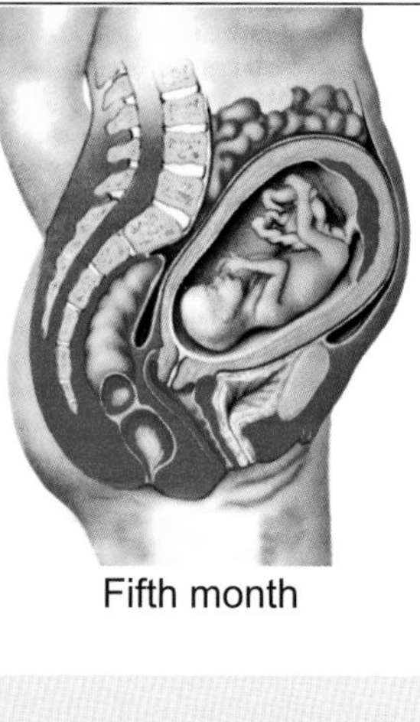

Fifth month

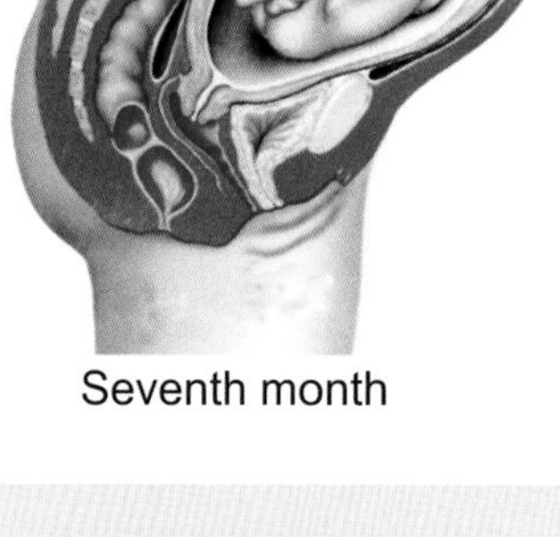

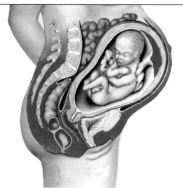

Seventh month

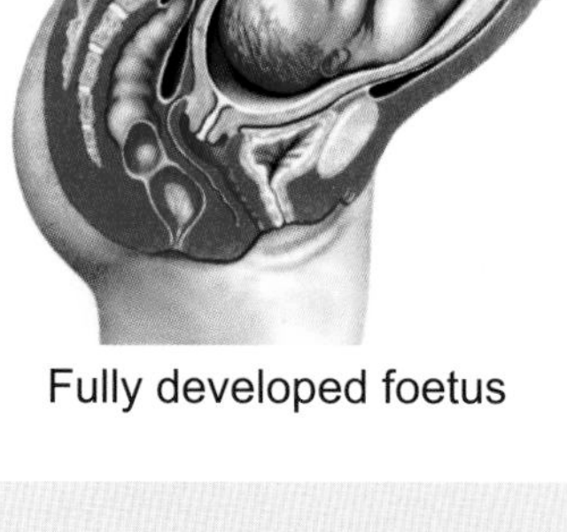

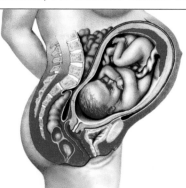

Fully developed foetus

develops in this month.

SIXTH MONTH

षष्ठे बुद्धिः। ...सुश्रुत शारीरस्थान

षष्ठे मासि गर्भस्य बलवर्णोपचयो भवति
अधिकं अन्येभ्यो मासेभ्यः । ...चरक शारीरस्थान

ṣaṣṭhe buddhiḥ ....Suśruuta śārīrasthāna

ṣaṣṭhe māsi garbhasya bala-varṇopacayo bhavati
adhikam anyebhyo māsebhyaḥ ...Caraka śārīrasthāna

Intelligence, strength and complexion develop during the sixth month, an indication that the foundation of these attributes have been laid during the foetal stage. In order to produce a strong, intelligent child, with a glowing complexion and healthy skin, the expectant mother must pay strict attention to her diet, health, lifestyle and behaviour throughout pregnancy, and especially during the sixth month. Adequate nutrition is, of course, extremely important.

The colour and complexion of the foetus are primarily affected by the fire element (*tej mahabhoot*). If the water element (*jal mahabhoot*) supports *tej*, then the foetus will be fair and light-skinned; if the earth element (prithvi mahabhoot) dominates then the skin will be darker. The proportion and balance of these elements ultimately depends on diet. **According to Ashtanga Sanghraha, four factors affect the baby's skin colour:**

1. **Pitruj-matruj** : means that skin colour is inherited from the parents.

2. **Deshaj :** the weather, average temperature and environment of the region of residence affect the skin colour.

3. **Kulaj :** the colour depends on the predominant skin colour of the ancestors and the family tree of the child.

4. **Mahabhutaj :** the predominance of a certain element in the diet of the mother is responsible for the colour of the skin of her unborn child.

One school of thought says that if the expectant mother consimes *sattvik* and liquid foods, which are free of impurities, her child will be fair-skinned (as far as possible given the other factors as well), and will have clear and glowing complexion. If she consumes dark coloured foods (which tend to increase *pitta*) then her child will have darker skin.

In general, if the mother wishes her child to have glowing and fair skin, she should eat ghee, milk, kheer, home-made butter, rice, buttermilk, tender coconut water, and *panchamrut* with saffron and gold, regularly. These foods not only affect the child's skin-colour but, as described earlier, also provide nourishment for their development.

SEVENTH MONTH

सप्तमे सर्वांगप्रत्यंगविभागः प्रव्यक्ततरः । ...सुश्रुत शारीरस्थान

Saptame sarvāṅga-pratyaṅga-vibhāgaḥ
pravyaktataraḥ ...Suśruta śārīrasthāna

The foetus is almost fully developed at this stage. All organs have essentially developed, lacking only in growth and maturity. Though the organs are still not fully grown, the child will be able to survive in the advent of a premature delivery.

Obviously, the ideal situation is for the baby to be born at full term (i.e. after nine months), when development is complete. There is no substitute for the nourishment that the mother's womb provides.

EIGHTH MONTH

अष्टमे अस्थिरी भवति ओजः ।
तत्र जातश्चेन्न जीवेत् निरोजस्त्वात् नैर्ऋत भागत्वाच्च । *...सुश्रुत शारीरस्थान*

Aṣṭame asthirī bhavati ojaḥ Tatra jātaścenna jīvet nirojastvāt nairṛata bhāgatvācca ...Suśruta śārīrasthāna

In this month, the Ojas (supreme energy), flows alternately between mother and child. The mother-to-be alternately appears extremely happy and enthusiastic (when the energy flows to her), or tired and drained (when the energy has transferred to the foetus). Because of this transfer of energy, delivery in the eighth month is not considered safe for either mother or child. *If premature labour does occur, the life of the one lacking Ojas at the time of labour may be in jeopardy, or will end up with a lifelong disability.*

NINTH MONTH

तस्मिन्नेकदिवसातिक्रान्तेऽपि नवमं मासं उपादाय प्रसवकालं इत्याहुरादशमान् मासात् । *...चरक शारीरस्थान*

Tasminnekadivasātikrāntelpi navamam māsam upādāya prasava- kālam ityāhurādaśamān māsāt ...Caraka śārīrasthāna

By now the foetus has developed completely. It is preparing itself for labour, and its journey to the outside world. A delay in delivery is not desirable, since the placenta that nourishes the foetus, begins to degenerate and dislodge itself from the uterine walls at full term. In cases of post-term delivery, the child may have long nails, or dry, rough skin at birth. So, it is in the interest of both, mother and child, for delivery to take place at around 9 months + 9 days of pregnancy.

NOURISHMENT OF THE FOETUS

The foetus is nourished primarily through the mother's diet, especially from her *rasa dhatu.*

स्त्रिया ह्यापन्नगर्भायास्त्रिधा रसः प्रतिपद्यते, स्वशरीरपुष्टये, स्तन्याय, गर्भवृद्धये च । *...चरक शारीरस्थान*

Striyā hyāpannagarbhāyāstridhā rasaḥ pratipadyate, svaśarīrapuṣṭaye, stanyāya, garbha-vṛddhaye ca ...Caraka śārīrasthāna

According to Charak,
Rasa dhatu is responsible for :

1. Nourishing the foetus.
2. Development of the breasts, so that good quality milk is produced, and
3. Nourishment of the mother.

Hence, the mother's *rasa dhatu* should be adequate, healthy and capable of providing for all of the above. As the foetus grows, the umbilical cord also develops, and transports the essence of this *rasa dhatu to it.*

मातुस्तु खलु रसवहायां नाड्यां गर्भनाभिनाडी प्रतिबद्धा साऽस्य मातुराहाररसवीर्यमभिवहति । *...सुश्रुत शारीरस्थान*

Mātustu khalu rasa-vahāyām nāḍyām garbha-nābhi-nāḍī pratibaddhā sālsya māturāhāra-rasa-vīryamabhivahati ...Suśruta śārīrasthāna

One end of the umbilical cord is connected to the umbilicus of the foetus, the other to the uterus. Blood vessels form an intricate network at the site, where the cord connects with the uterus, and this network is known as the placenta.

Being already assimilated in the mother's

body, *rasa dhatu* is accepted by the foetus, as it is, through the placenta. Since all nutrients are delivered in usable form, only a negligible amount of waste is produced by the foetus.

The moment a woman begins to plan pregnancy, she should regulate and control her movements, behaviour, and lifestyle. This reduces the chances that the placenta gets implanted in an undesirable manner in the uterus.

Inside the uterus, the foetus floats in a special fluid, known as the amniotic fluid. According to Ayurved, this fluid is formed from an abundance of *Prithvi* (earth element) and *Jal mahabhoot* (water element).

As the foetus increases in size, the quantity of amniotic fluid increases proportionately. The foetus almost swims in the amniotic fluid, which protects it from external injuries, and facilitates movement. There is normally about 900 to 1000 ml of amniotic fluid around the baby, but this may vary depending on the season, and the individual constitution of the mother. All this fluid is replaced every 3 to 4 hours.

The foetus swallows around 400 ml of amniotic fluid every day, but because of the fluid's special composition, this causes no adverse effects. The fluid is merely expelled by the foetus, through the urine.

The ancient sciences explain that any problems which may result from the foetus swallowing the fluid can be corrected by carrying out the *Annaprashan sanskar*. (See Chapter on Sanskaars)

The amniotic fluid also ensures that there is no undue pressure exerted on the foetus when the uterus begins contracting during labour. It actually facilitates the movement of the foetus. The amniotic fluid is released when the membranes rupture, which precedes the process of labour. This is commonly known as the 'waters breaking'.

At full term, the amniotic fluid naturally begins to decrease. Nowadays there are many cases where the amniotic fluid reduces suddenly and unexplainably during the eight or ninth month of pregnancy. This is obviously detrimental to the health of the foetus.

The importance of the Five Elements (*panchmahabhoot*), in the growth and nourishment of the foetus, is outlined as follows:

तं चेतनावस्थितं वायुर्विभजति, तेज एनं पचति,
आपः क्लेदयन्ति, पृथिवी संहन्ति, आकाशं विवर्धयति । ...*सुश्रुत शारीरस्थान*

Tam cetanāvasthitam vāyur-vibhajati, teja enam pacati, āpaḥ kledayanti, pṛthivī samhanti, ākāśam vivardhayati ....Suśruta śārīrasthāna

The element of Air (vayu) is responsible for all divisions occurring in the foetus, right from the first division of the cells, to the division of all body parts and organs.

The element of fire (agni) provides the necessary energy for the development of the foetal organs, and is responsible for the various essential transformations taking place.

Water (jal) imparts moisture and lubrication to the organs, binds them together and helps to nourish the unborn child.

Earth (prithvi) gives stability and density to the physical body and contributes to its structure.

The element of space (akash) provides optimal space for all these changes to take place at the

correct time.

The foetus gains shape and form because of these Five Elements. If, for some reason, these elements do not remain balanced and in their natural form, the child may exhibit the following defects :

- The imbalance of the Element of Air (*Vayu mahabhoot*) causes unnatural cell division, leading to various anomalies such as the growth of extra fingers, the absence of an anal aperture, or fused openings of bladder and rectum etc.
- The imbalance of the *Agni mahabhoot* (Element of Fire) leads to skin defects, allergies, digestive disorders and various eye problems.
- Aberrations in the *Jal mahabhoot* (Element of Water) results in inadequate nourishment of the foetus, decreased amniotic fluid and hydrocephalus (excess water in the cranium of the foetus).
- Abnormalities of the *prithvi mahabhoot* (Element of Earth) cause instability, which could result in miscarriage, underdevelopment of the foetus, brittle bones or short stature.
- Aberrations in the *Akash mahabhoot* (Element of Space) lead to congenital defects, such as openings in the septum of the heart, deformities of the heart chambers or abnormalities of the ear.

The following shows the relationship between each element, and the senses and body parts:

Mahabhoot	Senses and body parts
Vayu	sense of touch, skin
Agni	sense of vision, eyes, jatharagni (digestive fire)
Jal	sense of taste, tongue, fatty tissue, phlegm, muscle, mansa dhatu, semen
Prithvi	sense of smell, nose, general physical structure
Aakash	sense of sound, ears, mouth, voice, throat, the hollow organs of the body

Additionally, the three *doshas* - *vata*, *pitta*, *kapha* and the seven *dhatus*, namely *rasa*, *rakta*, *mansa*, *meda*, *asthi*, *majja* and *shukra*, have a significant influence on the development of various organs.

Ayurved describes the formation of all organs in detail. Some of the more important of these are described below.

Heart - श्लेष्मरक्तप्रसादात् । ...*सुश्रुत शरीरस्थान*

śleṣma-rakta-prasādāt ....Suśruta śarīrasthāna

The heart develops from balanced *kapha*, and the essence of *rakta*.

Lungs - रक्तफेनप्रसादात् । ...*सुश्रुत शरीरस्थान*

Rakta-phena-prasādāt ...Suśruta śarīrasthāna

The lungs develop from the foam (extremely thin saccules) of the essence of *rakta dhatu.*

Liver and Spleen - यकृतप्लीहानौ शोणितजौ । ...*सुश्रुत शरीरस्थान*

Yakṛta-plīhānau śoṇitajau ...Suśruta śarīrasthāna

The liver and spleen mainly develop from *rakta dhatu*.

Kidneys - रक्तमेदप्रसादात् वृक्कौ । *...सुश्रुत शारीरस्थान*

Rakta-meda-prasādāt vṛkkau ...Suśruta śarīrasthāna

Kidneys develop from the essence of both *rakta dhatu* and *meda dhatu* (fatty tissue).

Testes - मांसासृक्कफमेदप्रसादात् वृषणम् । *...सुश्रुत शरीरस्थान*

Māmsāsṛk-kapha-meda-prasādāt vṛṣaṇam
...Suśruta śarīrasthāna

The essence of *mansa*, *rakta* and *meda dhatus*, and balanced *kapha*, contribute to the development of the testes.

According to Ayurved, all hollow organs are formed in the following way. *Pitta* acts on *rakta dhatu* as well as balanced *kapha,* together, to produce their essence. When this essence is then acted upon by *vata*, the hollow organs are formed. These are organs like the intestines, uterus and bladder.

Skin - शुक्रशोणितस्याभिपच्यमानस्य क्षीरस्येव सन्तानिकाः सप्त त्वचो भवन्ति । *...सुश्रुत शरीरस्थान*

śukra-śoṇitasyābhipacyamānasya kṣīrasyeva santānikāḥ sapta tvaco bhavanti ....Suśruta śarīrasthāna

Ayurved compares the formation of the skin to the formation of a layer of cream on milk being heated. This transformation is a continuous process from the moment of fertilization throughout the development of the foetus.

An important fact to note: Although it is true that the foetus develops entirely from its parents, the different characteristics of each organ are not inherited from each parent equally. Some organs exhibit a predominantly maternal influence, while others are more influenced by the father

In general, all soft structures and organs are influenced by the mother, while the hard, firm organs are influenced by the father.

Skin, rakta dhatu, mansa dhatu (muscles), meda dhatu (fatty tissue), umbilicus, heart, pancreas, liver, spleen, stomach, large and small intestine, rectum, anus, kidney and urinary bladder are influenced by the mother. Hair, beard, moustache, body hair, teeth, bones, ligaments, semen and blood vessels are influenced by the father.

- **Since the heart of the foetus has developed substantially by the fourth month, it is able to transmit its cravings through the mother.**
- **It is necessary that cravings (*dohaale*) be satisfied in order to ensure the physical and mental health of the baby.**
- **The foundations of intelligence, complexion and strength are laid down during pregnancy - a fact that should be kept in mind by the mother.**
- **An adequate quantity of amniotic fluid is essential for the proper nourishment of the foetus.**
- **The woman should regulate her behaviour, lifestyle, and physical movements from the moment she begins to plan her pregnancy. This reduces the incidence of problems which may occur during the formation of the placenta.**

Some possible foetal defects

It is only natural to wish for a child who is bestowed with all possible positive qualities. We want that children should be physically and mentally excellent, intelligent and artistic. This can by no means be taken for granted. A child's imperfections will only come to light at birth or shortly after. The following are some general causes for such issues:

1. A family history of hereditary problems, and/or defects in the sperm or egg: These could include all kinds curable and non-curable diseases, diabetes, asthma, thalassaemia, obesity, increased *pitta* tendencies, acidity, headaches, weak eyes, certain kinds of mental diseases, and skin disorders. All these may be passed on to future generations. Such problems may manifest at different stages during life, but subtle indications of their presence can be seen early from childhood. For example, if there is a history of diabetes in the family, children tend to be either obese or extremely underweight, complain of burning micturition (urination), exhibit poor eyesight, and are generally weak. In many cases, however, the presence of increased blood sugar is detected only after the person reaches the age of 35-40.

2. Ignoring the guidelines related to menstruation, as laid down by Ayurved: These practices followed before pregnancy also help the foetus after the woman has conceived. If the guidelines related to lifestyle and behaviour are not followed, the resulting disturbances may have an adverse effect on the foetus. It could even cause certain abnormalities. This is especially true for those organs developing with maternal influence.

3. Problems arising in the parents-to-be, either before conception or while conceiving: We have already learned that both male and female reproductive cells should be healthy. Diseases like malaria, jaundice and tuberculosis have long-lasting effects on the body. If either partner has recently suffered from any of these, they should make sure that they have been completely cured before conceiving. If not, the reproductive cell could be affected, consequently leading to disabilities in the child.

If either parent has regular late nights or is under severe physical or mental stress at the time of conception, the foetus could develop certain physical or mental abnormalities. The necessary precautions to be taken at the time of conception have already been outlined earlier.

4. Partial defects in sperm or egg: The ideal pre-condition for a healthy baby, is the presence of healthy reproductive cells. In some cases, the baby may be born with congenital defects which are only noticed after birth. For example heart defects (valvular or septal), lack of a kidney, absence of the uterus, or inadequately developed ovaries. In these cases it is possible that only the corresponding part of the reproductive cell (either sperm or ovum) had some defects.

Acharya Charak describes such conditions

in the following way

यस्य यस्य ह्यवयवस्य बीजे बीजभागे वा दोषाः प्रकोपमापद्यन्ते, तं तमवयवं विकृतिराविशति ।

... चरक शारीरस्थान

Yasya yasya hyavayavasya bīje bīja-bhāge vā doṣāḥ prakopam-āpadyante, tam tamavayavam vikṛtirāviśati ...Caraka śārīrasthāna

Modern genetic science refers to genes and chromosomes. Ayurved describes similar functions in verses like the one above. These, of course, are now being studied with the help of advances in modern science. Certain congenital diseases arise when people intermarry in the same family or caste (consanguinity).

5. Problems during pregnancy: If diet, behaviour, or lifestyle guidelines are ignored, or if the mother is unhappy, the foetus may develop defects. Any ailment suffered by the mother during pregnancy, whether minor or major, could also affect the unborn child. Disorders such as urinary infections, white discharge, mild fever, malaise, frequent coughs, colds or sore throat, should be cured completely during pregnancy. The child's cravings expressed through the mother - *dohaale* - should be fulfilled to avoid any impairment to mother or child.

6. Problems during labour: Prolonged labour, physical trauma to the child during labour, or undue pressure given by the mother at an inappropriate time, can cause defects in the child.

E.g. If labour is difficult, the child may be unable to breathe, and the ensuing loss of oxygen could cause brain damage.

7. Inappropriate postpartum care: The newborn needs a few days to slowly adapt to the external environment. It is in an extremely delicate and sensitive state during this adaptation period, and needs great care and attention. Any serious infections occurring during this time, can lead to undesirable long-term effects.

8. Fate / destiny that which is beyond our control: There is often no obvious explanation for defects which may appear in the baby. In such cases, the cause may stem from past lives, or may be due to the effect of planetary positions. Ayurved clearly refers to this as, Devādiprakopanimitta vikaraḥ samupalabhyante

MISCARRIAGE AND BLEEDING DURING PREGNANCY

During the first trimester, the embryo is in an unstable and delicate condition.

Any harm or damage at this point could lead to a miscarriage. Any bleeding that occurs during this time could be very harmful for the embryo. It has not yet been properly formed and could easily be expelled with the blood. Ayurved refers to this as *Garbhastrav*. Once begun, it is difficult to bring under control.

The complete development of the foetus occurs during the second trimester of pregnancy, and any bleeding occurring during this time may cause it to be expelled. This is known as *Garbhapaat*, or miscarriage. However, since the foetus has stabilized by then, it is possible to prevent this occurrence with prompt and correct treatment.

SIGNS OF MISCARRIAGE

- Spotting or mild bleeding, accompanied by a sticky discharge.

- Back ache and lower abdominal pain. After the fifth or sixth month, the pain feels like labour pain.

- A feeling of weakness and general uneasiness.

The causes of miscarriage are outlined as follows:

व्यवाय व्यायामकर्शनाभिघातातिमात्रसङ्क्षोभियान अप्रियावलोकन श्रवणादयः । ...*अष्टांगसंग्रह शारीरस्थान*

Vyavāya vyāyāma-karśa-nābhi-ghātātimātrasaṅkṣobhiyāna apriyāvalokana vaṇādayaḥ ....Aṣṭāṅgasaṅgraha śārīrasthāna

- Intake of inappropriate food. Insufficient diet or incorrect dietary habits.
- Excess traveling.
- Incorrect physical exercise, or over-exercising.
- Sexual intercourse during the first trimester, or excess sexual activity in the latter part of pregnancy.
- Accident or physical trauma.
- Excess physical activity.
- Frequent late nights or sleeping during the day.
- Constant suppression of the urge to urinate or defecate.
- Overexposure to the sun, or staying in a hot site for a long period of time.
- Habitually sitting in incorrect postures or squatting.
- Exposure to news, noise or visual stimulation, which causes mental stress and strain.
- Emotions such as extreme anger, jealousy, fear, anxiety or sadness.
- Internal examination, if incorrectly performed, could also damage the foetus. It should be avoided as far as possible, unless absolutely necessary for diagnostic purposes.

Measures to Stabilise the Foetus

There are remedies to help avoid such issues and provide stability to the foetus from an early stage. Acharya Charak recommend the following measures, which are known as *garbhasthapan* (giving stability to the foetus). Should any of the above problematic situations occur unintentionally, these procedures, either done as precaution, or after, can help nullify or reduce such negative effects. They should ideally be followed throughout pregnancy.

ऐन्द्री-ब्राह्मी-शतवीर्या-सहस्त्रवीर्याऽमोघाऽव्यथाशिवाऽरिष्टा-वाट्यपुष्पी-विष्वक्सेनकान्ता इति दशेमानि प्रजास्थापनानि भवन्ति । ...*चरक सूत्रस्थान*

Aindrī-brāhmī-śatavīryā-sahasravīryā-amoghā avyathā-śivā ariṣṭā-vāṭyapuṣpī-viṣvaksenakāntā iti daśemāni prajā-sthāpanāni bhavanti

....Caraka sūtrasthāna

These remedies are most effective when done from the 4th to the 16th day of the menstrual cycle - the fertile period (*rutukaal*) - in the preparation for conception. They can be continued throughout pregnancy. They strengthen the uterus and facilitate easy conception. Their effects last very long and months later, they will help ensure an easy and timely labour. Several such remedies are described below.

Boil milk with shatavari (Asparagus racemosus), brahmi (Herpestis monniera), vidarikand (Ipomoea digitata), guduchi (Tinospora cordifolia), bala (Sida cordifolia), jeevak, rushbhak and consume regularly. Ghee prepared with the same herbs is as useful. These herbs help to cool, nourish and strengthen the body.

If possible, powder these herbs and boil with water. Add the resulting decoction to bath water on pushya nakshatra (the occurrence of the pushya constellation).

Make provision for a small herb nursery at home. Plant shatavari, brahmi, gulvel and durva. Once ready, pick and dry them (in shade). Wrap them into small bundles with cotton, muslin or silk cloth. Keep these bundles under the mattress or pillow of the woman attempting to conceive.

Month-by-month diet recommendations have already been outlined. It is important that they are followed religiously to ensure proper nourishment of the mother and her unborn child.

All of the above remedies are such that they can be quickly initiated at home. However, if bleeding or spotting occurs, medical consultation should be sought without delay!

What Should You Do In the Event That Bleeding Occurs During Pregnancy?

Irrespective of the cause, the following measures will be helpful:

1. The expectant mother should sleep on a soft and comfortable mattress, and her feet should be elevated.
2. Apply *Shatadhauta ghruta* on the lower abdomen, below the navel, in a thick layer (i.e. like a *lep*).
3. Soak a cloth in cold cow's milk and place on the lower abdomen, below the navel. The cloth can also be soaked in a cold decoction made of herbs which are cooling and help to constrict blood. The decoction should be made from dhayati (Woodfordia floribunda), behada (Terminalia belerica), umber (Ficus glomerata), and pimpal (Ficus religiosa).
4. Make a paste of the blue lotus (Nelumbium speciosum) and durva (Cynodon dactylon). Mix the paste with *ghee*. Soak a cotton swab in this mixture and place it in the vagina. If you cannot prepare the above mixture, use *Shatadhauta ghruta* instead.
5. The pregnant woman should eat *shingada sheera*.
6. Another useful recipe is as follows. Take any one of the following - the blue lotus, shoots of the banyan, licorice, or the raw fruit of umber. Boil this herb in cow's milk and water, and strain. This milk should be cooked with brown / red rice and candy sugar, into a *kheer*. It should eaten cold with honey.
7. Make sure the pregnant woman is never under any mental stress in this condition. She should engage in pleasant and cheerful activities.
8. Keep the mother's diet light at this time. A thin *khichadi* made of mung and soft rice, or *mung kadhan* (mung soup), cooked in pure ghee, are recommended foods

Nowadays more and more women complain about some bleeding during pregnancy. While this does not necessarily lead to an abortion or miscarriage, but it needs to be treated, since it is surely detrimental to the Foetus. The main reasons for bleeding and spotting are:
a) a weak uterus and b) an unstable foetus

Since bleeding or spotting could be harmful to the foetus, just halting the discharge is not enough. You need to take measures to strengthen the uterus. A weak uterus may result in disorders in the placenta, inadequate nourishment of the breasts, and under-development of the organs such as the spleen, liver, and lungs, in the foetus (i.e. those organs which develop from *rakta dhatu*).

The Risk Of Miscarriage

For women who have a history of miscarriage or those who have specifically been warned by their vaidya or doctor that they are at risk of miscarriage, Ayurved suggests the following remedies to safegaurd the foetus.

Ayurvedic medicines known to arrest this process are *Garbhapaal Ras*, *Shatavari ghrut*, or *Laghumalini Vasant*, which can all be administered as a prophylactic. Please do this taking the woman's constitution into consideration and after medical consultation.

PREVENTING MISCARRIAGE - MONTHLY REMEDIES

1st month - In the first month of pregnancy, the foetus needs time to stabilise. Cow's milk with powders of licorice, sandalwood and raktachandan (red sandalwood - Pterocarpus santalinus), and raisins as well, are all very helpful.

2nd month - A decoction of nagkeshar and lotus stem in milk is advised. Boil 150ml (1 cup) of milk with 10g each of nagkeshar and lotus stem and 600ml (4 cups) of water. Boil until the decoction reduces to approximately 150 ml again. Strain, and sweeten with candy sugar before drinking.

3rd month - Drink milk with sugar and a powder made from padmakashtha (Prunus malus), sandalwood, wala, lotus stem and nagkeshar

4th month - Take a little milk in a mortar. Add some pieces of the rhizome of the banana plant, petals of the lotus and the root of wala. Grind it with a pestle until it is like a paste. This paste should be eaten by the pregnant woman.

5th month - Consume a mixture of the blue lotus (neelkamal), lotus stem, renukabeej (Piper aurantiacum), nagkeshar and padmakashtha with water. The herbs should be mixed very well with water, and consumed.

6th month - A handful of special black soil (dhekud) that has been heated in a fire, some red geru (gairik) and some burned cow dung, should be soaked in water. This water should be strained. Add sugar and sandalwood to the mixture before drinking.

7th month - A powdered mixture of wala, gokharu, nagarmotha, lajalu (Mimosa pudica), nagakeshar, and padmakashtha, should be taken with honey.

8th month - A powered mixture of Lodhra and pimpli (Piper longum) should be taken with honey.

These remedies are useful upto the eighth month. They should be initiated with the guidance of a vaidya. Ayurved suggests these remedies so that a vaidya can help you in case there is a tendency towards miscarriage.

If miscarriage or bleeding does occur in spite of these measures, the woman may have to undergo uterus cleansing, and certain specialized treatments available in Ayurved. There is a general misconception that a woman who suffers a miscarriage, or undergoes MTP (medical termination of pregnancy) in the first trimester, does not need any medical therapy. It should be noted that a miscarriage should be treated as a mini-labour, and the type of care administered for labour, as clearly defined in the Ayurvedic texts, is absolutely necessary in such cases.

A simple but effective guideline for therapy after a miscarriage or MTP is that therapy should continue for as many days as the number of months the pregnancy lasted, i.e. if miscarriage or MTP occurs in month four, the woman should undergo four days of all the suggested therapy. This is an approximate measure of the duration of therapy required based on the extent of trauma.

THERAPY AFTER MISCARRIAGE OR MTP

Food

Rice cooked until soft, mixed with herbs that increase digestive fire, such as dry ginger, black pepper, long pepper, chitrak (Plumbago zeylanica), and chavya (Piper chaba),is recommended at this time.

As an alternative, these herbs could also be mixed with mung dal soup.

The normal addition of spices used in Indian cooking through fodni etc. should not be used in these recipes at all. Even salt should be used minimally.

Ginger and jaggery balls, taken in the mornings, in these conditions, are very helpful (see Special Recipes).

Remedies to Help Balance Vata

This condition leads to a lot of vata imbalance. This should be alleviated with the following measures.

- A vata-pacifying oil like **Santulan Abhyang Sesame Oil** should be used for massage for at least fifteen days.
- Smoke therapy (with **Santulan Shakti Dhoop**), to the genital region to purify the uterus, twice or three times a week. Once the bleeding stops after a miscarriage, a cotton swab soaked in medicinal oil (like **Santulan Femisan Oil**) should be placed in the vagina overnight, for at least a month.
- The woman should be administered a decoction made from gulvel, pittapapda (Fumaria officinalis), vala, nagarmotha (Cyperus rotundus), sandalwood, coriander and bala, for eight to ten days.
- Complete rest for at least a week. Housework involving water, any exposure to wind, or late nights, should be avoided. There should be abstinence from sexual intercourse for at least a month.
- All drinking water should be boiled in the manner suggested earlier and food should be light and simple.

After a traumatic experience like this, it is of utmost importance that the woman takes care of this vata imbalance. If left untreated, problems such as weight gain, especially around the waist and abdomen, and disturbances in the menstrual cycle, could arise.

Subsequently, medications and a diet that strengthens the uterus should be continued. In fact, all the care that needs to be taken as prescribed in this book to plan for conception should be done with care and in detail before trying to conceive again. Having done all this, conception can be planned again after a period of three to four months.

In cases of abortion or miscarriage in the later months (in the sixth or seventh month), the above-mentioned remedies should be applied as well, along with the other precautions which are taken postpartum. These should be followed for about 30-45 days. Due to the accompanying depression, many women fail to take adequate care of themselves, and this may affect their health and future pregnancies.

It is important to keep a watchful eye on the growth of the foetus. In some cases, the foetus stops growing even if there are no signs of miscarriage. This condition can happen in two cases: 'upvishtak' and 'nagodar'.

This shlok explains Upvishtak
यस्याः पुनरुष्णतीक्ष्णोपयोगात् गर्भिण्या महति संजातसारे गर्भे पुष्पदर्शनं स्यात् अन्यो वा योनिस्त्रावस्तस्या गर्भो वृद्धिं न प्राप्नोति निःस्त्रुतत्वात् स कालम् अवतिष्ठतेऽतिमात्रं तम् उपविष्टकम् इति ।

...चरक शारीरस्थान

Yasyāḥ punaruṣṇatīkṣṇopayogāt garbhiṇyā mahati sañjātasāre garbhe puṣpadarśanam syāt anyo vā yonisrāvastasyā garbho vṛddhim na prāpnoti niḥsrutatvāt sa kālam avatiṣṭhate~timātram tam upaviṣṭakam iti ....Caraka śārīrasthāna

In the later stages of its development when the foetus has grown in size, if the mother consumes hot and spicy food or strong medicines, she may suffer from vaginal bleeding. In this situation, insufficient nourishment is then passed on to the foetus, which could impair its further growth. In extreme cases, growth ceases altogether, a condition which is called upvishtak. However, in general, this situation does not lead to miscarriage, as the foetus is already quite well-developed.

In the situation known as *Nagodar*, growth also comes to a halt, but in this case, the foetus begins to reduce in size. There are various explanations for this condition: reduced intake of food, or a diet which is lacking in nutrients; insufficient intake or complete absence of items such as milk and ghee in the diet; excessive fasting, eating stale food, or food which increases vata.

In both conditions, where the foetus is still alive, treatment should commence immediately, to ensure that the growth process is restored. The remedies to stabilize the foetus, as outlined earlier, are also useful here.

If correct treatment is not begun on time, the foetus may die. This is called intrauterine death and its symtoms are as follows:

- Heaviness in the lower part of the abdomen, which feels cold on touch.
- Absence of foetal heartbeats or any foetal movements.
- Abdominal pain, not accompanied by contractions or vaginal discharge.
- Breathlessness and unease.
- Difficulty in movement.

If any of these symptoms arise, a doctor should be consulted immediately.

The foetus dying after 28 weeks of gestation, just before the onset of, or during, labour. Ayurved calls this condition as 'mrutagarbha' (stillbirth). This can occur if guidelines that are contraindicated during pregnancy are practised or if serious complications develop during labour. Stillbirths are more common if the baby is premature.

- **Children born out of consanguinity are more likely to have congenital defects.**
- **If the pregnant woman does not follow the prescribed diet, the possibility of miscarriage is increased.**
- **If the risk of miscarriage does exist, measures to stabilize the foetus should be initiated immediately. Taking advantage of these remedies is also beneficial in a normal pregnancy, even if there is no risk of miscarriage.**
- **If miscarriage does occur, purification and strengthening of the uterus must be performed. The postpartum protocol (in terms of diet and lifestyle) should also be followed.**
- **Neglecting any abnormal symptoms during pregnancy is not advised. Prompt action, consultation with a medical practitioner, and appropriate treatment, is of the utmost importance.**

Yoga during pregnancy - 1

Earlier generations of women were used to doing household chores themselves. This ensured that their bodies remained flexible, and the need for separate physical exercise did not arise. Our modern lifestyle has made life 'easier', but our bodies have become less flexible. The muscles used during childbirth remain under-utilized in our day-to-day lives. While many muscles participate in childbirth, attention is usually, and mistakenly, focused on the abdominal and pelvic muscles with respect to labour. In reality, the thigh, back, neck, and even the facial muscles, directly or indirectly participate in this process. Strengthening these muscles as well, through specific exercises, will ensure a smooth delivery.

During pregnancy, all physical movement should be carried out with care to avoid problems for the mother and the unborn child. This does not mean that exercise or routine work should be avoided; on the contrary, too much rest and relaxation can prove disadvantageous, and hinder natural labour. The expectant mother should continue to carry out simple, routine household chores, as well as specific exercises beneficial for pregnancy. Another important advantage of such exercises is that they help to bring the foetus into its natural birth position in the womb, necessary for an easy and natural delivery.

The duration of pregnancy is divided into three phases, known as the first, second, and last trimesters. One can maximise the benefits of exercises by focussing on those that are meant for each trimester. Do consider the growth of the foetus and the physical changes occurring in the mother at this time.

Let us first take a look at the exercises that are suitable throughout pregnancy.

WALKING

This is the simplest and easiest form of exercise, and can be done easily throughout pregnancy. It uses all the muscles of the thighs and hip joints, which help in maintaining their flexibility, thus facilitating natural birth. Walking in the also improves blood circulation and increases the intake of fresh air and oxygen. This can help reduce morning sickness and maintain enthusiasm throughout the day, especially in the first trimester. Walking in the morning is ideal. But if this is not possible, walking at any time, except after lunch, is fine. Do not walk too fast or too slow, and avoid talking. Decide your pace keeping the weight of the foetus into consideration. A daily walk of at least 15 minutes in the first trimester, 30 minutes in the second trimester, and 45 minutes in the third trimester, is recommended.

Walking during the third trimester is very important as this helps to engage the head of the foetus in the pelvic brim. (The head also descends due to the effect of gravity during the walk). All of these factors increase the likelihood of a natural vaginal delivery.

During the 7th or 8th month, the woman may experience swelling of the feet, but walking should be continued in spite of this. If necessary, rest after a walk using a pillow to elevate your feet.

Many women avoid walks, giving an excuse of lack of a suitable area for walking. All you need is a small space. You can always walk around even a small garden.

SUKHASANA, PADMASANA, VAJRASANA

These *asanas* are different types of sitting postures, which help increase the flexibility of the hip joints and strengthen the flexors and extensors of the hips.

Padmasana

You should perform pranayam in the morning while sitting in one of the first two *asanas*. Everyday chores such as cutting vegetables, making chapatis, writing or other household tasks may also be done while sitting in *sukhasana*, rather than standing or sitting on a chair with dangling feet. If it is possible, attempt doing such chores while sitting in *padmasana*.

Vajrasana is good for the legs, thighs and waist

Vajrasana

muscles. Sitting in this posture after lunch, helps to pacifies *vata*, and improve the digestion. Try and cultivate the habit of sitting in vajrasana for at least a few minutes a day. If it is difficult to maintain this posture, placing a thin pillow between the heels and the buttocks could be helpful. These three asanas can be safely practised throughout pregnancy.

DEEP BREATHING

All of us tend to breathe in a shallow and superficial manner. This tendency may increase during pregnancy especially when there is a feeling of heaviness in the lower abdomen.

During pregnancy the expectant mother needs more than regular oxygen for herself and her baby. Shallow breathing in the chest is not enough for her needs. Instead of breathing from the chest alone, focus on moving the abdominal muscles while breathing as well. Try and take long and deep breaths.This is extremely beneficial and increases oxygen supply.

Practice deep breathing first thing in the morning. Five minutes of deep breathing exercises, while still sitting in bed, is a good way to start the day.

HOW TO BREATHE: Sit in *sukhasana*, place both hands lightly on the abdomen, and inhale deeply. During the inhalation, the abdomen should move outwards (this movement can be felt by the hands). Exhale slowly and steadily, feeling the abdomen moving inwards. The hands should not push or exert any pressure on the abdomen.

Practise breathing like this regularly every morning and also several times during the day. If you feel restless, mentally stressed, anxious, nervous or fearful, practise deep breathing. This breathing exercise also helps to reduce nausea and morning sickness.

PRANAYAM

As explained earlier, during pregnancy, the woman requires more oxygen than usual - about one and half times more. An adequate supply of oxygen will ensure the proper growth of the foetus. In addition, it promotes mental peace, prevents irritability and depression, fosters sound sleep, and reduces frustration and fatigue.

Both simple deep breathing and pranayam should be practised daily by the pregnant woman without fail. The former increases life energy or life force (*pranashakti*); the latter helps balance the *Pran* and *Apana* functions. If *pran* functions well, typical first trimester complaints, such as nausea and morning sickness, are less severe.

Apana is responsible for bodily functions such as urination, defecation, and, most importantly, a natural vaginal delivery. The regular practice of pranayam thus helps ensure a timely and natural birth.

Incorrectly practised *pranayam* is harmful, and so should be learned from an expert. Ideally one should practise pranayam at sunrise. Practise a second time between 4 and 6 pm (when the stomach is not too full), if time permits. Five minutes practice is good enough to begin with. Gradually you can go up to 15 minutes. Practise *pranayam* slowly. It should not be done in a hurry even if you have very little time. Fewer, but more relaxed, repititions are better than more repititions done in haste.

In all pranayam, as in all breathing, there are three distinct phases of taking breath - inhalation (purak), holding the breath [both with lungs full and lungs empty] (kumbhak) and exhalation (rechak). Inhalation (purak) is generally easy and effortless. Take care that the neck and chest do not stiffen during the breath-holding phase (kumbhaka). The exhalation phase (rechak) must be done slowly and carefully. If you hurry during this phase it can cause dry cough and irritation.

Pranayam should be practised in an open, clean, and quiet space. This not only helps the mind to stay calm and cheerful, but makes concentrating on the breath easier as well.

Shavasana

If you have no previous experience of pranayam, just start with simple deep breathing - inhale as deeply and slowly as possible with the abdomen moving outwards. Then exhale very slowly, to completely empty the lungs. Once this becomes easy, one can progress to pranayam.

Deep breathing and pranayam, performed in this manner, are refreshing, raise the mother's fatigue tolerance during the process of childbirth, and help her to withstand the pain of labour. The rechak phase (exhalation) increases flexibility of the abdominal muscles, which in turn, facilitates the process of expelling the foetus during natural birth.

Aumkar gunjan is the best form of *pranayam*. Regularly chanting *Aum* provides all the benefits of *pranayam*, and cultures the foetus with *Aumkar*. This culturing helps the development of various mental functions in the foetus, such as memory, grasping power, intelligence and concentration.

SHAVASANA AND YOGANIDRA

Shavasana can be practised easily throughout pregnancy. It is a great *asana* with which to end an exercise session. It can also be practised at night just before sleeping. At first, it should be practised with the help of a qualified practitioner so you can learn how to relax all the parts of the body in the appropriate sequence, and help keep your mind focussed.

The best form of *Shavasana* is *Yoganidra*. *Yoganidra* adds music and simple vocal instructions to the exercise and is even more effective than *Shavasana*. The numerous beneficial effects of healing music have already been described earlier. Since Yoganidra is available in an audio CD with precise guidance and music, it can be practised independently of a teacher.

Expectant mothers often feel restless due to the various physical and mental changes occurring during pregnancy. Shavasana and Yoganidra encourage mental peace and help maintain hormonal balance. They foster peaceful sleep which is an absolute must during pregnancy. As the foetus grows, the pregnant woman will complain about back and neck aches, and find her movements restricted. Shavasana gives instant relief by helping all the muscles of the body to relax. Regular practice increases pranshakt in the body and improves blood circulation. The growing foetus also benefits from this. Very, importantly, Shavasana and Yoganidra will help prevent high blood pressure in the last trimester.

All the exercises in this chapter may be performed throughout pregnancy.

- **Any awkward or inappropriate physical movement should be avoided during pregnancy. Specific exercises, to increase the likelihood of a natural birth, should be performed.**
- **Walking is the best exercise, and should be done in accordance with one's capacity.**
- **Pranayam and deep breathing should be practised regularly, to meet the increased oxygen demand during pregnancy.**
- **Shavasan should be practised during the entire pregnancy to foster mental peace.**
- **Sukhasana, padmasana, and vajrasana, should be performed regularly to maintain flexibility of the hip and pelvic joints.**

Yoga during pregnancy - 2

In the first trimester, the foetus is not completely stable. Therefore, you should not practise any difficult *asanas.* Some asanas are not practical in the last trimester because the foetus has increased very much in size. It is easiest to do asanas in the second trimester, and hence this time should be used to the maximum.

Follow all the instructions carefully to avail of all the benefits and to exercise all the muscles involved, properly. These asanas should be integrated into the daily routine, along with walking and pranayam.

Recommended prerequisites:
1. Offer a prayer before starting
2. Face east or west while performing the exercises.
3. Choose a location sheltered from draughts
4. Practice yogasanas after morning ablutions, and never on a full stomach
5. Clothes should neither be too tight nor too lose during practice.

All asanas should be first learned from an expert, and then practised independently. Keep in mind the condition of the body and its flexibility, as well as, the state and strength of bones and joints. The asanas should be performed only within the limits of your comfort.

SHAKTISANCHARAN (ENERGY FLOW)

1. Sit in sukhasana, hands resting on the thighs.
2. While inhaling, slowly raise the arms sideways up to 60 degrees, as shown in the illustration, with thumbs facing upwards and fingers lightly flexed to form a fist. The arms should be straight.
3. Continue to breathe slowly and deeply. Each cycle of inhalation and exhalation should last for about 20-30 seconds initially.
4. To complete the exercise, while inhaling, raise both arms above the head, with palms facing outward, in such a way, that the backs of the hands touch each other. Exhale.

Shaktisancharan

5. Inhale again, and while exhaling, lower the arms slowly and place them again on the thighs.

Note : The eyes should be steady and focused, or, alternatively, they may remain closed lightly.

As you get better at this asana, you should hold your arms up in the illustrated position and breathe slowly and deeply for up to a minute, for the best effect of this exercise. If there is discomfort in the arms while doing the asana, they should not be lowered suddenly. The above sequence should be followed through to completion.

This asana strengthens the neck, shoulder and back muscles, and improves the supply of pran (life energy) to these regions. It leads to an improved flow of energy in the body, especially in the spine. This improved flow of energy, along with deep breathing, increases the tolerance for pain, and is thus helpful during labour.

This asana should be a part of the daily exercises throughout pregnancy, if possible.

Butterfly

SANTULAN KRIYA BUTTERFLY

This asana should be performed as follows in the first trimester:

1. Sit in sukhasana
2. Slowly bring the feet, one after the other, as close as possible to the groin, as shown in the illustration. The hands can then be placed on the knees.
3. Breathing deeply, remain in this position for 30 seconds, then, while exhaling, stretch the legs straight out in front. With practice, the time can be increased to 60- 90 seconds.

   From the fourth month onwards, the technique should be changed as follows:

1. Sit in sukhasana
2. Bring the feet close together as described earlier.
3. Hold both feet with the hands
4. Steadily and slowly move both knees up and down as far as possible, like the wings of a butterfly. Exhale while moving the legs towards the ground and inhale as they move up. Do not jerk or do this movement hurriedly.

Hold the asana for about 60-90 seconds. With practice it should be possible to touch both knees to the ground.

This asana facilitates the contraction-extension capacity of the buttock and pelvic muscles. It also strengthens the muscles of the thighs, legs and pelvis, which aids the process of labour.

SANTULAN KRIYA SNEHA (LOVE)

Regular practice of this kriya improves the ventilation of the lungs and stimulates them, and increases life energy. It also opens and activates the heart centre.

Sneha - Love

1. Stand erect with feet 15-20 cm apart and pointing slightly outwards. Keep the arms straight down on either sides.
2. Raise the arms, then fold them, and gently tap the chest with fingertips of both hands while inhaling.
3. While holding the breath make loose fists, and gently tap the chest with the palm-side of the fists. Do this only as long as you can comfortably hold your breath.
4. Exhale through pursed lips while lowering the hands to the sides.

Repeat 6-7 times. This asana may be practised throughout pregnancy.

HRUDAYACHAKRA UNMEELAN (CHEST BALANCE)

This asana, activates the heart centre, strengthens the contractile power of the chest muscles, and consequently increases the capacity of the lungs. It stimulates the circulation of rasa and rakta, which helps prevent complaints like breast engorgement, or rigidity of the chest muscles. The

Hrudayachakra unmeelan -1

Hrudayachakra unmeelan -2

neck and shoulder muscles are also exercised, and, if practiced regularly throughout pregnancy, this asana can guard against the sagging of the breasts, which is often seen after childbirth.

1. Sit in sukhasana or vajrasana.
2. Hold the hands in the 'namaste' pose (join your hands like in prayer) in front of the face, with elbows touching each other. The upper arms should be parallel to the floor. Exhale fully.
3. Inhale slowly, and open the arms fully, as shown in the illustration, until they are parallel to the ears.
4. Exhale and bring the arms back to the original position. Repeat this procedure about 10 times.
5. To finish, inhale deeply, and while exhaling, place the hands on the thighs.

GOMUKHASAN (COW FACE POSE)

Gomukhasan brings similar benefits. Since we have normally lost much of our flexibility, it may be difficult to grasp the hands behind the back. If this is the case, holding one end of a handkerchief, or a small towel, in each hand behind the back, is helpful. You can easily look up Gomukhasan in any book on yoga.

KAAK BAITHAK (COCK POSE)

This is a squatting position as required when using an Indian-style toilet. The use of this type of toilet is preferable for pregnant women for just this reason. This asana strengthens and increases the contractile power of the major pelvic and waist muscles. In addition, the buttock, thigh, knee and calf muscles, which will aid the process of natural delivery, are strengthened.

The following steps should be followed for the first trimester:

1. Sit in sukhasana.
2. Stretch both legs straight out in front, with the feet about 3-4 cms apart.
3. Rest the palms of both hands on the floor next to the buttocks, parallel to the body.
4. Slowly, while pressing the palms to the ground for support, bend the knees and sit in the squatting position.
5. Fold the hands into the namaste position (as

Gomukhasana

Hand positions in Gomukhasana

Kakbaithak in in First Trimester

shown in the illustration) and breathe steadily for one minute. If required, use the hands to support yourself by holding on to something in front of you (perhaps the led of a chair).

6. Return to the sukhasana position by reversing the above steps.

From the fourth month onwards this *kaak baithak* asana should be done as follows:

1. Stand and hold on to a strong, stable support at chest level, such as a door handle, keeping about 22-25 cm between the feet.
2. While inhaling and holding on to the handle for support, slowly move downwards as if sitting on a chair. The thighs should be parallel to the floor.
3. Exhale while returning to the standing position.

If done in this manner, all the benefits of the asana are obtained, without undue pressure being exerted on the abdomen or uterus.

If you are not accustomed to this position, there may be initial discomfort in the thighs. In this case, the kriya should only be performed as many

Kakbaithak after 4th month

times as comfortable. Once a certain proficiency is attained, however, it should be repeated 10-12 times.

After completion, bring the legs together and gently massage the thighs and legs to help reduce fatigue. This asana is very helpful in ensuring that delivery is normal and natural.

MERUTARANG-SPINAL FLEXES

This kriya benefits the entire spine, and increases tolerance for the stress and strain of labour. It also enhances the contractile (flexion and extension) abilities of the spinal muscles, as well as the blood circulation to this area. The kriya should

Merutarang Type 1-1

Merutarang Type 1-2

be practised from the fourth month of pregnancy until delivery.

There are three variations of this kriya, for the upper, middle and lower sections of the vertebral column respectively.

Type one

This benefits the lower one-third (sacral) part of the spine. In addition, it stimulates the 1st (muladhar) chakra, which aids the process of labour.

1. Sit in sukhasana
2. As shown in illustration 1-1, hold both feet tightly with the palms. The thumbs should face upwards and the fingers should be on the soles of the feet.
3. Concentrating on the sacral region, inhale deeply into the abdomen while holding the back erect. While exhaling, relax the sacrum (the back may hunch a little while doing this). Inhale and make your back erect again very slowly. Since the hands are grasping the feet and soles securely and the neck is erect, only the lower third of the spine is affected by this asana. The whole asana and its movements are very subtle. The main benefit is derived from concentrating on the lower third of the back during this asana.

Repeat this procedure five times in the beginning, and 12-15 times, once a certain level of proficiency has been reached.

Note : No jerks or sudden movements need occur during this kriya. The contraction and relaxation should be rhythmic and harmonious. As pregnancy progresses, and the foetus grows in size, a pillow may be placed between the thighs and the floor for support.

Type two

This benefits the middle (lumbar) region of the spine. In the early stages, the foetus will not experience this kriya, but as its development progresses, it will also enjoy the kriya. This will be felt by the mother-to-be. As already described, the foetus responds to movements made by its mother.

This kriya activates the 2nd chakra

Merutarang Type 2-1

2-2. Straighten the back again while inhaling. Since the neck remains erect while one is sitting in vajrasana, the specific area affected is the lumbar region.

Repeat this procedure five times in the beginning. Once proficient, it may be increased to 12-15 times.

Precautions to be taken are the same as mentioned in type one above.

Type three

This kriya is targeted at the upper one-third of the spine (thorax). Regular practice stimulates the heart and the Anahat (hruday) chakra.

Merutarang Type 2-2

Merutarang Type 3-1

(swadhishthan), and the adrenal glands, which help in reducing fatigue and weakness. All three types of this kriya, particularly the second, should be included in daily yoga practice.

1. Sit in vajrasana.
2. Rest the hands on the knees keeping the arms and shoulders relaxed.
3. Inhale deeply while concentrating on the lumbar region and keeping the back erect. While exhaling, relax the lumbar region by hunching the back as shown in illustration

Merutarang Type 3-2

1. Sit in sukhasana
2. Rest the hands on the knees, keep the elbows straight and shoulders relaxed.
3. Inhale deeply, while concentrating on the upper third (thoracic region) of the spine, and keep the back erect. While exhaling, relax the thorax by hunching the spine as shown in illustration 3-2. Inhale and straighten the spine. Since the arms remain immobile from the elbows upwards, this asana remains focused on the thoracic region.

Repeat this procedure five times in the beginning. Once proficient, it may be increased to 12-15 times.

Note : make sure that the arms remain straight.

Other precautions are the same as described in type one. These three types of merutarang should be done diligently, 12-15 times each, for best results. A break of two - three minutes between each set is advised.

ARDHA MARJARASANA (SEMI CAT POSE)

This asana provides the same benefits as merutarang, is simple to practise, and can be performed at all times. As the foetus and the uterus grow in size, there is an increased strain on the muscles of the abdomen and the back. Ardhamarjarasana can help relieve this strain, and should definitely be practised during the last trimester. It may even be used during the first stages of labour in case there is extreme back pain. It can help make the pain more bearable at that time.

1. Sit in vajrasana.
2. Slowly assume a crawling position, keeping both hands straight below the shoulders and both knees below the buttocks as shown in the illustration. Both arms and legs should be in a straight line. The soles of the feet should be relaxed.
3. Inhale.
4. While exhaling, raise the back upward, and lower the head between the arms - as shown in the illustration.
5. While inhaling, straighten the spine. Do not go into the reverse bend of the spine - where the spine moves downwards towards the ground - during pregnancy!

Repeat this procedure five times in the beginning, and, once proficient, increase to 12-15 times.

All of the asanas should be done rhythmically, with no jerks or sudden movements, and ones

Ardhamarjarasana

breathing should remain even throughout.

Since the reverse posture is not permitted during pregnancy, this is only ardha (half) marjarasana. Complete marjarasana is contra indicated.

All throughout pregnancy it is advisable to be careful while rising up from a horizontal or sitting position. In fact, it is recommended that one assume the posture of this exercise if you need to get up from the floor or bed before rising up completely to stand. This posture should be also assumed while getting up from the kaak baithak (described earlier).

The asanas described so far affect almost all of the muscles. Many more and similar asanas can be learned and practised regularly. However, describing all such asanas goes beyond the scope of this book, therefore we have limited ourselves to the most essential exercises.

SIMPLE EXERCISES - STRETCHING

The expectant mother often feels tired, weak, fatigued, or listless. At such times, instead of avoiding exercise altogether, perform some of theses simple exercises outlined below. After consultation with a doctor, they may even be practised when bed-rest has been prescribed.

For Kriya 1-5, it is advised that you lie on your back. If necessary, a thin pillow may be placed under the waist. Hands should be at the sides, parallel to the body.

Kriya no. 1

1. While inhaling deeply, extend the feet downwards towards the ground (1-1)
2. Exhale and straighten the feet again. (1-2)
3. While inhaling, flex the feet (toes stretch towards the body) (1-3)
4. While exhaling, return to the original position. (1-2)

Repeat five times.

Note : make sure that the heels remain steady and do not move during the kriya.

Kriya no. 2

1. At the ankles and wrists, rotate the feet and hands, first clockwise then anticlockwise, five times.

Note : make sure that the heels and arms remain firmly on the ground. Only the hands and

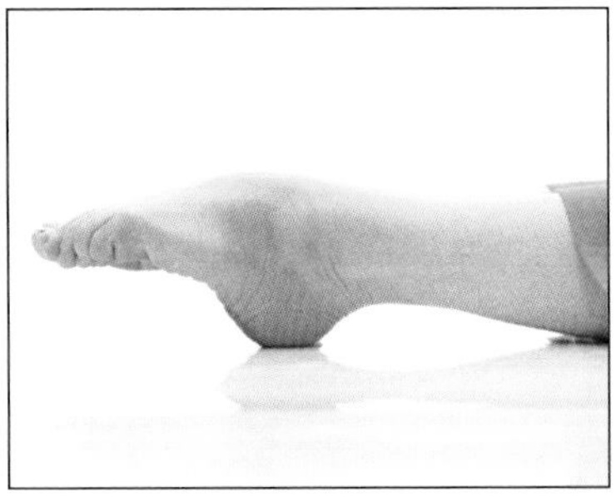

Stretch Kriya 1.1

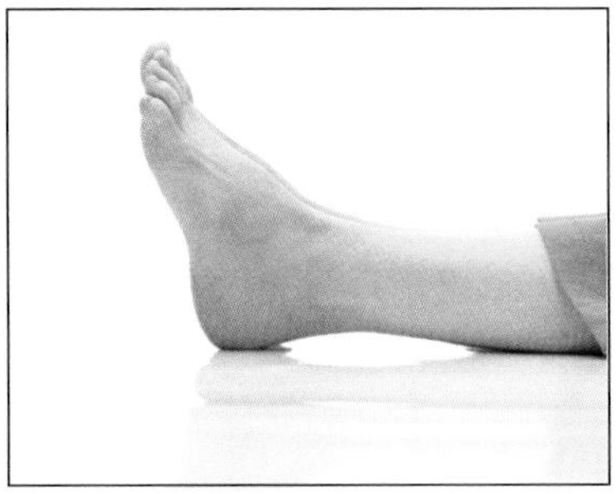

Stretch Kriya 1.2

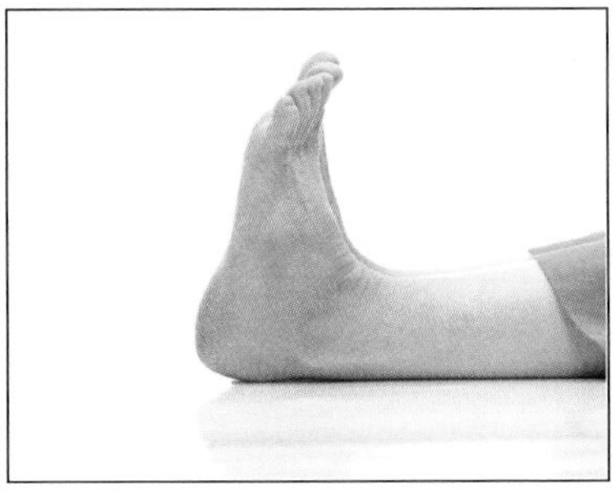

Stretch Kriya 1.3

the feet should be rotated.

Kriya no. 3

1. Place the hands on the floor slightly above the head, palms facing upwards.
2. While inhaling, stretch the arms upward and the feet downwards, as if being pulled in opposite directions.
3. Exhale and relax.
5. Repeat this five times.

Kriya no. 4

1. While lying flat on the back, grasp one knee with the hands and bring it as far as possible towards the abdomen (flexion of knee and hip joints). Hold this position and breathe deeply for about 5 times.
2. Straighten the leg.
3. Repeat with the other leg.

Kriya no. 5

1. While lying flat on the back, bend both legs and bring the knees towards the abdomen. Maintain this position for about five breath breathing cycles.

Note : Make sure that there is no undue pressure and strain on the abdomen, while doing Kriyas 4 and 5. These kriyas benefit the back and waist, and reduce tension in the pelvic muscles. They also help to expel gases.

To conclude, straighten the legs, turn on one side, come up onto all fours (ardhamarjasana) before rising up completely. Exhale as you stand up.

Kriya no. 6

1. Stand with the feet about 10-12 cm apart.

Stretch Kriya No. 6

2. Interlock the fingers of both hands behind the back as shown in the figure.
3. While exhaling, stretch the hands backwards and upwards as far as possible.
4. Inhale and bring the hands back to the relaxed starting position.

Repeat 5-10 times.

After completing the above exercises, sit straight, supporting the back against a wall, with the legs stretched out, or lie down on the back for three to five minutes, breathing calmly and slowly.

The exercises help to improve circulation and although very quick, they have a positive effect on the muscles as well.

Other important points for daily life:

- The expectant mother should always stand erect.
- While sitting, she should keep her back straight, or use a pillow for support, in case of discomfort.
- Her breathing should be normal, slow and steady at all times, especially while doing any work or exercise.
- Sleeping on the side rather than on the back is advised. As the uterus increases in size, the position as shown in illustration 21, with a pillow between the knees, is recommended.
- Do not bend the back when reaching down to pick something up. The correct method is to squat (bend at the knees and lower the body slowly). Inhale while going down and exhale while getting up.
- If you want to sit in one place for a long time, instead of a chair, it is better to sit on the ground against a wall in sukhasana, or with the legs stretched out. This improves the flexibility of the pelvic region.
- The bed used for sleeping should not be too high. Instead of immediately lying on the back, lie first on the side then turn onto the back. If necessary, a small pillow can be placed below the waist.

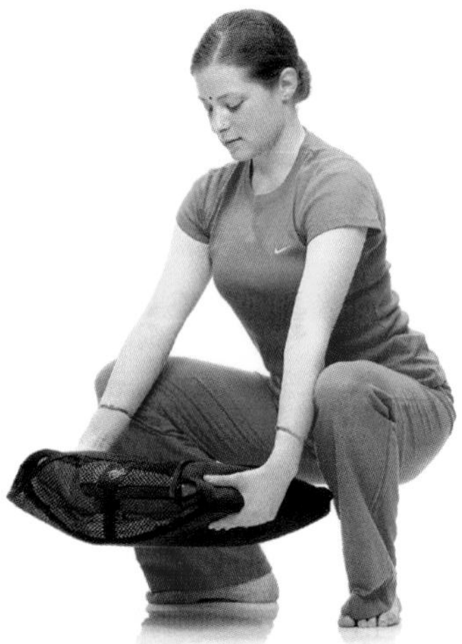

The ideal posture for a pregnant woman to lift objects from the floor

Apart from these exercises, appropriate routine movement also helps to ensure normal delivery. In fact, during pregnancy, everyday movement should only be done in ways that are ideal for the human body. Sitting, standing, assuming restful postures or carrying and picking things up, can all be done in suitable and unsuitable ways, depending on our habits. All the unsuitable and improper movement results in a build up of vata imbalance, and should be avoided as much as possible.

The ideal posture for a pregnant woman to sleep in

- Perform all asanas within your comfort limit.
- Unless otherwise specified, breathe normally and steadily while doing the exercises. Wherever possible, follow the breathing technique as mentioned.
- Do not disrupt the exercise routine, even if there is tiredness or fatigue?
- All movements during pregnancy should be done with caution and due awareness.
- When doing asanas and exercises, concentrate on the body part that is expected to benefit from them.

Preparations prior to delivery

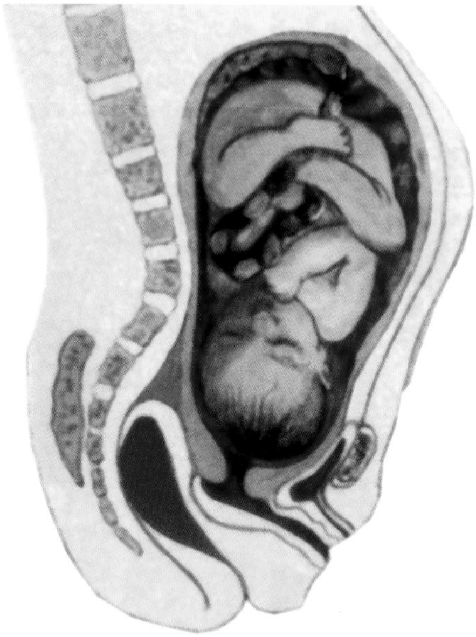

Natural Position of the Foetus

We have already learned that the foetus is suspended in the amniotic fluid present in the uterus. When small in size, the foetus moves in all directions: up, down, sideways, and even turns upside down. As its size increases, however, its movement become more restricted.

Prakrut asan refers to the natural position of the foetus in the uterus, and is described in the following *shloka* from the *Sushrut Sharirsthan*.

आभुग्नोऽभिमुखः शेते गर्भो गर्भाशये स्त्रियाः ।
य योनिं शिरसा याति स्वभावात् प्रसवं प्रति ।।

...सुश्रुत शारीरस्थान

ābhugnolbhimukhaḥ śete
garbho garbhāśaye striyāḥ
Ya yonim śirasā yāti svabhāvāt
prasavam prati ...Suśruta śārīrasthāna

The head faces downwards, and the legs are bent towards the body. This is the Prakrut asan of the foetus. This position is ideal for natural childbirth.

गर्भस्तु मातुः पृष्ठाभिमुखो ललाटे कृताञ्जलिः
सङ्कुचिताङ्गो गर्भकोष्ठे । *...अष्टांगहृदय शारीरस्थान*

Garbhastu mātuḥ pṛṣṭhābhimukho lalāṭe
kṛtāñjaliḥ saṅkucitāṅgo garbha-koṣṭhe
...Aṣṭāṅgahṛdaya śarīrasthāna

This shloka, from *Ashtanga-hruday Sharirsthan*, states that *while in the uterus, the foetus lies naturally with its face turned towards the mother's spine, its body bent, and with both hands together in front of the head.*

If this position changes for any reason, natural labour may be difficult. In Ayurvedic literature, a condition in which the foetus is in an unnatural position is called *moodhgarbha*.

The primary reason for *moodhgarbha* is the mother moving incorrectly or inappropriately during the pregnancy. Several cause are listed below.

- Too much physical work.
- Lifting heavy objects.
- Too much travelling.
- Inappropriate or excess exercise, too much walking or running.
- Trauma to the abdomen due to a fall, or injury caused otherwise.
- Severe jolts, possibly due to swinging

of the legs while sitting, swinging on a swing, or travelling on bad or pot-holed roads.

- Sitting incorrectly or squatting when not required.
- Attempted abortion.

If you suppress natural urges such as urination and bowel movements, eat very dry or very spicy or any other gas producing foods, you could prompt *moodgarbha*. Another instance in which a normal vaginal birth may be difficult is if the placenta is attached to the lower rather than upper part of the uterus.

As explained above, the easiest position for delivery is when the foetus' head is downwards with the face turned towards the mother's spine. If, instead of the head, the face, shoulders, or hands are lowest, it is called *moodhgarbha*. In some cases, during childbirth, the buttocks, knees or legs emerge first instead of the head, a situation referred to as 'breech'. Sometimes the foetus lies horizontally (parallel to the ground) in the uterus. Ayurved calls this condition *parigh* (transverse presentation) and it is the most difficult presentation for labour.

The natural position of the foetus is important because it helps the head to become engaged in the pelvic area (brim), during the eighth or the ninth month of pregnancy. This engagement means that the baby's head actually gets fixed into the area meant for it, just before delivery. The position does not change thereafter and then the head can emerge first during delivery.

Once the baby's head is engaged, its movements naturally decrease. This may cause some concern at first, but it is natural. The reduction in movement helps to ensure a proper delivery and there is usually no need to worry.

The pregnant woman should continue to take regular walks towards the end of pregnancy to help the baby's head descend and fit into the pelvic brim. In case of a primigravida (first pregnancy), the head usually engages in the eighth month, and the expectant mother should take longer walks from this month onwards. In the case of second or subsequent pregnancies, the head usually engages in the ninth month, so she could extend her walks during this time.

From the point of view of *doshas*, the main cause of *moodhgarbha* is an imbalance in *vata dosha*, especially in the *apanvayu*, which can manifest itself in several forms, as described in the *Sushrut Nidansthan*.

स यदा विगुणानिलप्रतिपीडितोऽपत्यपथम् अनेकधा प्रपद्यते तदा सङ्खया हीयते । *...सुश्रुत निदानस्थान*

Sa yadā viguṇānila-pratipīḍito~ patyapatham
anekadhā prapadyate tadā saṅkhayā hīyate

....Suśruta nidānasthāna

When apanavayu gets disturbed and enters the birth canal, it causes several different types of moodgarbha.

In this context, I recall a patient who has been one of many who was under my care for the entire duration of their pregnancy. Till the seventh or eighth month, the development, weight, and position of the foetus was perfect. In the eighth month, she inadvertently moved a heavy box, and immediately felt the baby turn inside her abdomen. A visit to the gynaecologist confirmed that the foetus had shifted from its original position and had become slightly horizontal. This incident occurred some time ago, and the treatment then consisted of administering gentle abdominal massage, to slowly move the baby back to its correct position. The woman subsequently delivered at full term, without any further complications.

In this manner, it is possible for experienced doctors or midwives to correct minor problems. More serious problems could, however, require surgery, and extreme care should be taken to prevent such situations occurring at all.

Delivery is much easier if the mother can, through her breathing, control the speed of the baby's descent and her contractions, during a particular stage of labour. Earlier, midwives would generally take care of this, motivating and instructing the expectant mother accordingly. As this has now become rare, the mother-to-be should make an effort to learn these breathing techniques from trained teachers during the ninth month.

In the ninth month, the woman should mentally prepare herself and her baby for the coming birth. A fully grown nine-month foetus is now a 'baby', has an independent identity, and is sensitive. So the mother can, and should, interact with her baby during this month. She should tune in to her inner self and talk to the baby as if it were there in front of her, telling it how eager the entire family is to welcome it. She should also tell the baby that being born vaginally (the natural birth process) will make it easier for both of them. She should explain that everything is going to be simple and easy. Some readers may find these points ridiculous, but those who have actually gone through this process, and experienced it, know how true and important this is. Such an inner dialogue is made clearer with the help of regular meditation and listening to healing music. Both these activities should be done more frequently in the ninth month.

The mother should devote maximum time to the coming child. It goes without saying, that leaving the house should be avoided unless necessary. The mother should not involve herself in unnecessary activities.

The attendant doctor, and the lying-in hospital have a vital role to play in the natural delivery process. They should be selected carefully.

Natural labour is beneficial for both the mother and baby, and the appropriate diet, behavior and exercises, which facilitate this, have already been described. Besides these, the following measures should be followed in the ninth month.

- A cotton swab soaked in **Santulan Femisan Oil** should be applied to the vagina.
- Application of **Santulan Kundalini Oil** (containing herbs which pacify *vata*), from the tail-bone to the waist.
- Massaging the breasts with **Santulan Suhrud Oil** and the lower part of the abdomen with **Santulan Rose Beauty Oil**.
- A light diet, and early dinners (by 7 p.m.). Ensure that bowel movements are regular.

If the guidelines outlined for every month are followed properly, the muscles of the lumbar, pelvic region and the back, become supple, lubricated, and flexible. All of this will lead to the birth of a healthy and illness-free child, can occur naturally at full term, without any problems.

All the above-mentioned guidelines, help to balance *vata dosha*, and maintain *apanvayu*, and so, contribute to an easy and timely delivery.

DELIVERY MISCONCEPTIONS & BELIEFS

As full term approaches, questions and doubts about delivery-related issues will arise, and possibly be compounded by interactions with friends and family. The following points should erase some of those doubts:

The Time of Delivery

Generally 'full term' denotes 280 days of pregnancy (Refer to the chart to calculate the expected due date or EDD). However, the EDD is only an approximation, and delivery may not necessarily occur on that day. The baby may possibly be born eight days before or after this date, i.e. within a time frame of 15 days around the EDD. Do not fix a particular date in your mind according to the EDD calculator or you will end up anxious if delivery doesn't occur on that very date. Labour pains that commence naturally are beneficial for normal vaginal birth without complications. There should be no unnecessary worry about the timing of delivery.

It has also been observed, that women whose menstrual cycle lasts less than 30 days, tend to deliver before the due date. Conversely, those women who have a cycle of more than 30 days often deliver after the expected due date. However, the reason for the commencement of labour pains, at a particular point, exact reason for the pain has never been fully understood.

False Labour Pains

The uterus is a muscular organ, and to expel the foetus during labour, the muscles begin to contract. This causes labour pains, which are in no way similar to abdominal aches and pains. Pain, in the absence of uterine contractions, is called 'false labour pain' and many women, especially those in their first pregnancy, may experience such pain. At times they are similar to labour pains, but with no outcome.

It is important to know the difference between false and true labour pains, else it could lead to uncertainty, and unnecessary distress. False labour pains can occur at any time and anywhere in the abdomen, at times above the umbilicus, or in the sides or the back, and they are generally irregular. True labour pains, on the other hand, begin in the lower abdomen, and are fairly regular. The reasons for false labour pains could be flatulence, indigestion, constipation, or irregular bowel movements. False labour pains are dull or weak pains. Unlike true labour pains, they do not become stronger. False labour pains can be experienced even if the date of delivery is not imminent.

Remedies for false labour pains

1. Eat food that is light and easy to digest
2. Eat a mixture of ginger juice and honey
3. Drink hot or warm water regularly
4. Apply **Santulan Rose Beauty Oil** on the abdomen
5. Chew on roasted bishop's weed seeds

If these provide no relief then you should consult a doctor.

Are Labour Pains Unbearable?

Of course natural labour is quite painful, but it has natural causes, and the reward is sweet and fulfilling.

If you have taken care to follow the guidelines in this book to prepare for labour, it should be easier to bear. Here is a quick reminder of the guidelines.

1. Regular practice of breathing techniques and *asanas* to keep the muscles required for labour flexible.
2. Massage and internal oil applications to keep *apanavayu* balanced and the birth canal lubricated.
3. The application of herbal pastes (*lep*) as suggested in this book.

In labour, it is advisable to remain relaxed and not focus on the pain, as that will just increase the stress. The process of birth should be experienced with a calm, peaceful mind and a joyful attitude.

Nowadays, many women are inclined to think that they can avoid labour pains by undergoing surgery. However, it should be remembered that labour pains only last for a short time, while the side effects of surgery last throughout life. Another disturbing trend is the use of painkillers during labour. This has one major disadvantage. Since the woman cannot feel her contractions after painkillers, she cannot apply adequate pressure at exactly the appropriate times during delivery, and this could cause problems during childbirth.

Like it has been explained earlier, if you follow all the guidelines from the beginning of pregnancy, the natural process of birth can progress smoothly.

Caesarean vs Normal Birth

During my travels abroad, around 20-25 years ago, I noticed a surprising trend. In cases where the due date for delivery fell on a weekend, the pregnant woman was administered various drugs to induce labour on the Friday just before (to free up the weekend), or a Caesarean section was performed to fit the doctor's schedule rather than wait for the baby to be delivered at its own time.

Over the years though, many women have begun again to choose to deliver the baby at home with the help of a trained nurse or midwife. This is the result of an increased awareness all over the world of the importance of natural birth. Natural labour is best for the health of the mother and her child.

The Disturbance of Apanavayu

During labour, *apanvayu* moves downwards, and pushes the baby out. Once the foetus grows to a certain optimum stage, *apanvayu* is automatically activated.

If a Caesarean section is performed, *apanvayu* becomes active at an inappropriate time, and moves in the wrong direction, resulting in an imbalance of *vata dosha*. This, in turn, could lead to excessive weight gain, increase in abdominal girth, and lax abdominal muscles after the operation.

A Caesarean section should be performed only if there is a genuine and pressing necessity. In the case of a Caesarean section you need to ensure all the more that you follow all the practices outlined in this book to ensure that vata dosha remains as balanced as possible.

Returning to original form

It is said that going through the process of childbirth is like beginning a new life all over again. To ensure a return to the original pre-pregnancy state, the mother has to make a lot of effort after delivery to pacify vata dosha, and allow enough time for regeneration.

The after-effects of a C-section make it very difficult to carry out the remedies necessary to deal with vata dosha after childbirth. The Caesarean section incision, the stitches, and the resultant blood loss, need time to heal. Besides restricting certain movements, it also restricts the woman from practising certain yoga asanas and exercises. On the other hand, after a natural vaginal delivery the woman will get back to regular movement within 3-4 days.

In any case it is very important that the woman

who has just given birth should have oil applied all over her body. Even if oil is not applied to the scar after a Caesarean section, it should certainly be used to massage other parts of the body, such as the buttocks, thighs and back. After a C-section it is even more important to have oil massages, smoke therapy and fomentation to balance disturbed vata.

Preparation for breast-feeding

The body becomes progressively ready for the birth process as early as the eighth month of pregnancy. In the breasts, the changes necessary for milk production also take place. After a natural delivery, the production of milk starts immediately, which does not necessarily happen after a Caesarean delivery. With a Caesarean, medication is sometimes required to help the mother start the flow of milk.

Easy acclimatization after natural birth

For the child, the most important benefit of the natural vaginal delivery is that the birth occurs in gradual stages, and the baby emerges from the birth canal very slowly. This helps the baby to get acclimatized to the outside environment, and breathing, crying and other movements happen relatively easily.

The scenario is quite different in a caesarean birth. The child is abruptly presented to the outside environment. Owing to this sudden shock, the newborn needs more time to acclimatize itself to the outside world.

Other Serious Side Effects Of the Caesarian Section

Surgery also weakens the abdominal muscles. This could cause a hernia in the future. The uterus, a very important organ, is also weakened by the surgical incision, and this could affect hormonal balance and, in turn, overall health. Since the uterus is weakened, women who have had a Caesarean, are advised to have two children at the most. Furthermore, **if the woman has a weak constitution**, a second child is not advisable at all, or special care is required for her to conceive again. In some cases, the weakened uterus cannot bear the weight of the full-term foetus during the second pregnancy, and a Caesarean is again advised beforehand. If a second conception occurs before the scar on the uterus has healed, after the first caesarian, this can also lead to complications.

After a natural delivery, it is easier for the uterus to contract and slowly return to its normal shape and size. It has been observed that after a Caesarean section, the menstrual cycle post-delivery begins earlier than expected, which has a negative effect on breast milk production, and the health of the mother.

Other Issues

प्रजातायास्य नार्या रुक्षशरीरायास्तीक्ष्णैः अविशोधितं रक्तं वायुना तद् देशगतेनातिसंरुद्धं नाभेरधः पार्श्वयोर्बस्तौ बस्तिशिरसि वा ग्रन्थिं करोति, ततश्च नाभिबस्त्युदरशूलानि भवन्ति सूचीभिरिव निस्तुद्यते भिद्यते दीर्यते इव च पक्वाशयः, समन्तादाध्मानमुदरे मूत्रसङ्गश्च भवति इति मक्कल लक्षणम् ॥

Prajātāyāsya nāryā rukṣa-śarīrāyāstīkṣṇaiḥ aviśodhitam raktam vāyunā tad deśagatenātisamruddham nābheradhaḥ pārśvayorbastau bastiśirasi vā granthim karoti, tataśca nābhibastyudaraśūlāni bhavanti sūcībhiriva nistudyate bhidyate dīryate iva ca pakvāśayaḥ, samantād-ādhmānam-udare mūtrasaṅgaśca bhavati iti makkala lakṣaṇam

The above verse illustrates the situation, where a woman with a "dry intestinal system" (dryness in the body), delivers a child, and the impure blood, which is not completely discharged or removed with medicines having penetrating properties, subsequently obstructing the flow of vayu. This blood then accumulates behind the umbilicus, the bladder, or laterally to the bladder, forming a knot, which causes pain in the abdomen, bladder, or umbilical region, or a pricking pain in the large intestine. Furthermore, the area around the stomach bloats, and there is difficulty in passing urine. This condition is called *makkal*.

Nowadays, most women do not follow diet guidelines, or behaviour and lifestyle precautions, which result in a *vata* imbalance throughout the pregnancy. In such cases, labour may not begin naturally once full term is complete, and may have to be induced with drugs. This can further increase the vata imbalance.

The healthier and better alternative, is to work towards natural labour and birth, right from the beginning.

- **The foetus should be in 'prakrut asan' to ensure a natural, normal delivery.**
- **This prakrut asan can change through inappropriate movement by the mother.**
- **Regular exercise supports the prakrut asan of the foetus.**
- **Breathing techniques can be used when labour is in progress to make the pain bearable. These techniques should be learned and practised in advance.**
- **A natural, normal delivery is ideal for the health of the mother and the child. All efforts made to ensure this, should be encouraged.**

Delivery

SYMPTOMS OF THE ONSET OF LABOUR

Ayurved outlines the signs and symptoms of the onset of labour as follows

जाते हि शिथिले कुक्षौ मुक्ते हृदयबन्धने ।

...सुश्रुत शारीरस्थान

Jāte hi śithile kukṣau mukte
hṛdaya-bandhane ....Suśruta śārīrasthāna

A woman who feels emptiness on both lateral sides of the abdomen, whose heart feels free from bondage or heaviness (a lessening of pressure around the heart), *is shortly going to deliver her baby.*

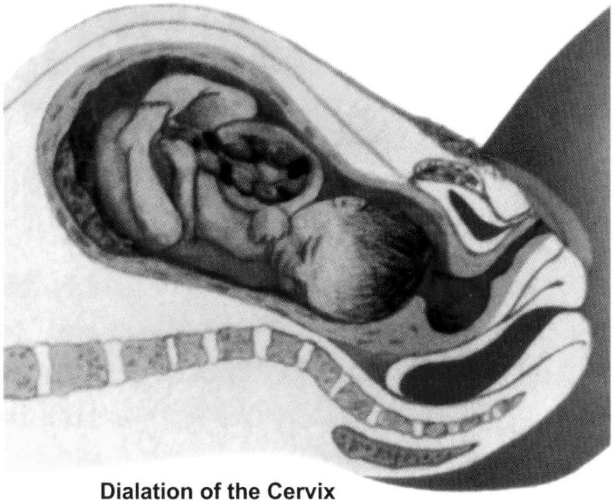

Dialation of the Cervix

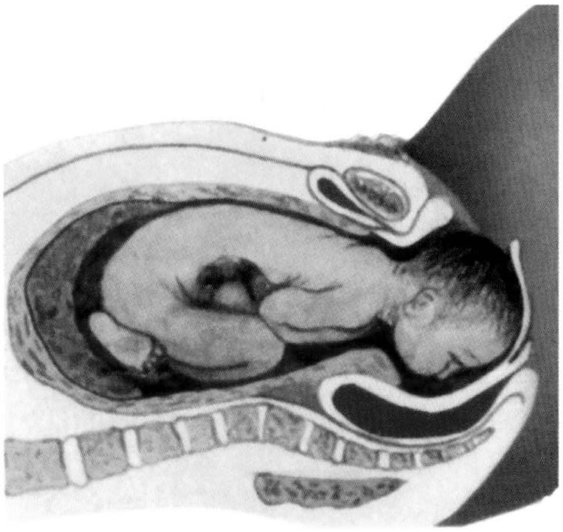

Position of the baby during delivery

As the time of delivery draws near, the baby descends into the pelvis (this is called 'lightening'). This changes the general shape of the abdomen. The downward shift of the foetus relieves pressure from the upper part of the abdomen and the mother can now breathe more easily. But there is now extra pressure on the urinary bladder and neighbouring organs (as the uterus rests on the bladder at this time). This leads to an increase in the frequency of urination or defecation. It also becomes difficult to walk around, or sit on the floor, and the thighs feel heavy. The lower abdomen (below the umbilicus) feels bulky. If it is a woman's first pregnancy these symptoms are evident around one week prior to the actual delivery. In subsequent pregnancies they occur only three to four days before delivery.

How long does it take for the baby to be born? Or how long does labour last?

Across the world, about 130 million women give birth each year. Each process of labour is of a different duration. The mother and child go through different stages, from the onset of pains, until the actual birth of the baby.

The following is a description of the process of labour.

तस्यास्तु खलु इमानि लिंगानि प्रजननकामभितो भवन्ति, तद्यथा क्लमो गात्राणां, ग्लानिराननस्य, अक्ष्णोः शैथिल्यं, विमुक्त बन्धनत्वमिव वक्षसः, कुक्षेः अवस्रंसनम्, अधोगुरुत्वं, वंक्षण-बस्ति-कटि-कुक्षि-पार्श्वपृष्ठ निस्तोदः, योनेः प्रस्रवणं, अनन्नाभिलाषश्चेति । ...चरक शारीरस्थान

Tasyāstu khalu imāni liṅgāni prajanana-kāmabhito bhavanti, tadyathā klamo gātrāṇām, glānirānanasya, akṣṇoḥ śaithilyam, vimukta bandhanatvamiva vakṣasaḥ, kukṣeḥ avasramsanam, adho-guurutvam, vaṅkṣaṇa-basti-kaṭi-kukṣi-pārśva-pṛṣṭha nistodaḥ, yoneḥ prasravaṇam, anannābhilāṣaśceti ....Caraka śārīrasthāna

SIGNS OF LABOUR

- *A general feeling of weariness, weakness and listlessness, which may even be noticeable on the face.*
- *The eyes lose their shine, and there is a feeling of fatigue in the breasts and chest area.*
- *Loss of appetite.*
- *Pain and discomfort in the back, waist and lower abdomen.*
- *Watery, or, at times, slightly sticky discharge from the vagina (the discharge of the mucus plug).*

The time, from the onset of these symptoms until the placenta is delivered, is called *prasavakriya* in Ayurved (labour or delivery). It has three distinct stages.

FIRST STAGE THE LATENT PHASE

The cervix remains closed throughout the pregnancy. During the labour process the foetus enters the vagina through the cervix, passes through the vagina, and ultimately, emerges from the external vaginal opening.

In the first stage, the cervix slowly dilates and stretches, so that the head of the foetus can pass through. In some women, this occurs easily, without too much discomfort, but others may have a lot of pain.

In such cases, the pain is inconsistent but has a particular pattern when it occurs. At first, the pain occurs every 10-12 minutes, and lasts for about half a minute. Slowly, as time passes, both the intensity and frequency of the pains increase. Towards the end of this phase, contractions generally occur every three to five minutes, and last for about 45 seconds.

The first stage can last for anywhere between a few hours up to two days. In case of a first pregnancy, this stage usually lasts for 12-24 hours.

On rare occasions, at the end of the first stage, the mother may have the urge to push the foetus out, even though the cervix is not yet fully dilated. Do not give in to this urge since the baby's head may press on the undilated cervix, and cause swelling in the cervical area. This could obstruct the later stages of labour, so no pressure should be exerted during this phase. The breathing techniques described earlier, help to regulate this stage of labour, and, in particular, to control the urge to push. This allows the cervix to dilate properly.

The pregnant woman should consciouly breathe deeply in this phase. This prevents muscle fatigue and helps conserve strength for subsequent phases, when it is really required.

Towards the end of this phase the pains will begin to occur at regular intervals of approximately five minutes. When this happens it is time to apply **Santulan Balant Lep** (a medicinal paste) around the umbilicus. This paste should be kept handyy in advance and applied around the umbilicus in a circular motion. This application helps expedite the next phase of delivery.

Apply a *vata*-pacifying oil like **Santulan Abhyang (S) Oil** to the pregnant woman's waist, back, thighs and lower abdomen. The oil should be warm during application. It helps *apanavata* move in the right direction, making the process of labour easier.

The woman in labour should pay close attention to the frequency of the contractions. She should note when each contraction starts and stops. As labour progresses, contractions should be stronger, have smaller intervals in between them and also last longer each time. As she goes further into labour they should occur at closer intervals and last longer. If the contractions happen to be irregular i.e. they differ in intensity - some being heavy and the others less intense, and if the intervals between them are irregularly long or short, it does not bode well for a natural delivery.

In the case of irregular contractions, Ayurved suggests that inhaling the fragrance of herbs, such as *koshtakolinjan*, *kalalavi* (Gloriosa superba), proves beneficial. Dhoop to the genital area, with herbal mixtures such as *madanfal* and *guggul*, or *devdaru* and *guggul* will prove helpful.

The application of **Santulan Balant Lep**, as mentioned above, along with gentle massage of the waist, pelvis and back with warm **Santulan Abhyang Oil**, help to alleviate the complications.

The pregnant woman's bowel movements should be regular when she goes into labour. It has often been observed that irregular bowel movements, or constipation, lead to irregular contractions.

Food intake during labour: A major question that people have about labour is regarding the food that the pregnant woman can eat during this time.

She should continuously sip liquids like fresh fruit juices, water with salt and sugar or *sherbet*. Solid food should be avoided. For lunch or dinner, soft liquid rice, soups, liquid *khichadi* or pureed rice, are fine. The intake of fluids should not be in excess though. It is important merely to ensure that the body is supplied with a sufficient amount of salt and sugar, to provide adequate energy to the muscles.

The traditional custom of eating *sheera* (please refer to the chapter on Special Recipes) when labour pains start, or before leaving for the hospital, has some logic. *Sheera* is satisfying, strengthening, and lubricating. The ghee used in *sheera* is easily absorbed, and is an internal lubricant, which keeps the intestines supple and prevents constipation. The sugar used in *sheera* is assimilated slowly and provides energy for the effort that is going to be made.

SECOND STAGE

अस्यां अवस्थायां पर्यङ्कमेनारोप्य
प्रवाहयितुम् उपक्रमेत । ...*चरक शरीरस्थान*

Asyām avasthāyām paryaṅkmenāropya
pravāhayitum upakrameta ...Caraka śarīrasthāna

During the first stage of labour, the woman may still be mobile, but it is advised that she lie down in the second stage, which starts with the complete dilation of the cervix, and ends with the delivery of the foetus. This phase begins with the rupture of the amniotic sac, but as the head of the foetus blocks the birth canal, not all of the amniotic fluid is expelled. The remaining fluid then helps create pressure, which pushes the foetus downwards. At this stage, the active participation of the woman is needed to push the baby out. This augments the contractions that are also pushing the foetus. She should push when a contraction begins, and continue to push until it stops. Applying pressure before or after the contractions is not favourable for the delivery or for the foetus, and only tires the mother unnecessarily.

Charak Samhita explains this phase in the following lines:

अनागतावीर्मा प्रवाहिष्ठाः या ह्यनागतावीः प्रवाहते व्यर्थमेवास्यास्तत् कर्म भवति, प्रजा चास्या विकृता विकृतिमापन्ना च, श्वासकासशोषप्लीहप्रसक्ता वा भवति । अनागतकालं गर्भमपि प्रवाहमाणा यथा चैषामेव क्षवथ्वादीनां सन्धारणमुपघातायोपपद्यते, तथा प्राप्तकालस्य गर्भस्याप्रवाहणमिति । सा यथानिर्देशं कुरुष्वेति वक्तव्या स्यात् । तथा च कुर्वती शनैः पूर्वं प्रवाहेत, ततोऽनन्तरं बलवत्तरम् । *...चरकसंहिता शारीरस्थान*

Anāgatāvīrmā pravāhiṣṭhāḥ yā hyanāgatāvīḥ pravāhate vyarthamevāsyāstat karma bhavati, prajā cāsyā vikṛtā vikṛtimāpannā ca, śvāsa-kāsa-śoṣa-plīha-prasaktā vā bhavati
Anāgata-kālam garbhamapi pravāhamāṇā yathā caiṣāmeva kṣavathvādīnām sandhāraṇamupaghātāyopapadyate, tathā prāpta-kālasya garbhasyāpravāhaṇamiti
Sā yathā-nirdeśam kuruṣveti vaktavyā syāt
Tathā ca kurvatī śanaiḥ pūrvam pravāheta, tato~nantaram balavattaram ....Caraka śārīrasthāna

Contractions generally occur at intervals of two to three minutes, lasting for approximately 1-1½ minutes each time. The woman should breathe deeply in the interval between contractions, so that she can give adequate pressure when they occur.

Pressure should be exerted from the neck and shoulders, and the exercises done for these muscles, throughout pregnancy, prove useful here.

The Ayurvedic texts recommend that other women be present during labour. These should not be just any women, but should fulfill the following requirements.

स्त्रियश्च बह्वयो बहुशः प्रजाताः सौहार्दयुक्ताः सततमनुरक्ताः प्रदक्षिणाचारा प्रतिपत्तिकुशलाः प्रकृतिवत्सलाः त्यक्तविषादाः क्लेशसहिन्योऽभिमता । ...चरक शारीरस्थान

Striyaśca bahvayo bahuśḥ prajātāḥ sauhārda-yuktāḥ satatamanuraktāḥ pradakṣiṇācārā pratipattikuśalāḥ prakṛtivatsalāḥ tyakta-viṣādāḥ kleśasahinyo~bhimatā ....Caraka śārīrasthāna

In addition to nurses and doctors, women present at the birth should have the following qualities -

A loving and helpful nature, experience and knowledge of childbirth, mental strength, and the ability to encourage and understand the woman in labour.

They should also be known persons, related to the woman, and be present for the entire duration of delivery. They should also be able to show confidence in natural procedures that will work in the pregnant woman's favour in the long run.

Ayurved has outlined a specific *mantra*, to be whispered in the ear of the woman, during the final stage of labour:

कर्णे चास्या मन्त्रम् इमम् अनुकूला स्त्री जपेत्,

**"क्षितिर्जलं वियत्तेजो वायुर्विष्णुः प्रजापतिः ।
सगर्भां त्वां सदा पान्तु वैशशयं च दिशन्तु ते ॥
प्रसूष्व त्वं अविक्लिष्टं अविक्लिष्टा शुभानने ।**

कार्तिकेयद्युतिं पुत्रं कार्तिकेयाभिरक्षितम् ॥'' इति...चरक शारीरस्थान

Karṇe cāsyā mantram imam anukūlā strī japet,

''Kṣitirjalam viyattejo vāyuḥ Viṣṇuḥ Prajāpatiḥ
Sagarbhām tvām sadā pāntu vaiśalyam ca diśantu te

Prasūṣva tvam avikliṣṭam avikliṣṭā śubhānane
Kārtikeyadyutim putram ārtikeyābhirakṣitam''
iti ...Caraka śārīrasthāna

"May the Earth, Water, Sky, Air, Fire, Vishnu, and Prajapati, protect you and your child. May they also help you to have a safe delivery. May your baby be born without undue effort. May the baby be as brilliant as Kartikeya and may Kartikeya himself protect it."

This mantra should be chanted when the woman is bearing down with the contractions.

With strong contractions, the head of the foetus gradually moves forward, and after it emerges, the shoulders and then the rest of the body follow. In the first pregnancy, this stage can last for about two hours, and for about half an hour in subsequent pregnancies.

Nowadays an episiotomy - an incision in the perineum made to facilitate the easy emergence of the foetus - is carried out routinely, without really assessing if there is a need for it. Normally, the mouth of the vagina is optimally dilated and relaxed at this stage, so that the foetus can come out easily. Stitches given after an episiotomy, can restrict the woman's movements while sitting or standing, and, in some cases, may also cause problems during sexual intercourse in future.

As soon as the foetus emerges, the vaginal area should be covered immediately, to prevent *vata* from entering the uterus.

The second stage of labour ends with the birth of the child, heralding the onset of the third stage.

THIRD STAGE

Once the baby is born, the uterus becomes somewhat smaller in size, thereby loosening the placenta, which is attached to the uterine wall.

Due to the strong contractions, the uterine muscles have by then become fatigued, and the spontaneous expulsion of the placenta begins only after a short break of about fifteen to twenty minutes. The intensity of the contractions is fairly mild by this time, and generally not too distressing. The expulsion of the placenta takes around 30 minutes after the birth of the child. When the placenta reaches the vagina it can be gently removed manually. There is absolutely no need to exert undue force, either by pulling the umbilical cord, or the woman exerting pressure to push it out.

Pulling at the umbilical cord before the placenta has naturally detached from the uterine wall can cause haemorrhage, which could endanger the mother. However, if the placenta is not expelled after 30-35 minutes, it must be removed with special measures.

Ayurved has recommended certain remedies for expulsion of the placenta if it does not expel on its own. They are as follows:

- Smoke therapy using *bhojpatra* (Betula bhojapatra) and *guggul* (Balsamodendron mukul) or similar herbs.
- Application of a paste made of ghee cultured with the root of the rice plant, to the genital area (vagina and surrounding area).
- The application of a paste made from the root of the kalalavi (Gloriosa superba), finely ground and applied on the woman's palms and soles.

- Ingesting a mixture made from *pimpli* (Piper longum), cardamom, *bor* (Zizyphus jujuba), *bid lavan* (a kind of salt) etc., which helps the uterus to contract.

The delay in the expulsion of the placenta can be due to the obstruction of the movement of *apanvata*. Ayurved suggests a special *basti* to help this situation.

तदास्थापनमस्याः सह वातमूत्रपुरीषैर्निर्हरत्यपरामासक्तां
वायोरेवाप्रतिनुलोमगमत्वात् । अपरां हि वातमूत्रपुरीषाण्यन्यानि
चान्तर्बहिर्मार्गाणि सज्जन्ति । *...चरकसंहिता शारीरस्थान*

Tadāsthāpanamasyāḥ saha vāta-mūtra-
purīṣairnirharatyaparāmāsaktām
vāyorevāpratinulomagamatvāt
Aparām hi vāta-mūtra-purīṣāṇyanyāni
cāntarbahirmārgāṇi sajjanti ...Caraka śārīrasthāna

Normally, waste products such as gases, urine, and faeces are excreted from the body. If this does not occur, then the placenta may be blocked within the body. In such cases, the administration of special basti helps to regularize the flow of apanvata. This facilitates the evacuation of waste products, and leads to the expulsion of the placenta.

However, this *basti*, called *asthapan basti*, should be administered only under the guidance of an expert *vaidya*.

The final measure suggested, if all this does not work, is to remove the placenta by hand.

A clean pair of hands with clipped fingernails are required for this procedure. The hands should be smeared with an oily substance, such as ghee, and inserted into the vagina. The umbilical cord should be used for guidance, and followed gently to reach the placenta, which should then be tenderly dislodged and removed from the uterine wall. Only a doctor or a trained nurse should carry out this procedure.

It is also important to ensure that the entire placenta is expelled, and that nothing remains. The expulsion of the whole placenta ends the third stage of labour and completes the process of delivery.

The next phase of care for the new mother (she is called *sutika* in Ayurved) will last several months and is described in detail in the following chapters.

The entire process of delivery can last up to 12-24 hours for the first pregnancy, and about 4-12 hours for successive pregnancies.

Some women report that even their first labour only lasted four hours. It is possible that their constitutions may be such that they did not feel the pains of the first stage, and therefore they assume that the entire labour process consists only of the last two stages. Nature must take its course and the first stage has to occur for the next two to take place. Women who do not realize when the first phase came and went should consider themselves very lucky indeed.

The reason we have gone into such detail about the process of childbirth is that some women have no idea about the birth process. Incomplete or superficial knowledge may cause them to fear delivery, or they may assume that childbirth is a very difficult test to go through.

With good guidance a woman can prepare herself well throughout pregnancy for delivery. Preparations will provide courage and help her go through labour with relative ease.

In Ayurvedic terminology a woman who has just delivered a child (post-partum) is called *sutika*. As per Ayurvedic science, women who have just delivered should be given a number of treatments to help them return to a balanced state.

As described earlier, *vata* regulates and controls the entire delivery process. After carrying the foetus for nine months, the uterus is suddenly empty after delivery and the woman is tired after labour. All of these factors contribute to an increase of *vata* in her body. The main aim of these treatments, done immediately after childbirth, is to pacify this *vata* as soon as possible.

The first treatment to be administered is a gentle massage to the sutika's lower abdomen, below the umbilicus, with warm, *vata*-pacifying oil. Her back should be massaged a little as well.

पीडयेत् घट्टमुदरं गर्भदोषप्रवृत्तये ।
महता अदुष्टपट्टेन कुक्षिपार्श्वे च वेष्टयेत् ॥

तेनोदरं स्वसंस्थानं याति वायुश्च शाम्यति । ...काश्यपसंहिता खिलस्थान

Pīḍayet ghaṭṭamudaram garbha-doṣa-pravṛttaye
Mahatā aduṣṭapaṭṭena kukṣi-pārśve ca veṣṭayet
Tenodaram sva-samsthānam yāti vāyuśca śāmyati

...Kāśyapa khilasthāna

The remnants of childbirth should be removed from the uterus immediately after delivery. To achieve this, the abdomen of the sutika should be pressed gently (to whatever extent she allows) and a belt tied around the abdominal region. This helps the abdomen return to its pre-pregnancy state and pacifies *vata*.

The sutika should now be allowed to rest a while. After she has recovered a little, warm **Santulan Abhyang (Sesame) Oil** should be applied to her entire body and she should have a bath with warm water afterwards. After the bath she should be administered *dhoop* on her entire body, especially around the genital area. The herbs used for *dhoop* should have *vata*-pacifying properties such as those in **Santulan Shakti Dhoop**.

As a result of the intense physical work during labour, the new mother is usually tired, and begins to feel hungry by this time. If this is the case then Ayurved suggests that she should first be given a specifically medicated ghee to eat. The amount of ghee is to be determined by an expert Ayurvedic physician after checking her general health, appetite, physical strength, and the strength of her digestive fire (Agni) into account.

If she is not able to ingest this ghee, then she should be given a decoction (*kadha*) of *Dashamool. Dashamool* is a set of ten specific roots of herbs that are excellent for pacifying *vata* (your vaidya or Ayurvedic medical shop will be able to guide you about this). The dashamool herbs should be bought beforehand in case they are required. To prepare the decoction, a handful of all the herbs should be boiled with four glasses of water, until the liquid is reduced to one quarter (one glass) of the original amount. This liquid should then be strained, and two spoons of pure home-made ghee added to it. It should be consumed by the sutika while still warm. This herbal decoction helps to pacify and balance vata and protects the sutika from post-partum diseases.

After this the sutika can be given a meal of liquid rice, or rice cooked with mung dal. Add a good quantity of pure ghee and a little dry ginger powder, *pimpli* powder and a pinch of *saindhav* (rock salt) for taste and to make the meal a little spicy. Liquid rice can be eaten at any time. It immediately satisfies hunger without leaving a feeling of heaviness. It is very easy to digest and there are no chances of any imbalance being caused by it. The meal also pacifies *vata* and helps relieve tiredness.

- **A woman pregnant for the first time will show signs of the onset of labour a whole week in advance of delivery.**
- **Santulan Balant Lep should be applied at the end of the first stage of labour, to help keep the duration of labour under control, and make the whole process easier.**
- **In order to conserve and maintain her strength, the mother-to-be should eat sheera or a soft, liquid food.**
- **The abdomen of the post-partum woman should be bound by a sufficiently tight belt to help remove the remnants of childbirth from the uterine cavity and pacify vata.**

4

Care of the woman after delivery...

After delivery, the new mother and her baby require special care. Ayurved gives detailed guidance about the care to be taken, including lifestyle advice and specifc dietary guidelines, during this extremely sensitive situation. These guidelines throw new light on the ingrained practices and customs already prevalent in the Indian tradition.

Care of the 'Sutika'
(a woman who has just given birth)

It is entirely natural, that a woman who has had a baby looks very different from her earlier self. But now a days the after affects of the childbirth begins to show on a woman's body. It may be difficult to judge in this generation whether a woman is married or not just by looking at her, but it is much easier to tell whether or not she has had a child. However, Ayurvedic practices are effective enough to help make it very difficult for people to tell whether you have had a child or not. Every woman wants to be admired. Mothers love to hear compliments such as "you do not look like the mother of two children!" This can come true for any pregnant woman who follows pre-natal and post-natal guidelines set down in Ayurved.

The special and necessary post-delivery care, is described in the following lines:

तस्यास्तु खलु यो व्याधिरुत्पद्यते स
कृच्छसाध्यो भवति असाध्यो वा,
गर्भवृद्धिक्षयितशिथिलसर्वधातुत्वात्, प्रवाहण
वेदनाक्लेदनरक्तनिःस्रुतिविशेषशून्य शरीरत्वाच्च,
तस्मात्तां यथोक्तेन विधिनोपचरेत् ॥ ... *चरक शारीरस्थान*

Tasyāstu khalu yo vyādhirutpadyate
sa kṛcchasādhyo bhavati asādhyo vā,
garbha-vṛddhi-kṣayita-śithila-sarva-
dhātutvāt, pravāhaṇa vedanā-kledana-
raktaniḥsruti-viśeṣa-śūnya śarīratvācca,
tasmāttām yathoktena vidhinopacaret

.....Caraka śārīrasthāna

After delivery, the new mother is very weak, sensitive and susceptible. She has provided nourishment and energy to the child during its entire development, undergone the exertion and resulting fatigue of labour, and blood loss, during and after delivery. Any health problem, arising during this time, could be difficult to treat, and in some cases, impossible to cure. Administering special remedies (to strengthen and protect her) *can provide the necessary care and attention, right from the beginning of the post partum phase.*

There are three post-partum phases as described below:

1. **The first ten days:** Immediately after the delivery the new mother is tired and she will surely have some vaginal bleeding. She requires special attention at this time.
2. **The first 45 days:** It is important to follow the guidelines that are meant to help the uterus contract to its normal size again. Diet, medicine and body care that ensure the adequate production of breast milk are recommended during this time.
3. **Until the reappearance of menstruation:** The time until the recommencement of menstruation is included in the post-partum period, so the woman is 'sutika' during this entire phase. Paying careful attention to diet, behaviour and lifestyle, ensures the adequate production of breast milk and maintains hormonal balance. This also prevents weight gain, and helps her to regain her former physical shape.

TREATMENT FOR THE SUTIKA

Massage

Every morning for the first ten days she should apply Abhyang Oil all over her body and especially to her waist, back and breasts. If the weather is cool, the oil should be warmed prior to use. Applying oil on the entire body should take about 25-30 minutes, and the oil should be fully absorbed in the skin.

Herbal Bath

1 to 1½ hours after the oil massage, take a bath with warm water. Instead of soap, use herbal pastes like **San Massage Powder**. The powder is to be mixed with chickpea flour and milk cream to be made into a paste (or as directed on the product). These herbs act like a skin moisturizer and help to balance vata and help to reduce stretch marks, the slackening of the skin and prevent the accumulation of fat.

After a bath smoke therapy with **Santulan Shakti Dhoop** for the genital area is recommended every day for at least the first ten days.

Smoke Therapy & Hot Fomentation

The next therapy is hot fomentation. When possible, the use of charcoal or dried cow dung cakes is recommended. These are lit, and pieces which do not release smoke, are to be used.

Method: a traditional bed (khaat), made of interwoven cord ropes, is the most suitable for this therapy. Cover the bed with a thin muslin cloth. The Sutika should lie down on it (see image). A metal container with hot charcoal embers is then placed below the bed. The fomentation is done in this way, for approximately ten to fifteen minutes, after which specific herbs should be added to these charcoal embers, to transport the smoke to the entire body. Some of the herbs, which could be used here, are balantshop (Peucedanum graveolens), ova (Carum copticum), vavding (Embelia ribes), etc. **Santulan Shakti Dhoop**.

If a bed as described above is not available, any similar bed, having a mesh or net, can be used.

The heat should be felt all over the body, and especially at the waist. Herbal smoke and hot fomentation so administered, pacifies vata and helps to restore strength to the joints. Thus, it helps in preventing back ache, pain in the lumbar region, and similar complaints. If charcoal is not available, a hot water bottle, or electric hot-pads, can be used instead, and a heater should be used to warm the room. During the summer, as much fomentation should be taken as can be tolerated. The room should be kept comfortably warm during this entire therapy.

Covering the Ears

The ears should be protected with a scarf, not only for these ten days, but during the 45 days after delivery as well. A small ball of cotton or wool can also be placed in the ears, and be careful that the ears are not exposed to the wind or cold air, from a fan or an air conditioner.

Abdominal belt

A belt should be tied securely around the abdomen immediately after delivery, and this should remain in position, except when having a bath, during the day as well as the night. The belt supports the now empty and loosened abdomen, and helps to restore the waist to it's earlier girth.. It also prevents flatulence, and imparts a feeling of fullness and satisfaction after meals, which reduces the risk of overeating.

Duration of Treatment

The above-mentioned treatments, namely fomentation, full body massage, smoke therapy, and the tying of an abdominal belt, should be performed daily for the first two phases, i.e. for the first 45 days after delivery. They may then be tapered off gradually. E.g. fomentation and full body massage (abhyang) could be given every alternate day, then be reduced to three or four times a week, by the end of the third month. From the fourth month onwards, these can be done twice a week, until the start of menstruation.

After 45 days, it is not necessary to tie the abdominal belt, but smoke therapy should be continued until menstruation returns.

Pichu

Once the post-delivery bleeding has stopped completely, a cotton swab soaked in **Santulan Femisan Oil** can be inserted into the vagina daily, to help restore the hormonal balance, and strengthen the uterus

Padabhyang

Daily foot massage - *Padabhyang* (Please refer to the glossary of terms for this extremely important therapy) - helps balance vata and pitta, and increases physical strength.

The Sutikaghar - an ancient practice

Since most deliveries nowadays take place in hospital, it makes it difficult to put all of the above suggestions into practice, yet it is advisable to implement as many of them as possible.

To ensure that all the above are implemented completely and properly, in the earlier years, the concept of a 'sutikaghar' existed. This was a special place, built close to the main dwelling, where pregnant and post partum women resided, and where all the above-mentioned guidelines could be practiced with ease and to their best effect. A reference to the building of a sutikaghar, in accordance with Vastu-shastra guidelines, can be found in the Charak Samhita.

On an auspicious day during the ninth month of pregnancy, the expectant mother would move to the sutikaghar, where the child was then born, and all further procedures required for the baby and its mother were carried out. All the necessary facilities to heat water, bathe and administer herbal smokes (dhoop) were provided. The place was well equipped with everything required by the mother and the child. It was airy, well lit, and kept extremely clean. They were careful that there wasn't too much light or wind in the house, but that they adequately ventilated at the same time. Special herbal smokes and a collection of antiseptic liquids and herbs were available to ward off contagious infections.

Your own Sutikaghar

It is almost impossible to find such an ideal Sutikaghar today, but the family should try to provide a separate room for the new mother, when she comes home from hospital. The room should be prepared and kept ready beforehand, and located such that it is not directly accessible to visitors. In such a room, the handling of the newborn by outsiders and strangers should be prohibited, and it must be ensured that the mother and baby get enough rest.

Medicines for the Sutika

In addition to the above-mentioned external therapies, various medicines, to be taken internally, are recommended.

The drinking of dashamool kadha in the morning on an empty stomach should be continued for 10 days. This balances Vata and helps prevent post-partum disorders. Ayurved has stressed the importance of preventing post-partum fever, and Dashamool, which has fever-reducing properties (anti-pyretic in action), is ideal. It is best made fresh, but if this is not possible, then Dashamoolarishta, or similar ready-made kadhas (decoctions), which are specifically prescribed for this period, may be taken.

The uterus gradually expands during pregnancy, and should return to its normal size post-delivery. At such a time, treatments to purify the uterus and restore its former strength, are of utmost importance, as the future health of the new mother depends on these factors.

Trikatvadi vati: Prepare a mixture of equal amounts of powder of dry ginger, black pepper, pimpli (long pepper),cinnamon, cardamom, bay leaf, coriander seeds, and nagkeshar, and add enough jaggery, so that the mixture can be formed into small round tablets. Take two of these tablets, morning and evening, with hot water, for 45 days after delivery.

Sunth (Zingiber officinale**) goli:** one small round tablet, made from dry ginger powder, ghee, and jaggery, should be taken on an empty stomach, every morning, for 45 days after delivery.

Kala bol (the dry pulp of Aloe vera)**:** tablets made from kala bol are very useful for the purification of the uterus. As these are difficult to make at home, tablets made from kala bol and jaggery can be obtained from a vaidya (Ayurvedic physician). One or two tablets (depending on their size) should be taken every day, for 45 days.

Jaggery pacifies vata, and thus should be included in the diet everyday.

A special mixture, to purify the uterus and restore the abdominal girth to its earlier state, is described in the book *Yogaratnakar*.

प्रसूता वनिता वृद्धकुक्षिऱ्हासाय संपिबेत् ।
प्रातर्मथितसंमिश्रां त्रिसप्ताहात् कणाजटाम् ॥ ...*योगरत्नाकर*

Prasūtā vanitā vṛddha-kukṣi-rhāsāya sampibet
Prātar-mathita-sammiśrām trisaptāhāt kaṇā-jaṭām
....Yogaratnākara

The drinking of buttermilk mixed with pimpalmool (the root of Piper longum) *is recommended, every morning, for three weeks after delivery. This helps restore the uterus and the abdominal girth to their former status.* Half a teaspoon of Pimpalmool powder should be mixed with the required quantity of buttermilk and consumed.

Yet another simple remedy, useful in reducing the size of the abdomen, is a powder of turmeric and amla, mixed with ghee and honey. Good quality amla should be dried (cut them up and leave them in sunlight until dry) and powdered. Turmeric, washed thoroughly, should be ground into a powder and blended with an equal amount of powdered amla. Half a teaspoon of this mixture should be taken with honey and ghee, once or twice a day, for 45 days. This powder available commercially, are not always pure or of good quality, so it is better to prepare the powders before childbirth, and store them at home.

The new mother should drink milk with shatavari kalpa twice or three times a day. **San Rose, Santulan Lohit Plus, Santulan Rudhira**, are some of the herbal products recommended to help replace the blood lost during delivery and after.

Besides these, Ayurvedic medicines such as Jeerakadyarishta, Devadarvyadee kadha, Panchajeeraka gud, and Yavadi ghruta, may be taken as well.

Recommended treatments after the resumption of menstruation:

UTTARBASTI

Uttarbasti is extremely beneficial for the maintenance of health after menstruation has recommenced. It purifies the uterus, removes any residual vata imbalance, restores hormonal equilibrium, and helps regulate the menstrual cycle. Uttarbasti fosters the proper constriction and contraction of the uterus back to normalcy, helps remove any vaginal flaccidity, and prevents prolapse of the vagina and uterus.

An increased incidence has been observed, of the uterus remaining enlarged in size after the first delivery, which could be the cause of menstrual disorders in the future. To prevent such an occurrence, two to three Uttar bastis, performed under medical supervision, are advisable after childbirth. Proper care, diet, and therapies, done as explained above, ensure that the woman regains her pre-pregnancy state.

- Fresh decoction of dashamool, or ready-made dashamoolarishta, should be consumed in the first ten days after delivery.
- From a health point of view, the first ten days are the most important. So, optimum care must be taken during these days, preferably by following all of the Ayurvedic guidelines.
- For the first 45 days after delivery, regular oil massage, fomentation, smoke therapy, and wearing an abdominal belt, are very important for the health of the new mother.
- Ayurved has outlined special remedies to help restore the size to its original size after childbirth.
- Two to three uttar bastis should be taken after approximately six months, to help the uterus return to its normal size, and to restore the hormonal balance.

Diet after delivery

The Sutika, who breastfeeds her baby, must pay special attention to her diet, to maintain her own and her child's health

मितपथ्याशनान्मातुः पुत्रे तेषाम् असंभवः।
सुखोदयश्च धात्रीणां तस्मात् तदुपचारयेत्॥

... *काश्यप चिकित्सास्थान*

Mita-pathyāśanān-mātuḥ
putre teṣām asambhavaḥ
Sukhodayaśca dhātrīṇām
tasmāt tadupacārayet

.... Kāśyapa cikitsāsthāna

If the mother eats proper food in appropriate quantities, then she and her child will remain healthy.

The nursing mother should take precautions to avoid indigestion. If the mother has indigestion, her milk too may cause problems to the baby ranging from indigestion to skin diseases, heart disorders, asthma, and respiratory ailments. According to Kashyap Samhita, **the baby could also suffer mental disorders and planetary imbalances** (*Graharog*). The sutika's diet requires careful planning.

As already mentioned, if the woman feels hungry immediately after delivery, she can eat liquid rice, or liquified mung and rice seasoned with long pepper, dry ginger, salt, and homemade pure ghee. These are tasty, nutritious, satisfying, easy to digest and do not cause heaviness in the stomach. Both are suitable to be eaten as breakfast as well, in the days to come.

All Samhita (ancient texts), describe

the following very important factor, while considering the post partum diet. It is natural for the sutika to be weak, as a result of the strain of pregnancy, nourishing the foetus for nine months, labour, breast-feeding and vaginal bleeding. Considering this, a diet having the following qualities is ideal. That, which replenishes and strengthens the lost and weakened dhatus (body tissues), is rich in lubricating substances, and which is easy to digest, healthy, nutritious and satisfying. Eating even small quantities of food lacking in these properties is not recommended. Fasting is also detrimental to the health during this period.

Ghee and homemade butter should certainly be included in the diet. Ghee can be used in cooking, and should also be added to purify the cooked food while serving, i.e., spreading on chapattis, phulka, bhakri (all are different types of bread), or pouring a few drops on the rice, lentils or khichadi. Sheera should be eaten daily.

Dink ladus (see Special Recipes) should be eaten daily, for as long as the baby is breastfed. Care should be taken that the dink is of good quality. These ladus strengthen the bones, prevent back ache and pain in the lumbar region, and help regain strength and energy. The date powder, dink, and khus khus (poppy seeds), used in this recipe, nourish the hair, thus preventing hair loss.

Homemade butter, milk and coconut, are also beneficial for the hair.

Methi (fenugreek seeds) ladus can also be eaten for up to 45 days after delivery, (see Special Recipes). These help to restore the uterus to its former size, and enhance the quality of the breast milk. Ahleev (Lepidium sativum) also boosts production of breast milk and is nourishing. It can be eaten in the form of kheer, made with ghee, milk and sugar, or as a ladu with coconut.

In accordance with the principle 'like increases like', the new mother should be sure to drink a sufficient quantity of milk, so that ample breast milk is produced. A cup of milk with shatavari kalpa, is recommended twice or three times a day. She should continue to eat panchamrut as well as almonds which have been soaked in water overnight and peeled. All of these supplements are of tremendous benefit, and these benefits are passed on to the baby indirectly, through breast milk.

It is advisable to have fixed and regular timings for meals, and to eat only as much as is satiating, but does not cause a feeling of heaviness in the stomach.

The Kashyap Samhita also advises that vegetables be cooked in ghee (a fodni of ghee).

घृतभृष्टानि कूष्माण्डमूलकैर्वारुकाणि च । *...काश्यपसंहिता खिलस्थान*

Ghṛtabhṛṣṭāni kūṣmāṇḍa-mūlakair-vārukāṇi ca
....Kāśyapa khilasthāna

Not only vegetables, but also spicy dal/ lentils or soups, should be tempered with ghee. Mung dal is preferable, but tur dal can also be used occasionally, and the addition of sprouted methi seeds to the dal is also advised.

Vegetables such as kohala (Benincasa cerifera), bottle gourd (dudhi-Lagenaria vulgaris), smooth gourd (ghosali-Luffa aegyptiaca), ridge gourd (dodka-Luffa acutangula), gherkins (tondli - Cephalandra indica), bitter gourd (karela-Momordica charantia), padval (Trichosanthes anguina), parvar, zucchini, pumpkins, carrots and lady finger (bhendi- Abelmoschus esculentus), are excellent for the nursing mother, and boiled potatoes can be an occasional treat. Spinach, fenugreek (methi-Trigonella foenum-graeceum), maath (Amaranthus gangaticus), tandulja (Amarantus oleraceus) are good choices among the leafy vegetables, and can be also eaten occasionally.

कुलत्थयूषः सस्नेहलवणाम्लस्ततः परम् । ...काश्यपसंहिता खिलस्थान

Kulattha-yūṣḥ sasneha-lavaṇāmlastataḥ param
...Kāśyapasaṁhitā khilasthāna

Kashyap also recommends the occasional intake of kulith (Dolichos biflorus) soup, cooked with amsool (dried kokam fruits), in ghee. Kulith pacifies vata, and purifies the uterus, thus preventing post-partum vata imbalances. This soup can be included in the diet twice or three times a week. Besides this, mung dal soup, made with any of the above-named vegetables, is beneficial and nourishing.

Seasonal salads can be made using cucumbers, radishes, steamed carrots or cooked beetroot. Sprouted and steamed mung beans are also a good salad addition.

Apples, pomegranates, papayas, tender coconut or sweet grapes can also be occasionally included in the meal. The food should be prepared in a simple and sattvik manner; it should be tasty, without being too hot, or containing too many different spices.

Ayurveda recommends a specific remedy called as 'mudgayush yog'.

वह्नौ तप्तेन लोहेन मुद्गयूषं सुवापितम् ।
पीत्वेवं सूतिका नारी सर्वव्याधिन् व्यपोहति ॥ ...वंगसेन स्त्रीरोग

Vahnau taptena lohena mudga-yūṣam suvāpitam
Pītvevam sūtikā nārī sarva-vyādhin vyapohati
....Vaṅgasena strīroga

A piece of iron, which has been heated over a flame, is immersed in mung soup. If the new mother eats a soup like this, she will be protected from all diseases. An alternative method, which offers similar benefits, is to temper the food with a fodni that has been prepared in a small iron vessel. Dals, soups and other liquids, can be seasoned in this way. While pouring the fodni, the iron vessel can be dipped into the soup as well. Iron pot, pans or griddles, should be used to cook vegetables and chapattis, bhakri or fulka. This way, the food is cultured with iron during cooking, and this helps to replenish the body's supply of iron.

Cumin helps purify the uterus and is a good addition to the fodni; turmeric has antiseptic properties, helping to purify both, the blood and the breast milk, and should be used generously during cooking. Besides these, coriander powder, fenugreek seeds, ginger, fresh coconut, aamsool (dried kokam fruits), ajwain, asafoetida (hing), black pepper, cinnamon, bay leaf, coriander leaves and chilies (to taste) can be used in cooking. A cup of buttermilk with cumin powder, black salt (saindhav) and shahajeera (caraway) powder, should be taken after lunch.

उष्णोदकोपचारं च स्वस्थवृत्तमतः परम् । ...काश्यप चिकित्सास्थान

Uṣṇodakopacāram ca svasthavṛttamataḥ param
...Kāśyapa cikitsāsthāna

Drinking water should be boiled for 20 minutes every morning. It can then be kept in a thermos, and drunk warm, or as hot as possible, whenever required.

This helps the digestion process, and reduces fat at the abdomen and around the waist. Some may find it difficult to drink warm water in summer, so, during this season, it can be cooled to room temperature before drinking. In other seasons, especially in winter and in the rainy season, only warm water is recommended, and it is a must throughout the 45 days after delivery.

After meals a recipe of supari - a digestive and mouth freshner - as outlined in the chapter on Special Recipes can be taken. This also prevents flatulence, and helps purify the breast milk.

SUBSTANCES TO BE AVOIDED

Chavali (Vinga catiang), pavata (vaal-Dolichos lablab), chole (a type of chick pea), chick pea (Cicer arietinum), and other legumes which are heavy to digest. Also, vegetables which increase vata, such as capsicum, gavar (a type of bean - Cyamopsis psoralioides), spring onions (allium cepa), cabbage (Brassica oleracea), and cauliflower (Brassica botrytis). In addition, the inclusion of vegetables, such as onion, garlic, and eggplant is discouraged, along with eggs, non-vegetarian and stale foods. These are all tamasic in nature, and thus, must be avoided for at least six months after childhood. Non-vegetarian food is heavy to digest. If you cannot do without it, take it in a soup form, but only a minimum 15 days after delivery. Eggs should not be eaten at all. Sour yoghurt, lassi, shrikhand, fermented foods, pickles made from raw mango, tamarind, pineapple, ice-cold water or soft drinks, ice-cream, jack fruit, custard apple, and heavy foods like elephant yam (suran), are all to be strictly avoided. Fast foods such as *pav bhaji* and *panipuri* and burger and pizzas are also a taboo.

The diet and lifestyle, both need to be modified, depending on the place of residence, climatic conditions and the season when the birth has taken place. In the climate of northern India, for example, tamarind is forbidden, while it is considered beneficial in southern India.

Despite such variations, it is universally accepted that the post partum woman needs utmost attention.

- **A breastfeeding mother should take all precautions to ensure that she does not suffer from indigestion.**
- **The diet should include homemade ghee, fresh homemade butter, and dink.**
- **She should drink boiled warm water as far as possible.**
- **A non-vegetarian diet should be avoided for the first 15 days of delivery and as far as possible thereafter.**
- **Turmeric, fenugreek (methi) seeds, balantshop, shahajeera and ajwain, should be included in the daily diet to help purify the breast milk.**

Ideal practices for the new mother

As already described, Ayurved repeatedly emphasizes on specific diet, remedies and behaviour for all phases of life. Needless to say, the new mother is not an exception.

Acharya Sushrut has written the following, regarding the lifestyle to be followed:

क्रोधायासमैथुनादीन् परिहरेत् । ...सुश्रुत शारीरस्थान

Krodhāyāsamaithunādīn pariharet
....Suśruta śārīrasthāna

Things to be avoided

Anger, grief, excessive physical effort, sexual intercourse, sleeping during the day, talking loudly, traveling for extended periods, sitting in one place for too long, too much walking, contact with cold in any form, going out in a strong breeze, being exposed to the sun, overeating or eating foods that have opposing qualities (like milk and fruits), or foods contrary to the basic constitution of the person are all to be avoided.

The reasons to avoid the above activities are explained. All of these activities increase *vata* and should be avoided completely, especially during the 45 days following delivery. Even after this suggested time frame, it is best not to indulge in these activities too much, for a while.

Anger, grief and other forms of mental tension can affect the production of breast milk. It has been observed that in spite of proper diet and medication, breast milk may decrease if there is stress or tension at home. It is essential to ensure that the new mother remains happy, and in a stable and peaceful state of mind while she breast-feeds, especially during the first three to four months.

Other dietary measures like *Shatavari Kalpa*, *kheer*, or *ahleev ladus* should be continued regularly.

It is advisable to avoid sexual intercourse for at least 45 days after delivery, as this is the minimum time necessary for the mother's body to regain its strength.

Kapha and *pitta* increase if one sleeps during the day, and this can affect the quality of breast milk. Taking long naps during the day is discouraged when nursing the child. Sitting in one position for extended periods can cause lower back ache and pain in the lower abdomen. It is good to stand up or move at regular intervals.

Vata dosha, which is already out of balance, is further affected by contact with any form of cold. Examples of cold contact are

1. Taking a cold shower, washing up, or washing clothes or utensils in cold water.
2. Sitting continuously in an air-conditioned room or in a room with a cooler, or directly under a fan.

All of these could result in body ache, stiff or painful joints, and shivering.

Going out when there is a strong wind or in the hot sun, can also cause imbalance in *Vata* and *Pitta* respectively. The after-effects of this are fever and darkening of the skin. The new mother should keep a scarf tied around her head and ears for the first ten days, and small cotton swabs in the ears up until the 45th day after delivery. If she has to leave the house or be exposed to wind, she should wear a scarf without fail.

Most women gain weight after childbirth, especially around the abdomen and waist, and their bodies go out of shape. The main reason for this sudden weight gain is not pregnancy itself, but inappropriate care after delivery due to ignorance. This is further exacerbated by the use of contraceptive pills, which are usually taken immediately after the onset of menstruation, to prevent another pregnancy. Many such practices can have far-reaching effects that may be difficult to cure and that women are completely unaware about. They result in chronic backache, arthritis, rheumatism, loss of weight and hypertension. If the uterus does not return to its normal size, a woman's hormonal balance will not be restored, and subsequent conception could be difficult. The health of children born later may also be affected.

The Kashyap Samhita explains this in detail, giving an accurate and appropriate example. Acharya Kashyap states here:

यथा च जीर्णं भवनं सर्वतः श्लथबन्धनम् ।
वर्षवातविकम्पानामसहं स्यात्तथाविधम् ॥

तथा शरीरं सूतायाः खिन्नं प्रसवणश्रमैः ।
वातपित्तकफोत्थानां व्याधीनां असहं भवेत् ॥

...काश्यपसंहिता खिलस्थान

Yathā ca jīrṇam bhavanam
sarvataḥ ślatha-bandhanam
Varṣavāta-vikampānām-
asaham syāt-tathāvidham
Tathā śarīram sūtāyāḥ
khinnam prasavaṇaśramaiḥ
Vāta-pitta-kaphotthānām
vyādhīnām asaham bhavet

....Kāśyapasamhitā khilasthāna

Just like an old, feeble, and battered house is weakened and unable to bear the force of heavy rain, winds or earthquakes, a woman is weakened after delivery and is unable to tolerate the problems caused by vata-pitta-kapha dosha.

It is important to understand that a woman who has just given birth is extremely susceptible to many health issues. Prevention is far better than cure especially for the new mother, because the health of her baby also depends directly on her health. To enjoy her motherhood with good health she should be prepared to follow this entire set of guidelines for the recommended period of time.

Having emphasized the importance of rest, it should also be mentioned that after 45 days, she can safely walk around the house, on the terrace or in the garden. But she should not tire herself out.

A woman gains about ten to twelve kgs during pregnancy, of which she loses approximately 6 kgs in the process of delivery and just after. The remaining weight is lost gradually over a period of seven to eight months.

Today, women usually want to lose weight quickly, and are willing to experiment with exercise programs prevalent everywhere which focus on exercising until one is really tired out. These exercises, like gym and aerobic routines, even in their mild form may not be of much help in the long run. How much such exercises really contribute towards sustainable weight loss, is a matter of research, but it is certain that these exercises weaken the body. Weight that has gradually increased over the 9 months of pregnancy, is best lost gradually and by natural means. Yoga asanas and breathing techniques allow you to retain your strength and energy while helping the body become healthier and stay in shape.

Parvatasan

Yogasanas, which should be performed after three months are: Santulan Kriya Sthairya, Santulan Kriya Vistaran, Pavanmuktasan, Vishnushayanasan, Naukasan, Parivartit Chakrasan, Santulan Kriya Samarpan, and Suryanamaskar. Such exercises are simple to do, and should be done as the energy levels allow. Santulan Bhasrika, done along with these asanas, helps reduce fat and restore the thighs, abdomen, waist and buttocks to their original shape and size.

PARVATASAN (MOUNTAIN POSE)

The final posture in this asana resembles a mountain, hence the name. The practice of Parvatasan improves the flexibility of the spine, diaphragm, and intercostal muscles.

It also improves digestion. If done regularly throughout pregnancy, it ensures an easy and natural labour, and helps in reducing fat on the abdomen and excess on other parts of the body.

1. Sit in padmasana, ardhapadmasana or sukhasana.
2. Bring the palms together in the namaste pose in front of the chest.
3. While inhaling, raise both arms up, keeping the palms together, until the arms are fully stretched

Shalabhasan

upwards and come close to the ears. Stretch as much as possible.

4. While exhaling, slowly bring down the arms, rest them on the knees, returning to the original position.

SHALABHASANA (LOCUST POSE)

This asana strengthens the muscles of the abdomen, back and waist, improves digestion and trims the waist. It also reduces obesity and helps prevent menstrual disorders.

1. Lie on the abdomen with the insides of the feet touching each other.
2. Lay both arms next to the body, hands below the thighs with the palms facing upwards. The chin should be touching the ground.
3. While inhaling, contract the muscles of the lumbar region and buttocks and raise both legs simultaneously and as high as possible. The chin should remain on the ground and shoulders should be relaxed. Maintain this posture for three to five breaths (inhalation and exhalation).
4. Slowly lower the legs.

This asan should be practised for a minimum of three to five times.

Note : if it is difficult to lift both legs at one time, then lift one leg at a time, for the first few days.

SANTULAN KRIYA VISTARAN (EXPANSION)

This kriya makes the spine supple and strong, strengthens the lumbar muscles, facilitates expulsion of gases, improves digestive capacity, and helps the mother loose the weight gained during pregnancy.

1. Sit in vajrasana.
2. Bend forward and lie down on the stomach, bearing the weight of the upper body on the bent arms. The elbows should be perpendicular to the ground (see illustration). Place the index finger and thumb of both hands just behind the ears, and the other three fingers on the cheeks. The legs should be close to each other. Do not rest your chin in your palms. Look straight ahead.
3. Open the eyes and mouth wide, making sure there is no strain on any muscles.
4. Slowly inhale and exhale deeply through the mouth, mentally picturing a python sucking in its

Vistaran - Expansion

Pavanmuktasana

prey. A sound (like waves in the ocean) produced while inhaling and exhaling like this is normal.

5. Remain in this posture, and breathe deeply through the mouth, as long as it is comfortable. Then reverse the steps and return to the starting position.

PAVANMUKTASANA (WIND RELEASE POSE)

As the name suggests, this asana helps to relieve gas in the abdomen (Pavan means gas / wind). It helps improve digestion, and maintain regular bowel movements. It reduces back ache and lower back pain, and improves the functioning of the uterus.

1. Lie on the back, keeping both arms straight on the sides of the body, with the palms facing downwards.
2. Bend the knees at a ninety degree angle.
3. Interlock the fingers of both hands with the arms around the knees.
4. While exhaling, bring the bent legs towards the chest and abdomen.
5. Lift the head slowly and carefully and try to touch the knees with the forehead. Maintain this position for as long as possible, keep breathing normally.
6. While inhaling, bring the head slowly to its original position, and then slowly bring the legs down.

This asan can be done throughout the day, as many times as necessary.

Santulan Kriya Sthairya (GROUNDING)

Regular practice of this kriya keeps the spine flexible, stimulates the pituitary gland, improves digestion,and reduces abdominal fat.

1. Stand erect with the feet about 15-20 cm apart, and the toes pointing slightly outwards. Keep the arms straight down, almost touching the body, the hands in fists with the thumbs pointing downwards.
2. Keep the feet firmly rooted on the ground.
3. While inhaling deeply, lift the heels and rise up on the toes. Imagine that you are being pulled upwards by a thread attached to the top of the

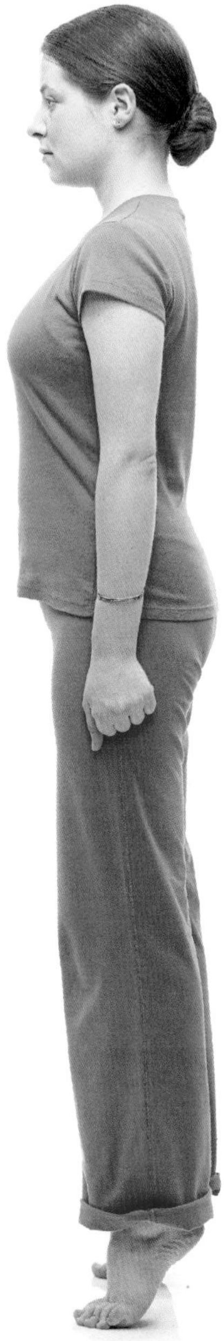

Sthairya - Grounding

Samarpan - Surrender

head.

4. Holding the breath, draw the abdomen inwards and upwards. Concentrate on the sahastradhar chakra (crown center at the top of the head). Maintain this posture as long as is comfortable.
5. Exhaling slowly, relax the abdominal muscles gradually, and bring the heels back to the ground.

Practise for a minimum of six to seven times.

SANTULAN KRIYA SAMARPAN (SURRENDER)

This kriya practiced regularly keeps the spine flexible, exercises the neck muscles, improves digestion, and reduces abdominal fat. It also helps one to become more humble, and creates an attitude of surrender.

1. Sit in vajrasan, and bring the palms in front of the chest in the namaste position. Inhale fully and deeply.
2. Keeping the palms together, extend the arms straight in front of the body, with the thumbs making a right angle with the fingers. The fingers should be pointing away from the body.
3. Bend forward slightly and touch the fingertips to the ground. While doing this do not bend the spine or the arms.
4. Look at the tips of the thumbs and exhale slowly, while sliding the palms along the ground, until the body is extended as much as possible. In this position, the abdomen and chest should touch the thighs, and the buttocks should not lift up from the heels.
5. Exhale completely, spread the arms slightly to allow the head to touch the ground. At this stage the breath should be fully exhaled and the arms straight. Remain in this position for a few seconds. Ensure that the buttocks are still resting on the heels.
6. Raise the head, inhale while looking at the tips of the thumbs, and slide the hands back towards the body.
7. Coming into the erect position, with palms in the initial namaste position, exhale completely.

This kriya should be repeated six to seven times.

Note : If you have problems in the neck, practise this kriya without lifting the head while rising up again as is instructed in point 6. You will still receive most of the benefit of the kriya.

Ayurved clearly explains the necessity of all these measures in this chapter, in the following shloka:

एवं हि गर्भवृद्धि-क्षपित-शिथिल-सर्वशरीरधातुप्रवाहण-

वेदना-क्लेद-रक्तनिस्रुत विशेषशून्यशरीराच्च पुनर्नवी भवति । ...*सुश्रुत शारीरस्थान*

Evam hi garbhavṛddhi-kṣapita-śithila-sarva-śarīra-dhātu-pravāhaṇa-vedanā-kleda-raktanisruta viśeṣa-śūnya-śarīrācca punarnavī bhavati ...Suśruta śārīrasthāna

A pregnant woman, who is weakened and thin, due to the growing foetus, the strain of delivery, and excessive blood loss, whose dhatus are depleted and feeble, will regain her original form (i.e. her youth), if she follows all of the above-mentioned guidelines.

A woman should consider having another child only when her physical strength is restored, after she has discontinued breast-feeding, and her regular menstrual cycle has recommenced. Conceiving by mistake during lactational amenorrhoea (this is called blind pregnancy), is not advisable.

Ideally, menstruation should recommence in seven or eight months after delivery. Menstruation causes breast milk to decrease and if it restarts earlier than this then the decreasing quantity of breast milk may prove insufficient for the baby. Generally menstrual periods only recommences when the baby's breast milk requirements automatically decrease with its age. No special measures are necessary to artificially restart menstruation. Any such measures will probably do more harm than good.

Women nowadays, do not usually wish for another child until the older one is grown up and somewhat independent. A very long gap between siblings is, however, not advisable, from the point of view of maternal health, development of the foetus, and a natural delivery. The Ayurvedic point of view is expressed in the following *shloka.*

निवृत्तप्रसवायास्तु पुनः षड्भ्यो वर्षेभ्य ऊर्ध्वं प्रसवमानाया नार्याः कुमारोऽल्पायुर्भवति । ...सुश्रुत शारीरस्थान

Nivṛtta-prasavāyāstu punaḥ ṣaḍbhyo varṣebhya ūrdhvam prasavamānāyā nāryāḥ kumāroḻalpāyurbhavati ...Suśruta śārīrasthāna

If there is more than a six year gap between two children, then the second child may have a shorter life span. It has been observed that, if the second pregnancy ensues five to six years after the first, there is an increased chance that conception could be difficult, or that the foetus could develop some abnormalities. There are greater chances of a spontaneous abortion, a stillbirth, or a difficult and complicated labour process.

Presently, society is witnessing a rapid deterioration of values. Corruption, misbehaviour, and disregard for rules, are on an increase. Respect for elders, humility, and discipline, are rarely-seen qualities. They have become almost strange and unknown ideas.

The coming generation is desperately in need of new values and Garbha Sanskar to revitalize society. Whether a couple has only one child or several, what is desirable is that they are helped to develop on all three levels, physically, psychologically and intellectually, in a proper way. Society needs children who are physically and mentally fit, and intellectually superior. To this end, Garbha Sanskar guidelines therefore act as an integral part of life, and will be beneficial for the future of the entire world.

- Anger, grief, anxiety or mental disturbance can adversely affect the production of breast milk.
- It is important to rest after childbirth, but this does not mean completely restricting all movements.
- The expectation that weight gained during pregnancy over nine months will be lost very quickly is inappropriate. It should be lost gradually, over six to seven months.
- Simple yoga should be started after three months of delivery. This help to restore the physical form, and give strength to the body.
- A gap of two to three years in age is an ideal time period between two children.

5

Baby Care...

In Sanskrit there is a saying... *Lalayet panchavarshani...* it means that the child should be pampered upto fve years of age. To understand what 'pampering' means, and to know exactly what has to be done to ensure a long and healthy life for the child, it is important to learn everything in baby care in detail from dietetics and lifestyle, to medicines.

Care of the newborn

In Ayurved, 'Jaatkarma Sanskar,' refers to the actions that are to be taken immediately after the birth of a child. These are to be carried out simultaneously with the care of the post-partum mother. Here is a list of things to be followed immediately after the birth of the child.

JAATKARMA SANSKAR

अथ जातस्योल्बं मुखं च सैन्धव
सर्पिषा विशोध्य । ...सुश्रुत शारीरस्थान

Atha jātasyolbam mukham ca saindhava
sarpiṣā viśodhya ....Suśruta śārīrasthāna

The mucus / secretions covering the face, eyes and nose of the newborn, should be removed. The child takes its first independent breath immediately after birth, and deposits on the mouth or nostrils may hinder this respiration. After thoroughly washing one's hands and clipping one's nails, the lips, palate, tongue, and the insides of the cheeks of the new born baby should be cleaned gently to clear any obstructing mucus, with a sterile cotton swab wrapped around the finger. The baby's cry signals the commencement of respiration. If the baby is exhausted from the process of delivery, this may be delayed, and in such cases, fanning the baby, gently patting its back, or sprinkling its body with a little water, helps. If these measures fail, then artificial respiration must be initiated.

If a baby cries immediately after birth it is an indication of its good health.

Once the baby is breathing satisfactorily, the following mantra should be spoken into its right ear:

अङ्गादङ्गात् संभवसि हृदयादभिजायसे ।
आत्मा वै पुत्रनामासि स जीव शरदां शतम् ॥

शतायुः शतवर्षोऽसि दीर्घमायुरवाप्नुहि ।
नक्षत्राणि दिशो रात्रिरहश्च त्वाभिरक्षतु ॥ *...अष्टांगसंग्रह उत्तरस्थान*

Aṅgādaṅgāt sambhavasi hṛdayādabhijāyase
ātmā vai putranāmāsi sa jīva śaradām śatam

śatāyuḥ śata-varṣo~si dīrghamāyuravāpnuhi
Nakṣatrāṇi diśo rātrirahaśca tvābhirakṣatu
...Aṣṭāṅgasaṅgraha uttarasthāna

This mantra is a prayer, that the child may have a long and healthy life, and that it may stay safe.

प्रथमं प्रमार्जितास्यस्य चास्य शिरस्तालु कार्पासपिचुना
स्नेहगर्भेण प्रतिसंछादयेत् । *...चरक शारीरस्थान*

Prathamam pramārjitāsyasya cāsya śirastālu
kārpāsapicunā sneha-garbheṇa prati-sañchādayet
...Caraka śārīrasthāna

After this, a small cotton swab dipped in pure ghee is placed on the fontanel (the opening at the crown of the child's head). If required, a small quantity of pure ghee and black salt, can be placed on the baby's tongue, to expel any residual mucus, or swallowed amniotic fluid.

The umbilical cord should be cut only after all this has been done. The manner in which the umbilical cord is to be severed is described below.

ततो नाभिनाडीमष्टांगुलमायम्य सूत्रेण बद्ध्वा छेदयेत् ।
...सुश्रुत शारीरस्थान

द्वयोरन्तरयोः शनैर्गृहीत्वा तीक्ष्णेन रौक्मराजतायसानां छेदनानाम्
अन्यतमेनार्धधारेण छेदयेत् । *...चरक शारीरस्थान*

Tato nābhi-nāḍīmaṣṭāṅgulamāyamya sūtreṇa
baddhvā chedayet ...Suśruta śārīrasthāna

Dvayorantarayoḥ śanairgṛhītvā
tīkṣṇena raukmarājatāyasānām
chedanānām anyatamenārdhadhāreṇa
chedayet ....Caraka śārīrasthāna

A piece of silk thread, should be tied tightly at a distance of eight fingers (4-5 inches approximately) from the baby's umbilicus, and a second thread should be tied tightly, a little distance away, from the first. Using a sharp instrument, the umbilical cord should then be cut in between the two threads. The threads and the instrument must be sterilized beforehand. This technique of tying the cord in two places, which is still prevalent today, helps to minimize blood loss.

Until the baby begins to breathe independently, its blood circulation takes place through the placenta, which is why the umbilical cord is still pulsing immediately after birth. Once respiration begins, the flow of blood is directed towards the baby's lungs, and no longer through the umbilical cord. Its blood circulation now changes direction, and passes through the heart-lung system of the baby, causing the pulsations in the cord to slowly decrease, and ultimately stop. The best time to cut the umbilical cord is when it stops pulsing. The time in between the baby starting to breathe and the cutting of the cord can be used to clean the baby's mouth, and place the ghee-soaked cotton on the fontanel etc..

Once the cord is cut, the umbilicus is covered with a soft muslin (or cotton) cloth. The muslin cloth can be tied around the baby's abdomen like a belt. This protects the cord from infection and prevents it from dangling. It can be fixed after the baby has been bathed.

Honey and Gold

The following Sanskar is one of the important procedures advised by Ayurved. It is completely safe and should be done as soon as possible after the baby is born.

अथ कुमारं शीताभिरद्भिराश्वास्य जातकर्मणि कृते मधुसर्पिरनन्तचूर्णं अङ्गुल्याऽनामिकया लेहयेत् । ...*सुश्रुत शारीरस्थान*

Atha kumāram śītābhiradbhirāśvāsya jāta-karmaṇi kṛte madhu-sarpiranantacūrṇam aḍgulya-anāmikayā lehayet ....Suśruta śārīrasthāna

**विघृष्य धौते दृषदि प्राङ्मुखी लघुनाऽम्बुना ।
आमथ्य मधुसर्पिभ्यां लेहयेत् कनकं शिशुम् ॥** ...काश्यप लेहाध्याय

Vighṛṣya dhaute dṛṣadi
prāṅmukhī laghunālmbunā
āmathya madhu-sarpibhyām
lehayet kanakam śiśum ...Kāśyapa lehādhyāya

Place a drop of honey and ghee (just honey is also fine) onto a sahan (a grindstone made from a particular material). Take a piece of pure gold (24 karat - not something that is part of or taken from everyday jewelry) and grind it in a coin-sized clockwise circle on the honey on the stone. The person grinding the gold should be facing east while doing so. Gently rub this mixture on to the baby's tongue, with the right hand ring finger.

This should be done daily for six months. According to *Kashyap Samhita*, this mixture has the following benefits

- increases the baby's lifespan
- improves the immune system
- increases intellect and memory
- protects the baby from negative energies
- it can help make the child so intelligent that he or she will be able to remember things that have been only heard once.

Oil The Baby

After this, ghee or gentle oil infused with vata-pacifying herbs, such as **Santulan Abhyang Coconut Oil**, should be applied very gently all over the baby's skin. This facilitates the easy removal of the sticky mucus-like substance that covers the skin of the newborn; if necessary, a little black salt (saindhav) may be added to the oil to aid the removal of the mucus. When this is done, the child should be bathed with clean, warm water.

Ayurved advises the use of *sarvagandhodaka* for the baby's bath. Boil water with the following herbs - cinnamon, bay leaf, cardamom, cloves, camphor, *nagkeshar* (Mesua ferrea), *kankol* (Cubeba officinalis), *agaru* (Aquilaria agallocha), *shilajeet* (Asphaltum) - and let the water cool until lukewarm and use it to bathe the baby. To make things easier, a decoction made from the above-mentioned herbs may be added to warm bath water instead. This decoction is not only fragrant, but it pacifies *vata* as well.

FIRST BREASTFEEDING

After bathing, the baby can be breastfed. Once both mother and child are clean, the right breast should be washed with water. The mother should then sit facing east, be in a pleasant frame of mind, and bring the child to her breast for feeding (the first breast feeding should last approx 30-40 mins). Suckling is an inborn natural reflex and comes easily to the baby. The breast milk, immediately after birth (called colostrum), is thick, and has a different constitution from the milk produced after a few days. This milk is important for the baby's overall development. A proper first-time feeding ensures adequate milk formation thereafter for the mother as well. Do not be mistaken that the mother has insufficient milk (since it is thick and not in large quantities in the beginning) and do not try to feed the baby any other milk from a bottle or with a spoon. If you do this, the baby will begin to reject the natural breast-feeding process. The baby usually sleeps immediately after its first feed.

The Sushrut Samhita advises the recital of the following mantra at this auspicious moment of the baby's first feed:

चत्वारः सागरास्तुभ्यं स्तनयोः क्षीरवाहिनः ।
भवन्तु सुभगे नित्यं बालस्य बलवृद्धये ॥

पयोऽमृतरसं पीत्वा कुमारस्ते शुभानने ।
दीर्घमायुः अवाप्नोतु देवाः प्राश्यामृतं यथा ॥ *...सुश्रुत शारीरस्थान*

Catvārah sāgarāstubhyam stanayoḥ kṣīra-vāhinaḥ
Bhavantu subhage nityam bālasya bala-vṛddhaye

Payo~mṛta-rasam pītvā kumāraste śubhānane
Dīrghamāyuḥ avāpnotu devāḥ prāśyāmṛtam yathā
...Suśruta śārīrasthāna

Oh fortunate woman, let all the four oceans produce milk in your breast, resulting in the progress of your child. As the Gods became immortal by consuming elixir (amrut), may your child too live a long life after drinking elixir in the form of your milk.

If possible, someone present should recite this mantra. If not, the mother should keep similar thoughts in her mind during breastfeeding

THE BENEFITS OF BREAST FEEDING

The secretion of mammary glands is called breast milk. Breast milk is a complete and wholesome food for the baby, and is therefore, considered to be an elixir. Thus the saying *'maturev pibet stanyam'* - the new-born should have only breast-milk. The followiong are the reasons why breast milk is so important for both the mother and the child.

- It is easily accepted by the baby, it keeps the baby healthy.
- Breast milk is complete in itself as it has all nutrients that are needed for the infant.
- The essence of all substances consumed by the mother, whether they be nourishing food, medication, nutritional supplements or rasayans, are assimilated by the baby through breast milk. Breast milk helps the development of intellect, the immune system, and physical and mental health of the baby.
- Breast milk is always fresh and pure and available whenever required by the baby. The risks resulting out of storage of other milk (e.g. the milk turning sour) are avoided. Breast milk is at the perfect temperature for optimal absorption

and contains natural immune antibodies and has anti-infective qualities.

- Breast-feeding strengthens the bond between the mother and the child. It will leave a powerful impression of security throughout life.

- Breast-feeding is also beneficial for maternal health. The reappearance of menstruation any time in the first five to six months after childbirth can be detrimental for her health. Breast-feeding protects the mother from this as menstruation will generally not recommence as long as the child is being breast fed.

The numerous beneficial effects of breast-feeding, have been confirmed by modern scientific research. It is an accepted fact that children who have been breast-fed, are generally better-nourished, healthier, and have stronger immune systems throughout life.

PRECAUTIONS WHILE BREAST FEEDING

Initially, breast-feeding may be difficult for both mother and child, but with due care and patience, both will become accustomed to it quickly.

For the first few days, the baby's milk requirements are minimal. During this time, the mother secretes thick milk called colostrum. The quantity of breast milk increases gradually. If the baby takes less milk than is produced, the residual milk remains in the mammary ducts, where it can cause a feeling of heaviness and a dull ache in the breasts. This excess milk should be removed with some gentle pressure else it could form clots which could block the mammary ducts, leading to discomfort for the mother, or even fever. It could also cause decreased breast milk production in some women. If required, a breast pump may be used to extricate the extra milk. But be cautious as the repeated indiscriminate use of a breast pump could lead to cracks in the nipples.

A quiet and calm place is best for breastfeeding. The mother should sit comfortably, ideally in a cross-legged position, on a soft seat. The baby should be held in such a way that the head is slightly above the level of its abdomen. Instead of the mother bending over, it is better to hold the child slightly higher on the arm, otherwise the weight of the breasts may cause breathing difficulties for the infant. The baby's head should not be entirely covered with a *sari pallu* or a cloth as it could smother the child or cause difficulty in breathing. The child may have to breathe through its mouth, and the air, which then reaches the abdomen, may cause vomitting and colic.

The breasts must be cleaned before each feed, and for this, a vessel should be filled with boiled water and kept covered ready for use. When the baby is ready to feed, the mother should wash her hands, then use a sterile cotton swab dipped in this water to wash her breasts, especially the nipples. Whenever the baby is hungry, this procedure should be followed. A new sterile cotton swab should be used each time.

In the beginning, babies can feed for around five minutes on each breast. The time can then be gradually increased to 10-15 minutes on each side. There is no hard and fast rule about how long the infant is to be fed. It depends on various factors, such as age, hunger and the infant's ability to suckle. The baby will usually feed up to 15-20 minutes and stop suckling once it is satisfied. Conversely, a weak or premature baby, may feed up to 30-35 minutes. The mother will normally be able to determine the baby's requirements within a few days.

It is important that the mother remains attentive to the baby's needs during nursing. Sometimes, too much milk gets secreted as soon as the baby is held close. This may be difficult for the baby to swallow. At such times, the flow may be reduced by using the index and middle finger above and below the nipple, to compress it gently.

After feeding, the nipples should be cleaned once again. The mother should apply pure ghee on the nipples once or twice a day to keep them soft and lubricated and prevent cracks and fissures. The baby should be fed alternately from each breast. Begin one session with the right breast, and next time, start with the left side. This balances milk production on both sides.

Ensure that there is no pressure on the baby's abdomen after feeding. This is best done by holding the baby with its back erect, close to the chest, and gently stroking its back.

The baby should be allowed to feed whenever it is hungry. The initial interval between feeds (when the child is hungry), is usually about 2½ to 3 hours, slowly increasing to three to four hours. If the baby is asleep at feeding times, it should not be woken just to feed. Similarly, it is not good to keep the child waiting for a set feeding time if it is hungry beforehand.

It is natural for a mother to worry about whether or not her baby is getting adequate milk, as there is no way of measuring how much milk has been consumed. But feeding the baby again and again out of this worry, say on a regimen of every two hours, may end up causing the baby indigestion.

If the child gains weight normally, sleeps soundly, feeds at proper intervals, is not irritable, has no digestion problems, and is quiet for two-three hours after feeding, then its needs are being adequately met.

The baby may vomit occasionally after a feed, but this should cause no concern. As long as it gains weight normally, sleeps quietly, and is not irritable, one need not seek medical advice for occasionally vomiting. Vomiting actually rids the baby's stomach of any excess accumulated *kapha* / phlegm. The incidence of vomiting usually reduces gradually, and ultimately stops when the child begins to turn onto its abdomen and crawl.

- **As soon as the child is born, a sterile cotton piece, dipped in ghee, should be placed on the child's fontanel. This strengthens and secures the child's brain and senses.**
- **A new-born should definitely be given honey and ghee with gold (as described in the chapter). This is the first sanskar to be performed after birth, and is paramount and vital for the progress of the child's health.**
- **Breast milk is the best food for a new-born.**
- **The first breast feed should be given 30 to 40 minutes after childbirth, to make matters easy for both, the mother and the baby.**
- **Breast-feeding is also very important for the mother's health.**

Breast-feeding

If possible, the baby should not only be breast-fed until it is six months old. Even if other food is given to the baby from then on, breast-feeding should be continued until the child is 12 to 15 months old.

Ayurved emphasizes the importance of breast-feeding to the extent where it suggests, that feeding be done by another woman (wet nurse / *dhatri*), if the baby's mother is incapacitated for some reason. The wet nurse should be of the same age as the mother and have a similar nature. If, however, neither the mother nor a wet nurse is able to feed the baby, the only other option is to feed the baby with cow's milk.

Today, it is not uncommon for many new mothers to not wish to breast-feed their babies. In such cases, the hormone injections or medication given to stop milk production certainly have a detrimental effect on the overall health and strength of the mother. In addition, the baby deprived of breast milk, does not get the benefits of breast milk which you have read in the previous chapter.

Such erroneous and unnatural instincts should definitely be discarded. On the contrary, while breast-feeding, the mother can experience a limitless joy, by watching the baby thrive and grow because of her milk.

BREAST MILK

A breastfed child is totally dependent on the mother's milk for complete nutrition. In turn, the quality of the milk is affected by the mother's diet and behaviour; what she eats or drinks, the lifestyle and speech habits she adopts, are some of the factors that influence the breast milk, and ultimately the baby. For this reason, the mother should take care of her own health.

Since breast milk is the child's only and complete food, it is imperative that it does not lack in any nutrients, is balanced, and is of optimal quality. It is necessary that the mother include **Santulan Shatavari Kalpa** in her diet right from conception. Other foods that help the production of breast milk and can be taken regularly are ahleev ladu, kheer, milk, and ghee. Healthy breast milk is defined below:

स्तन्यसम्पत्तु प्रकृतिवर्णगन्धरसस्पर्शम्, उदकपात्रे च दुह्यमानमुदकं व्येति प्रकृतिभूतत्वात् तत् पुष्टिकरमारोग्यकरं चेति । ...*चरक शारीरस्थान*

Stanya-sampattu prakṛti-varṇa-gandha-rasa-sparśam, udaka-pātre ca duhyamānamudakam vyeti prakṛti-bhūtatvāt tat puṣṭikaram-ārogyakaram ceti ....Caraka śārīrasthāna

- Breast milk should be clean, thin and at body temperature (not warmer).
- It should look white and have a shine (like the white surface of a conch)

- It should be sweet in taste.
- To test purity, add a few drops of breast milk to a glass of clean water. Imbalanced breast milk will not mix well with water.

Many women experience that the breast milk they produce has decreased. Possible reasons for this are outlined below.

क्रोधशोकावात्सल्यादिभिश्च स्त्रियाः
स्तन्यनाशो भवति । ...सुश्रुत शारीरस्थान

Krodha-śoka-avātsalyādibhiśca striyāḥ stanya-nāśo bhavati ...Suśruta śārīrasthāna

Anger, grief, lack of maternal love and empathy, fasting, over-exercising, excess anxiety or worry, can lead to reduced formation of breast milk.

Many women today are working, and this can cause constant physical and mental stress, in addition to time constraints, which may lead to neglect of dietary and behavioural guidelines prescribed in this book.

All the above-mentioned factors may cause a deficiency in the amount of milk produced. According to Ayurved, *rasa dhatu* and breast milk are closely interconnected. *Rasa dhatu*, being the first *dhatu*, is easily affected by minor changes in food habits, or the prevailing mental state, and this in turn affects breast milk.

Ensuring adequate production of breast milk

- Drink adequate quantities of milk with **Santulan Shatavari Kalpa**.
- Eat ahleev kheer or ahleev-coconut ladu twice a day.
- Eat sheera made with water chestnut-flour and jaggery.
- Add kheer, made from rice flour, khus-khus (poppy seeds), semolina, with sugar or jaggery, to lunch.
- Eat home made butter / ghee with candy sugar (khadi sakhar).
- Drink milk with half a teaspoon of shatavari churna and half a teaspoon of vidari (Ipomoea digitata).
- Mix together ¼ tsp of pimpli powder (long pepper), ¼ tsp of dry ginger powder (suntha), ¼ tsp of hirda powder, ½ tsp of jaggery with ghee and take the mixture with milk.
- **Santulan Lactosan** is a good herbal supplement for the mother while she is breast feeding her child.
- The breasts should also be massaged with **Santulan Suhrud Oil** to prevent sagging. Regular massage also helps to increase the production of breast milk.

The Quality Of Breast Milk

To ensure that breast milk remains optimal, the following preventive measures are advised.

- Turmeric - A sutika's diet should include a fair amount of turmeric in the form of powder. Ensure that the powder used is pure and preferably homemade. If can procure fresh turmeric root, include it in meals in the form of a pickle, made with ginger and salt. Use turmeric generously when cooking vegetables and lentils / dals as well.
- Hing (asafoetida) - This can also be used while cooking to help keep breast milk pure.
- Sprouted Methi (fenugreek) Seeds - These can be added to vegetables and lentils / dal *fodni*, also fosters the formation of good breast milk.
- Cumin (jeera) - This is excellent for purifying breast milk, and can be used to temper vegetables. The addition of jeera powder to buttermilk or vegetables makes them more

palatable.

- As described earlier, chewing some ajwain, balantshop (Peucedanum graveolens), or sesame, after meals, as supari or mouth freshener, also helps to purify the breast milk (See chapter on Special Recipes)
- Kulith (Dolichos biflorus) - Kulith soup is advised twice a week, as it helps maintain the quality of breast milk. It should be cooked in a cumin fodni, and the addition of aamsool (Garcinia purpurea) makes it tastier.
- Massaging the breasts daily with **Santulan Suhrud Oil** is also recommended.

Following these simple steps will prevent impure and unhealthy breast milk. If, for some reason, problems still arise, you need to visit an Ayurvedic physician.

DETERIORATION OF BREAST MILK

The taste, colour, smell and quality of breast milk may deteriorate due to:

- Over-eating by the mother, eating too much bitter/salty food or any stale food, eating too much of paneer (cottage cheese) and curd, sleeping in the afternoon, sadness, anger, grief, stress and inadequate sleep.

If breast milk is disturbed by vata dosha, it becomes frothy, slightly dark in colour and tastes bitter / astringent. Drinking such milk can cause the baby indigestion, flatulence, constipation, and inadequate weight gain.

If the breast milk is disturbed by pitta dosha, it becomes yellowish in colour, sour / bitter, and hot. On consuming such milk, the baby can have excessive sweating, loose motions, and a high body temperature.

If the breast milk is disturbed by kapha, then it is slightly salty, sticky, and heavy. If added to a glass of water, this type of breast milk will sink to the bottom. It can cause disorders, such as excessive salivation, increased sleep, swelling on the face, itching, and frequent bouts of cough and cold.

THE EFFECT OF THE DOSHAS ON BREAST MILK

Remedies for imbalances due to vata dosha

- Intake of dashamoolarishta and kumari asav, mixed with warm water, helps. Taking dashamula ghruta is also advised.
- Applying a paste of dashamool, hirda (Terminalia chebula), and licorice (Glycyrrhiza glabra) on the breast, helps to purify the breast milk. These ingredients are available separately in powder form. They should be mixed in equal quantities with water to form the paste.
- The intake, of a mixture of asafoetida and black salt (saindhav) with ghee, reduces disorders, such as abdominal pains, colic, and flatulence in the baby.

Remedies for imbalances due to pitta dosha

- Intake of panchatikta ghruta.
- The application of a paste made up of herbs, such as sandalwood, vala (Andropogon muricatus), anantmool (Hemidesmus indicus), having cooling properties, on the breast.
- Herbal preparations, such as pravalpanchamrut, kamadudha, bhunimbadi kadha, may be taken after consultation with an Ayurvedic physician.

Remedies for imbalances due to kapha dosha

- Intake of dry ginger powder mixed with honey

and ghee.

- The application of a paste of kadechirait (Swertia chirata), gulvel (Tinospora cordifolia), and triphala (mixture of amla, hirda, behada), on the breast is recommended.
- Herbal medicines such as pipplyadi powder panchakol powder, may be taken after consultation with a physician.

If the breastmilk is impure, imbalanced, or in decreased quantity, appropriate treatment should be started promptly. Breastfeeding is extremely important. It should only be stopped if you are not able to remedy its dusturbance or if milk is being produced in very small quantities. Please consult an Ayurvedic physician in such cases. Pure cow's milk is the only permissible substitute until the remedies are effected. Before feeding the baby with cow's milk, however, it must be cultured in the following manner:

Add ten to fifteen grains of vavding (*Embelia ribes*) or a spoonful of *laghupanchmool* herbs (mixture of five specific roots) to ¾ cup of milk and ¾ cup of water. Boil it, then cook on a low flame until the total quantity is reduced to one cup. Strain and allow it to cool to the around body temperature before feeding the baby.

The above treatment serves to make the cow's milk easier to digest. All of the nutrients from the mother's diet are automatically passed to the baby in the appropriate form and correct quantity through breast milk. To compensate for these deficiencies in cow's milk, preparations such as **Santulan Chaitanya Kalpa** made from herbs such as Ashwagandha (Withania somnifera), or kavach bij (Mucuna pruriens), can be mixed in the milk. This milk should then be strained through a clean cloth, before it is given to the baby. Maintaining strict hygiene and sterile conditions is of the utmost importance in the above process.

A very important point to be noted here, is that tinned or powdered milk is very difficult to digest, and should not be used. Bottle-feeding should be avoided as well, but, if in an emergency, the baby has to be bottle-fed, both, the bottle and rubber nipple, should be boiled for at least twenty minutes. If a cup and spoon are used to feed the child, these should also be adequately sterilized. Preferably use a silver cup and spoon for feeding.

- **For the first six months, the baby should be strictly breastfed. After that, even if other foods are introduced, breastfeeding should be continued till the child is 12 to 15 months old.**
- **If, for some reason, it is not possible to breastfeed the baby, cow's milk can be used as a substitute. This milk, however, should be cultured with herbs, and kalpas like Santulan Chaitanya Kalpa to provide the baby with adequate nourishment.**

For a healthy baby...

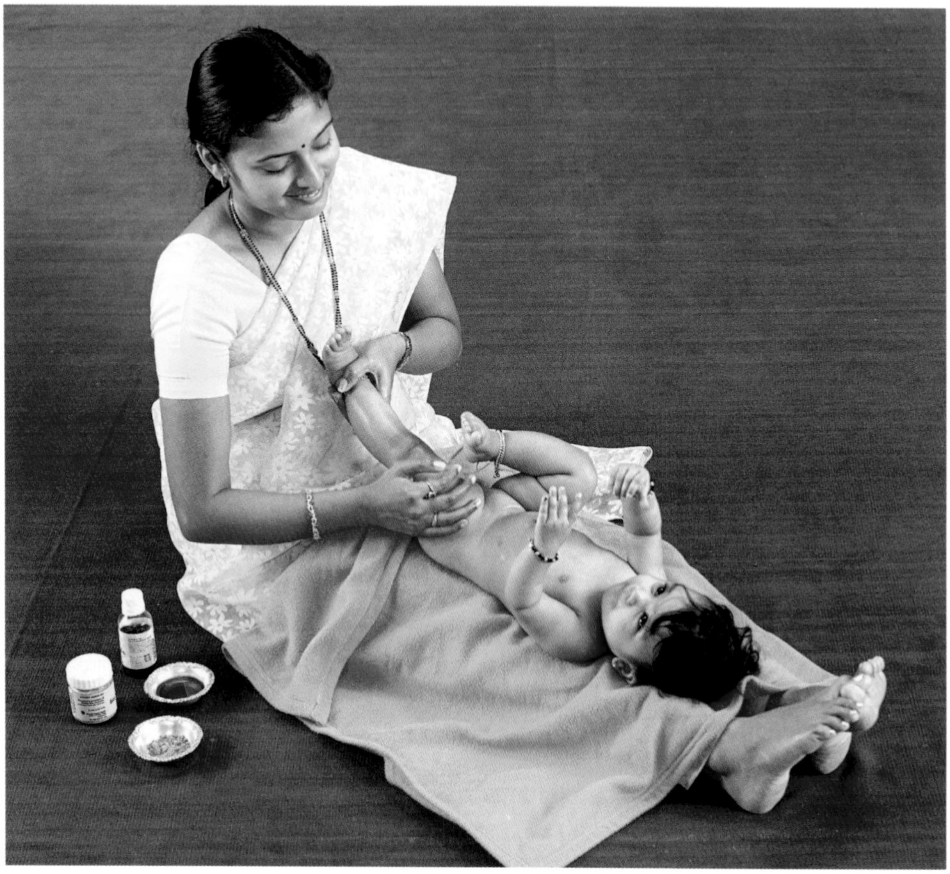

Babies grow very rapidly. Ayurvedic remedies, when integrated into the daily routine, improve the health and development of the baby, and in the long run are of tremendous help to the growing child. Some recommended Ayurvedic remedies, also part of traditional curative methods to encourage excellent development in the child, are as follows.

MASSAGE

Every morning before bath, the baby should be massaged gently (it is called *Abhyang* in sanskrit) with special herbal oils, such as **Santulan Abhyang (Coconut) Oil**. Applying pressure to the baby's body or rubbing its skin forcefully could cause injury. Try and apply the oil as if you're playing with the baby lovingly and with care. The baby will enjoy the experience, and cooperate completely!

The traditional and easiest position in which oil can be applied to the baby is shown in the picture above. The baby is to be massaged gently while placed on the legs extended out in front of you. If this position is not possible, the baby may be placed on a soft sheet laid on the floor.

How To Massage The Baby?

Begin with applying oil to the fontanel. Apply as much oil here as gets absorbed. Then put two to three drops of oil in the baby's navel and two to three drops in each ear. The massage should be done from the legs upwards; the direction of movement is from the soles to the feet and then the thighs. Massage strokes should generally be from the lower part of the body to the upper. Similarly, the palms, backs of the hands, then the arms should be massaged in this sequence. A similar upward movement is to be followed on the back, from the sacrum to the neck. On the abdomen, the strokes of the massage should be in a circular clockwise movement from the right to the left side. The massage oil should be lukewarm, especially in the rainy season and in winter. Give the baby a bath about ½ an hour after the massage.

Regularly massaging the baby will strengthen its bones and muscles. The baby's skin will become softer and will glow a lot more. Massage will also ensure adequate and normal physical growth for the baby, and will improve resistance to disease and will also boost the baby's immune system. A second application of oil in the evening will ensure sound sleep for the baby during the night.

It is advisable to continue giving the baby regular massages until the age of two. It should be a definite daily activity for the baby during the first eight to nine months, and subsequently the child can be given a massage once or twice a week up to the age of five.

BATH AND HERBAL PASTE APPLICATION

The water used to bathe the baby should be

neither too hot nor too cold.

As the baby's skin is extremely sensitive, susceptible and tender, the use of a bathing powders such as **Santulan Baby Massage Powder**, instead of soap, is recommended. Some of the main ingredients of such powders are sandalwood, *anantmool* and turmeric, with chickpea or *masur* flour

Santulan Baby Massage Powder should be mixed with fresh milk or cream to make a paste. Use this paste instead of soap while bathing the baby.

The room used for the baby's massage and

bath should be free of draughts of wind. Draughts can occur due to open doors or windows. Direct exposure to a fan or air-conditioner is just as bad. Immediately after bathing, the baby should be wrapped in soft muslin cloth, and dried gently.

SMOKE THERAPY - DHOOP

After bath, the baby should be exposed to *dhoop*. If one follows traditional methods of *dhoop*, the charcoal or dried cow dung (govarya) to be used for this purpose, should already be lit and kept ready when the child is being bathed. It is quite convenient now, though, to use electric dhoop pots or pans (available in the marketplace)

Sprinkle a small amount of **Santulan Tenderness Dhoop** on the electric pot and switch it on. The baby should then be held over the smoke that emanates from the herbal mixture.

If needed, a large sieved pot or pan may be placed over the dhoop pot so that the baby is not directly exposed to the heat. This also helps to ensure that the smoke spreads out more (see the image on the previous page). The smoke should reach all the parts of the baby's body, especially the fontanel, ears, anus, and genitals. Please ensure that the baby is not in any discomfort or feels choked or is touched by anything hot in this process.

Dhoop, taken daily, helps to ward off infections and prevents coughs, colds and fever. Since this therapy helps the overall growth and development of the child it should be administered daily for at least for the first six to eight months. As the baby grows older, and it becomes difficult to hold the baby in such a position, the child may be placed near the *dhoop* pot instead.

After dhoop, apply a pinch of *vekhand* (Acorus calamus) powder to the baby's chest and some finely powdered sangjira to the baby's abdomen, armpits, groin and chest. After this the child can be dressed.

This remedy helps removes excess or unwanted body hair on a child, and may be especially useful for girl babies . Mix turmeric and vekhand powder, or make them into a paste and apply it to the skin regularly. This considerably reduces future visits to the beauty parlour!

CLOTHES

The baby's clothes, sheets and bed linen should be made of soft cotton or silk. Ayurved recommends that all clothes used for the baby be treated with dhoop as well. The baby's clothes should be washed, dried in the sun - and then exposed to dhoop to sterilise them - before use. This practice is a must in the rainy season. In other seasons exposing only the baby's cloth diapers to dhoop may also be sufficient. Clothes and cotton diapers should be ironed to prevent microbial contamination.

Avoid making your baby wear tight clothes, especially undergarments. Cloth diapers should not be tied tightly onto the abdomen.

In the interests of convenience, there is an increasing tendency to use disposable diapers. These leave the genital region constantly moist and do not allow the area to be exposed to air. This causes an increased incidence in infection, inflammation, or rash (diaper rash) in the area. Avoid using disposable diapers as much as possible.

KAJAL

Kajal is great for the eyes. It is a myth that kajal can damage the eyes. Kajal, which has been prepared using traditional Ayurvedic recipes and guidelines, such as **San Anjan (black)**, is perfectly safe and excellent for the baby. It improves vision as well as the health of the eyes and gives them a glow. It has also been found that those who have been using Ayurvedic kajal since childhood, have fewer eye problems in adulthood.

Protecting The Ears And The Head

अहरहःश्चास्य श्रोत्रशृंगाटकं स्नेहाप्लुतेन प्लोतेन प्रच्छादयेत् । ...अष्टांगसंग्रह उत्तरस्थान

Aharahaḥścāsya śrotra-śṛṅgāṭakam snehāplutena plotena pracchādayet ....Aṣṭāṅgasaṅgraha uttarasthāna

A drop of lukewarm oil should be put in the ears every day, and then the ears should be protected with a cotton swab

After this, it is recommended to cover the baby's head and ears with a cap. Even in summer the baby should be wearing a cap on the head immediately after the morning bath, even if the baby sleeps during this time. The child should always sleep with its head in the east.

SLEEP

Sleep is very important for the baby's all-round development. Initially, babies sleep for 20-22 hours, waking up only when hungry or wet. When the baby falls asleep immediately after feeding, it is an indicator of good health.

The room where the baby sleeps should meet the following criteria. It should be warm, quiet, not frequented by people and away from loud or traffic noises. The baby should be kept away from draughts and not placed directly under a fan.

The baby's cot should be clean, soft and comfortable. Make sure the baby is always protected from insects and small animals, such as ants, mosquitoes and flies. It is not good to have the baby sleep only on its back, so it should be turned on to its side occasionally.

It has been observed, that maintaining one sleeping position for longer periods of time can result in an unnatural shape of the cranium, so it is recommended, that the head be supported in all three directions by the use of soft pillows, or soft cotton fabric rolls. When the baby is lying on its side, a pillow should be used to support the back as well.

Please allow your baby to sleep undisturbed and discourage visitors from trying to wake it. Noises like doorbells and telephone rings can disturb your baby's sleep, affecting its digestion and consequently its growth.

The duration for which the baby sleeps will reduce naturally as it grows. If your baby does not sleep soundly enough or has disturbed sleep you must take remedial measures immediately.

It is recommended that the baby sleep in its own bed, but near its mother. This enables the mother to keep an eye on her child and allows the baby to feel safe and secure.

Ayurved recommends the following regarding sleep for babies

बोधयेत् सहसा सुप्तं नो न चैनं समुत्क्षिपेत् ।

...अष्टांगसंग्रह उत्तरस्थान

Bodhayet sahasā suptam no na cainam samutkṣipet
...Aṣṭāṅgasaṅgraha uttarasthāna

It is not a good idea to waken a sleeping child suddenly. The baby should not be lifted without waking it up beforehand.

त्रासयेन्नाविधेयं च त्रस्तं गृह्णन्ति हि ग्रहाः ।
वस्त्रपातात् परस्पर्शात् पालयेत् लंघनाच्च तम् ।।
...अष्टांगसंग्रह उत्तरस्थान

Trāsayennāvidheyam ca
trastam gṛhṇanti hi grahāḥ
Vastra-pātāt para-sparśāt
pālayet laṅghanācca tam ...Aṣṭāṅgasaṅgraha uttarasthāna

Any unnatural or loud noises, abnormal shapes, frightening sights or situations, all of which have the potential to harm the baby, should be kept away.

Strangers should not be allowed to hold the baby when it is without clothes. The baby should not be swung into another person's arms, or thrown up into the air.

Such actions can cause grahabadha - lung or brain damage / disorders, or contagious diseases.

वर्षं स्ववसतेर्बाह्यं कुमारस्य न दर्शयेत् ।
दीपमातपमग्निं च रुपमन्यच्च भासुरम् ॥ *...अष्टांगसंग्रह उत्तरस्थान*

Varṣam svavasaterbāhyam
kumārasya na darśayet
Dīpamātapamagnim ca
rupamanyacca bhāsuram
....Aṣṭāṅgasaṅgraha uttarasthāna

In the first year especially, the child should be protected from excess heat, too much light, fire, and untoward and fearful images. This does not mean that the baby should be kept in a dark room. There should be adequate light, but it should not be so intense as to cause damage to the baby's eyes (indicated when the baby finds it difficult to keep its eyes open). Take care that the baby does not look directly into a light source. Often a baby's cradle is placed directly under a fluorescent light, or an electric lamp or the baby may be left to sleep near the television. The ability of a baby's eyes to react to light, by dilating and constricting its pupils, only develops after the seventh or eight month, so exposure to very bright light can cause permanent damage to its retina.

The hearing centres of the brain also begin their further development only a few months after the baby is born. Speech development also depends on these centres. The babies senses and consequently, these centres, should be protected from harsh exposure or injury until they have been properly developed. Any damage to these senses and nerves can lead to a lifelong disability in the baby.

Ayurved advises certain *raksha karma* (protective measures), to protect the baby from bacteria, negative energies and planetary influences. The following list of herbs and grains bundled together creates a protective atmosphere around the baby. Collect some finely ground *vekhanda* (Acorus calamus), *kushta* (Saussurea lappa), asafoetida (*hing*), yellow mustard seed, *atasi* (flax seeds), garlic and rice grain together. Make two bundles like this in silk cloth. Fix one bundle on to the door of the mother and baby's room and tie the second to the baby's cradle. Use a generous amount of the ingredients and tie the bundles loosely so that their fragrance spreads easily. According to Ayurved, this helps to prevent negative energies and germs from entering these rooms.

If you are able to carry out all the suggestion in this chapter you will ensure that your wonderful new-born will stay healthy and feel secure.

- When the natural progress of the child is supported by Ayurvedic treatments, it becomes healthy, which will prove beneficial throughout its life.
- Massaging the child is a must. Begin by gently rubbing oil on the baby's fontanel, and putting two or three drops in the ear and navel. Use oils like Santualn Abhyang Coconut Oil.
- Herbal smoke using mixtures like Santulan Shakti Dhoop, administered daily after a bath, will protect the baby from infections.
- If you apply Ayurvedic kajal in the eyes, it doesn't damage or trouble the eyes, instead it benefits the eyes and helps them remain healthy. Future eye disorders are also mitigated.
- For the child's physical, mental, intellectual progress, and proper digestion, it is important for it to sleep peacefully and adequately.

Diet for the baby

The baby's diet is divided into three types, on the basis of age and the type of food:

1. Ksheerap
2. Ksheerannad
3. Annad

For the first six months, the child should be breast-fed. This is the *Ksheerap* stage when the baby's sole nourishment is mother's milk.

After this, the phase in which the baby's main food is still mother's milk, but it can now also be fed other foods, is called the *Ksheerannad* stage. This phase lasts until the child is approximately two years old.

Then follows the *Annad* stage in which the baby shifts completely to solid food.

The *Ksheerap* (breastfeeding) stage has been described in detail in previous chapters.

***Ksheerannad* begins** with the ritual of *Annaprashan*. On an auspicious day in its sixth month, the child is fed a light, diluted semolina *kheer* (see Special Recipes) - its first food other than mother's milk - in a silver cup and spoon.

The following Shloka describes the beginnings of giving solid food to the baby

षष्ठेऽन्नप्राशनं मासि क्रमात्तच्च प्रयोजयेत् ।
चिराग्निषेवमाणोऽन्नं बालो नातुर्यमश्नुते ॥
भजेद्यथा यथाचान्नं स्तन्यं त्याज्यं तथा तथा ।।

...अष्टांगसंग्रह उत्तरतंत्र

ṣaṣṭhe annaprāśanam māsi
kramāttacca prayojayet
Cirāgniṣevamāṇo~nnam
bālo nāturyamaśnute
Bhajedyathā yathācānnam
stanyam tyājyam tathā tathā

.....Aṣṭāṅgasaṅgraha uttaratantra

After 'Annaprashan', the baby can slowly be given more and more solid food while the amount of breast milk it is given can slowly be reduced. The more gradual the increase in solid food the lower the chances that the baby will fall ill.

Kheer, fruit juice, vegetable soups, the water left over from cooking rice and mung dal or a liquid rice paste, are some of the foods that can be given to the baby between the ages of six months and one year.

All food should be introduced into the baby's diet very gradually. If the baby is able to digests the lightest or simplest food offered, then a new type of food can be introduced after an interval of ten to fifteen days.

E.g. begin with kheer for the first ten to fifteen days, then add fruit juices over the next ten to fifteen days. This can be followed by vegetable soup, and so on.

Cooked or prepared food should be given to the baby only once a day at first. Once the baby becomes used to it, it can be given twice a day. The best time to give the baby solid food is during the day, rather than the evening. Plan your baby's diet carefully according to these guidelines.

Baby food should be liquid/mashed, without any solid pieces, and should be neither cold nor too hot.

If the baby refuses to eat a certain food, don't force it, but try again in a few days. As the baby's taste buds get accustomed to different food, the baby will develop its own likes and dislikes. Your baby may acquire an aversion to foods which have strong flavour, are tasteless or strongly spiced. The baby's food should be cooked in a manner that makes it easy to digest. It is best if the mother tastes the food before giving it to the baby.

Add only a minimum amount of salt and sugar to the baby's food initially. Ready-made, tinned or bottled baby food has become very popular, but it will only put unnecessary pressure on the baby's digestive system at an early age.

KHEER: This soup-like sweet dish, made from milk, sugar and a grain like rice, semolina, poppy seeds or *nachani* (Eleusine coracana), is very healthy. About ½ or ¾ of a small cup of *kheer* may be given to the baby at one time.

FRUIT JUICE: The freshly squeezed juice of sweet seasonal fruits, such as grapes, pomegranates, sweet lime, apples or papaya, may be given to the child. Since apples are heavy to digest, they should be steamed, mashed and then strained to remove the juice. Papayas can be mashed by hand, and the pulp strained to extract juice. Two to three tsp of the juice of any one fruit can be given at a time. Another mistaken practice adopted commonly, is to feed the baby bananas. Bananas are best to be avoided until the baby is at least one year old.

VEGETABLE SOUP: Cook one or two of the following vegetables - bottle gourd (dudhi), red pumpkin, spinach, zucchini and carrot - in a little water, and puree it. Salt, sugar, ghee and finely ground cumin powder may also be added and about ½ a cup fed to the baby at one time.

RICE + MUNG LIQUID: Cook rice or a mixture of rice and mung dal in water. The ratio of water to grain should be about 8:1. The water leftover after cooking the rice and mung should be given to the baby. A little salt, sugar, ghee and cumin powder, may be added to the water for taste. About ½ a cup of this liquid can be fed to the baby. A little vegetable may also be cooked along with the rice + mung dal mixture for variety.

After the first year, the amount of liquid in the diet can be gradually reduced. For example, soft cooked rice or soft khichadi can be given instead of the rice-water. If necessary, this can be pureed in a mixer.

Fruit juice can be substituted with mashed, steamed apple, pear or mashed papaya, and in summer, about a quarter of mashed banana may be given. As bananas tend to increase Kapha dosha, they should be mixed with a little honey. The amount of fruit juice you give your child may also be increased by the time it is one year old. Introduce small pieces of chapati soaked in dal / lentil soup. This can be pureed too if necessary. Make sure that you increase the amount of food gradually.

Vegetables like lady fingers (okra), bottle gourd (dudhi), carrots, beetroot, ridge gourd (ghosali), potatoes, spinach, fenugreek (methi), or padval (snake gourd), may also be added to the dal / lentil soup / chapati mixture.

Grated fresh coconut, chopped coriander leaves, a pinch of chili powder, sugar and salt can be added to vegetables to improve their taste.

To improve the taste of vegetables for the baby,

freshly grated coconut, chopped coriander leaves, a pinch of chili powder, sugar and salt, can all be added as required.

The addition of homemade ghee to all of the above foods is a must. At least once a day, give the child khichadi, plain dal or spiced dal / lentil as these provide the necessary proteins for the baby's growth.

The development of the brains intelligence takes place primarily during childhood, and mental and physical growth occurs rapidly at this early stage. This development is enhanced enormously by a nutritious diet.

At this age the baby's food should be predominantly sweet-tasting. Items such as home made ghee or butter mixed with sugar should be in abundance. However, chocolates, pastry and cakes, though sweet in taste, are heavy to digest and best avoided.

Foods which are bitter and spicy/ pungent in taste, should be introduced into the diet as late as possible, and kept to a minimum.

The baby's digestive system is delicate and sensitive. Make sure to avoid food that is not easy to digest. This list includes legumes, such as chavali, peas, or sprouts, non-vegetarian foods, eggs, cheese, paneer, excess yoghurt, cake, biscuits and other products made from white flour (maida), sour fruits such as pineapple, orange, guava or custard apple. Avoid giving the baby these foods for the first two years at least. Fried foods and other ready made and processed food items should not be given to the baby.

Never combine milk or cream with fruits as this could cause a variety of allergies and skin rashes. If the baby suffers from colds or coughs, do not give it guava, custard apple, jackfruit, or strawberries.

At the age of two, the next stage i.e. ***Annad* begins**. Now, emphasis shifts to solid food in the baby's diet. By this stage the child will have milk teeth, and as chewing and swallowing improves, you should adjust the baby's diet accordingly.

It is a widespread misconception that once the child has been weaned, the need for milk reduces. Our bones continue to develop until the age of 16 and the growing child needs a lot of milk at least until then. In fact, people of all ages should regularly drink milk. Add **Santulan Chaitanya Kalpa** to milk to increase its benefits. Until the age of five, a cup of milk two to three times a day is an absolute must for children. Milk, as has been mentioned before, should be boiled properly, should not be taken after sunset and should be had warm.

From the age of two onwards, the child's diet should include a complete meal consisting of dal/ lentil soup, rice with ghee, vegetables, chapattis, a salad and buttermilk. If children become accustomed to this at an early age, they learn to eat all vegetables, fruits and soups.

At this stage, children haven't yet developed likes and dislikes, and even if they have started doing so, they can be altered to a certain extent. Keeping in mind their future health, vary their diet and feed them all types of vegetables.

A mother who proudly proclaims, "My child won't eat any vegetable other than potatoes," is, consciously or unconsciously, gravely neglecting her child's health. Similarly, parents who complain their child will only eat biscuits, chocolates or pizza, should ask themselves who is responsible for that. Aren't the parents the ones who introduce their children to such foods in the first place to be blamed?

The best mid-day snacks for children are, ladus made from mung dal and pure ghee, rajgeera ladu, raisins, figs, dry dates, almonds, *shashti shali lahya*, or *upma* (a preparation made from semolina). Children also love boiled potatoes mashed with homemade butter and a little salt. This could be made more interesting with small quantities of cooked carrots, bottle gourd (dudhi), or spinach added to the potatoes.

Children should have dinner by 7.30 or 8 pm. Dinner can consist of khichadi, soup, rice, *fulka* or mixed vegetable *paratha*. *Dhirdi* (salty pancakes), made of rice or chickpea flour, is a good change occasionally.

Mothers are often tempted to give one of the many commercial quick-to-prepare, instant baby foods to their children. However, it should be remembered that besides having been stored for a long time , these foods often contain preservatives and artificial food colouring. They are not only difficult to digest, but it is doubtful whether they have any nutritive value at all. Such ready-made foods may be used occasionally, in emergencies, but they are no alternative to fresh, wholesome, nutritious food prepared with love and attention at home.

In conclusion, the baby's food should be easy to digest, nutritious, easily assimilated by the body, and enriched with all the nutrients necessary for growth.

- **When the baby is six months old, the Annaprashan sanskar should be done, and the baby should be introduced to other foods. These foods should be increased very gradually, so that no pressure is created on the digestive system.**
- **The digestive capacity of the infant is limited. It is unable to break down heavy foods, hence, such foods should be avoided.**
- **Even when the child starts eating proper meals, it is imperative for him/her to have milk regularly, throughout childhood.**
- **The habit of eating a full meal should be inculcated right from childhood.**

'Rasayan' for the baby

Ayurved has mentioned special herbs / substances, to foster the baby's overall development. They are to be mixed with honey or milk and ground on sahan (a special stone) and given as a *chaatan* (a paste to be placed on the tongue or licked) to the baby. Such herbs are called *lehya*, and should be given to the child every day from its birth onward until recommended. They should preferably be administered by placing the mixture on the baby's tongue.

Earlier this book has described how gold ground in honey should be given to the child immediately after birth. The *Kashyap Samhita* advises continuing with this ground gold in honey , in the form of *chaatan*, for at least 6 months daily.

सुवर्णप्राशनं ह्येतन्मेधाग्निबलवर्धनम् ।
आयुष्यं मंगलं पुण्यं वृष्यं वर्ण्यं ग्रहापहम् ॥
मासात् परममेधावी व्याधिभिर्न च धृष्यते ।
षड्भिर्मासैः श्रुतधरः सुवर्णप्राशनाद्भवेत् ॥

...काश्यपसंहिता

Suvarṇa-prāśanam hyetan
-medhāgni-balardhanam
āyuṣyam maṅgalam puṇyam
vṛṣyam varṇyam grahāpaham

Māsāt parama-medhāvī
vyādhibhirna ca dhṛṣyate
ṣaḍbhirmāsaiḥ śruta-dharaḥ
suvarṇa-prāśanād-bhavet .....Kāśyapa

On a clean sahan, (a special type of

flat stone on which herbs are ground to a paste), a piece of pure 24-carat gold is ground with a small quantity of honey, in clockwise direction (see illustration), and this mixture is placed on the baby's tongue with a fingertip. A small one or two gram piece of gold is reserved especially for this purpose. A gold ring or other jewellery, that is worn daily, should not be used. The gold should be rubbed on the sahan with honey for around four or five circles, or till the honey changes its colour slightly. This paste should be given to the baby preferably at the same time every day, morning or evening, without fail. This paste is very well known to help develop the baby's intelligence, digestive fire (agni), strength and grasping power. It also helps the child attain longevity. That is probably the reason why our tradition says that the act of giving the baby this paste is auspicious, and blesses the child! According to Acharya Kashyap, it also protects the child against undesirable planetary effects, and infection from various microorganisms. If given for a month, it helps to increase the baby's comprehension and immunity; if given for six months, the baby develops excellent memory, and the ability to remember things, even if told only once.

WATER INFUSED WITH GOLD (Suvarnasiddha jala)

Like the above-mentioned gold paste, it is beneficial to give the baby water that has been infused with gold. In general, infants do not need water for the first six months, but drinking water is necessary as they grow older, especially in summer.

PREPARING GOLD-INFUSED WATER

Boil a litre of water on a low flame with a piece of gold, for convenience it can be attached to a silver chain. The water should boil until it is reduced to half. The water should then be cooled and given to the child lukewarm. If it is not possible to boil it for so long, it should be boiled for at least 20 minutes.

This gold-infused water augments the benefits of the gold paste mentioned above. To make the water easily digestible, a pinch or two of *ajwain* (Carum copticum), *balantshop* (Peucedanum graveolens), and *vavding* (Embelia ribes) and fennel seeds can be added during boiling.

BALAMRUT

Santulan Balamrut, a specially created herbal *rasayan* for children, should be given daily to the baby from the time it is ten days old up until the child turns two. It should be administered mixed with a little honey. It has been observed that children who have been given **Santulan Balamrut** on a regular basis, are good-natured, have an even temperament, cry less, and smiling a lot more. They have excellent overall development, and are less likely to fall ill.

BALGUTI

Another great Ayurvedic tonic is *Balguti*. Balguti is a remedy whose efficacy has been experienced countless times. It helps ensure proper digestion and bowel movement and improves the immune system, preventing colds, coughs, and fever. It helps the baby gain weight, and supports nourishment and helps in the overall development of the baby. Besides these benefits, several herbs in Balguti also strengthen the brain and bones, and help guard against worm infections.

The herbs used in Balguti, work best when ground in mother's milk. Alternatively, they may also be ground with gold-infused water. The herbs should be used whole, wiped dry, and stored in an airtight container. Ideally, Balguti should be given to the child daily until it is 15 months old, and for the first eight months at the minimum.

The herbs normally included in Balguti are listed and their benefits explained in the chapter on Balguti later on in this book.

A complete set of all of these herbs is available commercially, but you should ensure that they are pure and of good quality. It is also possible to buy a ready ground mixture of these herbs, but it is much better to freshly grind each dose as required. If made fresh at home, the dosage of any of the herbs can be altered as required, depending on whether the child has a particular problem. Also, readymade Balguti does not contain almonds or dry dates, which then have to be added later anyway.

In addition to all these rasayans, other herbs which nourish the brain, increase intelligence, grasping power and memory, such as *brahmi* and *jatamansi*, could also be given to your baby. One such lehya preparation that contains these herbs and can be easily administered to the baby is **Santulan Brahmaleen Ghruta** (add a few drops of honey for taste and give it your baby like *chaatan* described earlier). Since babies do not have teeth, *lehya* (softened paste) preparations are obviously very helpful in terms of delivering these important herbs to the baby.

This is the fastest period of growth and development in human life. You can imagine how helpful such potent food supplements will be in the baby's system at this age. Not only will the baby absorb these rasayans faster, but they will also have a greater and longer lasting effect on the baby's entire life, than if they are taken in adulthood. Rasayans are an imperative part of child care that bring lifelong positive results.

- **Ayurved says that if in the first six months, the baby is regularly given gold ground in honey, the baby will be intelligent and have an excellent memory.**
- **In general, infants do not need water for the first six months, but drinking water is necessary,**
  as they grow older, especially in summer.
- **The water should be boiled with gold, and a pinch of ajwain (Carum copticum), balantshop (Peucedanum graveolens), vavding (Embelia ribes) and fennel seeds.**

Child development milestones

There is an inexpressible joy in watching a child grow and develop. The entire family enjoys the child's day to day achievements, and takes great pleasure in describing these in intricate details.

A child develops gradually, in an almost programmed manner in accordance with Nature. These developmental milestones are described in this chapter. The changes are not visible overnight, but gradual progress is obvious over a period. If, for any reason, a particular milestone is not achieved within the stipulated time, (for example, the child is unable to hold up its head, turn over, or crawl within the given period), expert medical advice should be sought immediately.

A new-born child normally weighs between 2.5 and 3.5 kilograms. The child will normally lose a little weight in its first week, but rapidly put it back on in the second week, and continue to gain weight very quickly over the first year. After the first year its weight gain will become more gradual.

Although there may be variations on weight gain depending on diet and the baby's constitution, a child will gain approximately half a kilogram a month for the first year. A healthy Indian child will weigh between 2.5 and 3 kilograms at birth. Its weight will double at the age of six months, be three times at one year, 4 times at 2 years and 5 times at 3 years of age. Between the ages of 3 and 7 years the child will gain about 2 kg per year. From the age of 7 until puberty the child will gain about 3 kg per year. On average, the weight of a 3 year old will be 15 kg, of a 5 year old will be 18 kg and a 7 year old will be 21kg.

Many parents worry unnecessarily, if their child is not chubby. If the baby's development is normal, if it plays happily, eats and sleeps well, and if its physical and mental milestones are within the norm, there is no reason to be concerned. However, if the baby does not gain weight for 2-3 months and is irritable, does not feed properly, or is inordinately plump, then expert advice should be sought.

Holding Up The Head

The first important milestone is the baby being able to hold up its own head. This should be achieved by the age of 2½ to 3 months. The baby should be able to hold its head upright even when it is held on the shoulder or being lifted up from a lying position. Its gaze should also have stabilised by this age, so that it can follow the movements of objects in front of it.

Turning On The Side

A three-month-old baby should be able to turn over on its side independently. It should also begin to respond to those around it, and, for example, should show some facial reactions when spoken to. By this time, the child can usually recognise all members of the family.

Turning The Head, Grasping with Hands

By the fourth month, the baby begins to turn its head in the direction of any sound or noise nearby, and tries to grasp things with its hands. Gradually, it is able to hold small toys easily. The child also begins to articulate (i.e. make sounds when it is happy), and is able to turn on its abdomen.

Sitting Up

At the age of five months, a baby tries to sit up with support. It also tries to move forward on its abdomen, although often, babies tend to move backwards first. A child can sit up unsupported by the age of 6 months.

Crawling

The ability to crawl depends on the strength of the spinal cord, and the spinal muscles. Coordination (the ability of the arms and legs to move in a particular sequence) develops after the nervous system is fully developed. Since this takes a little time, the child usually begins to crawl properly at seven - eight months.

Teething

Teething, which also commences at this age, may cause excessive drooling. The desire to drink milk reduces automatically. The child becomes restless and exhibits the need to chew on something hard. Instead of a plastic teether, it is better to give the baby a piece of carrot, kharik (dry dates) or licorice, to chew on. Generally, the two lower front teeth erupt first, and all the milk teeth erupt between the age of six months to 1½ Years.

भक्षयेद् दन्तपवनं नास्थिरद्विजबन्धनः ।
तस्य तत्घट्टनात् क्रुद्धः कुर्यादन्तामयान्मरुत् । ...अष्टांगसंग्रह उत्तरस्थान

Bhakṣayed danta-pavanam
nāsthiradvija-bandhanaḥ
Tasya tat-ghaṭṭanāt kruddhaḥ
kuryādantāmayān-marut

....Aṣṭāṅgasaṅgraha uttarasthāna

Until the time the baby's gums harden and become strong, it is not advisable to use a toothbrush or datoon (herbal sticks) *to clean its mouth. This can disturb vata, and cause dental problems or malaligned teeth.*

This does not mean that the mouth should not be cleaned. Even a small baby's mouth should be cleaned every day. It should be cleaned with warm water, using a finger, only after the hands have been washed and the fingernails clipped. Once the baby is a year old, or has learned how to rinse its mouth, then herbal tooth powders, such as **Santulan Yogdanti**, may be used. This powder is not harmful even if ingested. By the age of four or five children can use a toothbrush to clean their teeth without help. They should still be supervised to ensure that they clean their teeth properly.

Responding To Its Name And Beginning To Make Sounds

By the 8th or 9th month the child recognises and responds to its name, and attempts to say simple words such as 'baba, mama, dada'. It reaches out to touch objects that are attractive. It will also go to someone other than the parent, if it likes that person. It learns to make actions like waving out, and tries to stand.

Standing Up

Using someone's hand, a bedpost, or a sofa for support, a 10 to 11 month old baby learns to stand up, and tries to take a few steps. It also tries to grasp tiny objects such as puffed rice or *lahya*, and put them in its mouth. Since the baby will pick up objects lying on the floor, you must be extra careful and vigilant at this time to prevent the baby from putting rubbish or dangerous objects in its mouth.

Walking And Eating

The child begins to walk unsupported when it is a year old. At this age, it should also wake up if it wets the bed at night. The baby will want to eat with a spoon, or drink from a glass independently. It will try to put a small glass/cup of water, or a spoon, in its mouth. The child's initial attempts will invariably result in spillage, or mess on the floor/table. Do not discourage the child. It will learn gradually, and should be allowed to eat by itself at least once a day, ideally from a plate with a high rim, so that it is easier to pick up the food with a spoon. If you do not allow the child to do this the child will become habituated to always being fed.

Instrustions And Bowel Movements

The child now also begins to understand when told not to do something or not to touch certain objects. The bladder-bowel timings also become regulated.

Music

Expose a child to good, melodious music from the age of 1-1 ½ years. The child will learn to appreciate good music. The child should also be made to listen to musical versions of traditional evening prayers, such as *Ramraksha*, *Hanuman Chalisa* and various common *Aaratis*, which help it learn these traditional compositions and instill faith in the child. The child also learns to memorise things by just listening to them - an ability that will result in several advantages throughout life e.g. while studying.

If the mother has listened to Garbha Sanskar or any other healing music during her pregnancy, the effect on the child will be visible even at an early age. You can see the extent of this effect because children become quiet easily when they hear the same music that they heard while in the womb.

Simple Words And Games

At the age of 1½ to 2 years, the child will begin to say simple words, especially the names of things it likes. It can now identify common household objects such as a fan, light bulbs, parts of the body such as nose, ear and hands, and can recognise animals such as a horse, cow, dog, or an elephant. It can also say its own name and listens very carefully when spoken to. The ability to run develops at this age and the child begins to enjoy indoor games such as hide and seek.

Simple Tasks

By the age of 2 or 3 years, a child learns to remove simple garments, slippers, and shoes from a cabinet for example. Doing these tasks independently gives it a feeling of joy and a sense of achievement.

Stories And Entertainment

The child also begins to enjoy stories, fables and children's songs and can do a number of things independently. At this age, the child will do things like look for reasons for not going to bed on time. It enjoys watching TV and talking to elders.

Parents and elders should reduce watching TV at this stage, to encourage the child to find new innovative ideas to entertain itself. Instead of watching television, playing in the open air with other children, which motivates the child to be creative, is best. Encourage the child to take up mentally stimulating activities.

Simple Sentences And Self Expression

By the age of three, children can construct simple sentences. Their vocabulary increases rapidly, and the child can memorise short poems and songs. It begins to play with toys such as dolls, cars, etc. on its own, and enjoys exploring and drawing, or simply scribbling, with coloured pencils and crayons. The child also begins to express itself by saying it feels hot or cold, hungry or thirsty, and to make decisions about what clothes or shoes to wear.

At this stage parents should not completely reject the child's preferences. On the contrary, you should encourage its independent thinking. Instead of scolding the child if it is stubborn, explaining why certain things are wrong, will help it differentiate between right and wrong, truth and lies, good and bad.

In this regard, it has also been observed that children exposed to Garbha Sanskar music while in the womb and after, are less stubborn, and are more calm and quiet in comparison with other children.

- **In the first week after birth, the infant loses weight, which is recovered in the second week. During the first year, on an average, children gain about ½ kg per month.**
- **If, for any reason, a particular milestone is not achieved within the stipulated time (for example, the child is unable to hold up its head, turn over, or crawl), expert medical advice should be sought immediately.**
- **If a 1 or 1½ year old child is allowed to eat one meal a day on its own, then the child becomes independent more quickly.**
- **Once the child turns a year old, it should be made to listen to musical compositions, like Ramraksha, Hanuman Chalisa, and other Aaratis. This increases the child's capacity to memorise and learn by listening.**
- **Do not bend to the wrong, stubborn wishes of the child. But instead of scolding the child, if parents explain properly, the child will not develop the tendency to become stubborn. It will start to understand the difference between right and wrong, good and bad, etc.**

Raising a child

Photograph: Shrikrishna Paranjape, Child: Harshad Dhumal

Parents and all the members of the family, play a very important role in sculpting the young child's personality. Children are not only sensitive on a physical level, but are mentally susceptible, and easily impressionable. They try to imitate people around them, so it is important to be aware of every tiny detail of what is done or said in front of a child. The following points should be taken into consideration, in order to ensure the child's successful physical, mental, and intellectual progress.

During the first three months, the child should not be handled more than is necessary. It should as far as possible be handled by the mother, grandmother or other women who are experienced with small children. As far as possible, visitors should be discouraged from holding the baby, or taking it on their lap. Holding the baby incorrectly for an extended period of time could cause discomfort, pain, or body ache to the child.

The head and neck should be carefully

supported, until the baby can hold its head up fully (at between three to four months). The new type of convenient baby carrier bag now available, that allows the mother to carry her baby and still have her arms free, does not provide adequate support to the baby's neck and back. The use of this carrier bag can have a negative effect on the infant's overall posture, and should not be used until the child is at least six months old. Even after that, it should be used only in rare and unavoidable circumstances.

Although it is very tempting to pinch a child's chubby cheeks, please avoid doing this. A baby should not be left unsupervised with other small children.

A child will begin to sit at the age of five - six months. There's no need to hurry this process up or force the child to sit before then. Even when the child starts to attempt to sit up, it is best to allow this only for short periods of time in the beginning. Prolonged sitting, at an early age, can cause the back to become rounded, or lead to permanent weakness of the spine. The same precautions are necessary when the baby learns to stand. It is best not to force a child to walk or put him in a walker. Let Nature take her course, and the baby reach its milestones at its own pace. There is no need to worry if a baby does not walk precisely at 10 months of age. Any forcible steps taken to hasten this may only cause regret later.

Instead of a swing / cradle, it is better to place the baby's bed on the floor, which provides adequate space, and allows the baby to look around. There is also the danger that the child may fall off a bed or cradle, once it is able to turn over independently.

Don't fix brightly coloured, harsh sounding and rotating toys, above the baby's cradle. A child may stop crying when it sees the toy, but this is more from being stunned than out of enjoyment. Such toys may also adversely affect the eyes.

मणयश्च धारणीयाः कुमारस्य । *...चरक शारीरस्थान*

Maṇayaśca dhāraṇīyāḥ kumārasya

....Caraka śārīrasthāna

Ayurved advises that children wear suitable precious stones and gems. There may be security or safety concerns with making the baby wear extremely precious gems. Even so, a small black tulsi and/or gold bead may be tied around the baby's wrist without much fear. The baby can wear a gold or silver chain of a suitable size, so that neither can it slip off over the head, nor can it be easily pulled off. Girls can wear anklets of silver or gold, and boys can wear similar anklets made of *panchadhatu* (a particular amalgam of five metals), but these should not fit too tightly.

It is important to talk to the baby as soon as it is born. It is a misconception that children cannot understand anything. The child should be spoken to using clear and proper words instead of baby talk. Avoid arguments, fights, shouting, or banging things around children, since they become aware of such things at a very early age. It is essential that family members are aware of how they speak among themselves. Derogatory remarks about rich and poor, black and white, or beautiful and ugly, should not be made in front of them.

Toilet training should be started when the child begins to sit, i.e. at five to six months, and voluntary bladder clearance (passing urine), should be encouraged after waking up in the morning, at bed time, as well as at regular intervals during the day. If an appropriate diet has been followed during pregnancy, the baby will not have a tendency to wet its bed and will grasp toilet-training faster. Infants who have been brought up in accordance with Garbha Sanskar have been known to sleep for six to seven hours at a stretch, even when only a month old.

The child does not know fear until two years of age, and any fear instilled at this time can have a lifelong effect, and may even cause mental abnormality. Fear is a natural instinct, and is present in everyone to some extent, but the action of adults should not add to this. Real or the imaginary ideas, such as the police or ghosts, should not be used to purposely frighten a child.

न ह्यस्य वित्रासनं साधु। तस्मात् तस्मिन् रुदत्यभुञ्जाने वाऽन्यत्र विधेयतामगच्छन्ति राक्षसपिशाचपूतनाद्यानां नामानि आह्वयता कुमारस्य वित्रासनार्थं नामग्रहणं न कार्यं स्यात् । ... *चरक शारीरस्थान*

Na hyasya vitrāsanam sādhu

Tasmāt tasmin rudatyabhuñjāne vā anyatra
vidheyatāmagacchanti rākṣasa-piśāca-
pūtanādyānām nāmāni āhvayatā kumārasya
vitrāsanārtham nāma-grahaṇam na
kāryam syāt ....Caraka śārīrasthāna

One should not scare a child when it is crying, eating, or being disobedient.

Give a child educational toys as it grows. Suitable toys have been clearly defined by Ayurved in the Charak Sharirsthan.

क्रीडनकानि खलु कुमारस्य तु विचित्राणि घोषवन्ति अभिरामाणि चागुरुणि चातीक्ष्णाग्राणि चानास्यप्रवेशिनि चाप्राणहराणि चावित्रासनानि स्युः । ... *चरक शारीरस्थान*

Krīḍanakāni khalu kumārasya tu vicitrāṇi
ghoṣavanti abhirāmāṇi cāguruṇi cātīkṣṇāgrāṇi
cānāsyapraveśīni cāprāṇaharāṇi
cāvitrāsanāni syuḥ ....Caraka śārīrasthāna

The toys should be:

- Of different types.
- Colourful and attractive.
- Produce sounds that are not harsh or irritating.
- Light and easy to handle.
- Without sharp or pointed edges, which could cause injury.
- Large enough, so that they cannot get into nostrils or the throat (for example coins or marbles).
- Non-toxic. This means that the materials and colours used in making the toy should not be harmful to the child.
- Ayurved goes on to say that toys should not be frightening, troublesome or unsightly.

It is better to buy fewer toys of better quality, rather than a lot of cheap, low quality toys. By the age of three or four, the child begins to develop its own likes and dislikes. Some may prefer cars and planes, others paper and pencil, so the child should be provided with toys according to its liking. These preferences should also be encouraged.

Encourage the child to participate in your daily activities, such as watering plants, picking flowers, or seasonal activities, such as making kites for *makarsankranti*, forts out of mud, or lanterns during Diwali and Christmas and so on.

The following verse gives talks about how a child's play area should be.

क्रीडाभूमिः समाकार्या निश्शस्त्रोपलशर्करा ।
वेल्लोषणकणाम्भोभिः सिक्ता निम्बोदकेन वा ॥

... *अष्टांगसंग्रह उत्तरस्थान*

Krīḍā-bhūmiḥ samākāryā niśśastropalaśarkarā
Velloṣaṇakaṇāmbhobhiḥ siktā nimbodakena vā

.....Aṣṭāṅgasaṅgraha uttarasthāna

The play area should be clean, leveled, and free of pointed objects. It should be cleaned with water mixed with disinfecting herbs like vavding, black pepper, long pepper or a decoction of neem leaves. Any commercially available disinfectant works just as well.

Children should sleep for 11-12 hours every day up until the age of three. A very young child will fall asleep the moment it is sleepy; however, as the child grows, it is better to fix a set bedtime, at about 8.00 or 8.30 p.m. Once children understand the concept of going out, watching television, or chatting, they begin to resist sleep. Parents and other family members, should modify their own routine, so that their children can follow a fixed schedule. Until the age of three or four, an afternoon nap is also recommended. Adequate sleep allows for the proper development of the brain.

As a child begins to crawl, stand, and walk, objects at home should be placed out of its reach. When the child learns to talk and play, the parents should respond correctly, and praise its efforts.

A certain amount of noise, mess & chaos are intrinsic to childhood. Don't set rules in either extreme i.e. neither have undue restrictions in place nor give the child unlimited freedom. Parents and family should also participate in these childlike activities, setting limitations only where and when required.

By the age of 2, children are intensely curious about their surroundings, and begin to question things. This trait should be encouraged, and an attempt should be made to answer every question in a way that the child really understands the answer. This will foster the child's intellectual development.

If there is a small age gap between two siblings, the family should not be particularly attentive to the older child. In the event that there are two or more children in the family, they should all receive equal praise and everything should be shared fairly between them.

A child should also be taught the joy of giving, for example, sharing sweets or giving gifts to others. This encourages the attitude of sharing.

It is a current trend to send children to school at an early age, and this is good, as long as it is limited to children of the same age group, and involves activities like playing, listening to stories, or reciting poems together. Try and see that there is no pressure on the child to memorise things or do homework. The behaviour of other children and teachers should not cause stress to the child or its parents.

Nowadays, there is a lot of discussion about how to correct children and the general opinion goes against punishing children or being strict with them. But if the child is wrong, then correcting him is not a problem. In fact, if the child is corrected, disciplined, and is inculcated with good habits, right from childhood, then it will be benefitted for its entire life.

The incidence of children exhibiting violent traits is on the increase, especially due to the influence of television, and this needs to be handled with great tact and care. It is better to acquaint children with traditional stories, such as the Ramayana, and other stories of valour and courage and traditional fairy tales, rather than introducing them to cartoons and modern fantasy stories which tend to be violent. Remember that watching TV for extended periods damages the eyes, and sitting in one place for a prolonged period will make the child lazy.

Common childhood diseases

If the child care is followed according to Ayurvedic principles, or according to suggestions given in this book, the chances of a child falling ill are minimised. Having said that, it is important to be acquainted with simple remedies for common childhood infections. Obviously, one should consult a doctor if symptoms do not subside and/or worsen, but it is better not to give strong medication or antibiotics to children. It is important to know at least a few common Ayurvedic remedies.

If problems occur in a nursing infant, the mother has to be treated along with the child. Ayurved has suggested that in some instances, the medication may be applied on the mother's breast, in the form of a paste, and removed just before the child is fed.

ABDOMINAL PAINS AND COLIC

Both infants and older children suffer from this complaint at some point in time. In a breast fed child, stomach ache is generally caused either by something in the mother's diet, or by indigestion.

The main question that arises in this case is - how do we know that the baby has abdominal pain? If the abdomen seems distended, or crying increases if it is touched, then one can safely assume that there is pain or colic. At such times, a paste prepared by grinding a piece of asafoetida (hing) in a few drops of hot water on a grindstone (see Balguti), should be applied on the area around the baby's navel while still warm. Instead of hing, dikemali can also be used. Another option is to prepare a paste with ajwain powder and apply it on the baby's abdomen. Mild fomentation done on the abdomen, generally gives instant relief. The method for fomentation is as follows: Heat a handkerchief on a griddle or a pan, and after ensuring that the temperature is bearable, place this on the baby's abdomen. It is recommended that the mother eat a mixture of ajwain, badishop, balantshop, jeera, and saindhav, after lunch or in the form of a powdered mixture with hot water. In addition, she should drink only boiled water and eat light, easily digestible food.

Slightly older children can be given **Santulan Annayog**, or pravalpanchamrut. These are tableted and so should be crushed into a powder before administering to the child with water.

CONSTIPATION

It is normal for a very young baby to pass stools seven to eight times a day, which may also be liquid in nature. However, as the baby's digestive system matures, the frequency reduces to once or twice daily (sometimes as early as the 2nd or 3rd month). At times there may be a tendency to pass hard stools, or to strain excessively. In such cases, the baby's abdomen should be gently massaged with castor oil. Soak 10-15 raisins in warm water for 10-15 minutes, strain, and give the baby this water to drink. Ensure that the mother's diet contains a sufficient amount of ghee, and that she drinks warm water.

Older children can be given ¼ to ½ tsp of hirda (Terminalia chebula) powder, or ½ teaspoon castor oil with warm water. This oil can also be applied to the anal region.

LOOSE MOTIONS

These are generally caused by indigestion, or impure water/food. This may also occur as a result of teething. Simple home remedies may be tried if the baby is feeding normally, is bright and chirpy, and passes only three - four loose motions in a day. If the baby seems drained and listless and has more severe loose motions, you should consult a doctor immediately.

An effective remedy is as follows. Suntha, ativisha, nagarmotha, and kakadshingi, should be ground with honey on a clean sahan (see Balguti), in a clockwise direction, for three - four turns, and the mixture should be fed to the baby. If the child cries before passing stools, this could be because of abdominal cramps. In this case, murudsheng should be added to the above mixture. For a day or two, the mother should eat only mung khichadi (rice and mung dal cooked together in water), buttermilk, and shashti shali lahya.

It is important to watch out for dehydration in the baby at this time. Add a pinch of salt, and a teaspoon of sugar, to a cup of boiled water, and give 4-5 spoonfuls of this at regular intervals to the baby.

Slightly older children can be given pravalpanchamrut, kutajarishta, or kutajaghana vati powder, after consulting an Ayurvedic physician.

The baby may also have loose motions when new foods are added to its diet, so take care when introducing a new food item. It is advisable to add new foods with consideration, and not to be strict about introducing them at a particular age.

VOMITING

Babies sometimes vomit after breast-feeding (for e.g. once out of several feeds a day). If weight gain proceeds normally, and the child is happy, there is no need to worry. Often the vomiting serves to remove any phlegm / kapha that may have accumulated in the stomach. However if vomiting increases (for eg. more than once a day) and this is accompanied by other symptoms such as a sour smell, or if the abdomen feels hard (to the touch), or the baby is restless, then medicines may be used. If it becomes listless, or vomits even more frequently, medical consultation should be sought immediately.

After feeding, it is advisable to hold the baby vertically near the torso, and gently rub its back in an upward direction beginning from the lower back. This generally prevents vomiting. Care should be taken to ensure there is no pressure on the stomach, or that the baby is not playfully put into an uncomfortable position. Grind pimpli and suntha three to four times each in honey on the grindstone. Given this paste to the baby. The mother should take extra care of herself so that her breast milk has absolutely no imbalances during this time.

Older children can be given medicines, like pravalpanchamrut and eladi vati churna.

REDUCED SLEEP OR RESTLESSNESS

We have learned earlier that the child needs adequate, sound sleep, and should wake up happily. Waking up with a cry, generally indicates that the sleep was disturbed. An oil massage given at bedtime, a drop of ghee in the baby's nose, and a little oil in the ears, a pinch of nutmeg powder gently massaged onto the head after bathing, or the application of a paste, made by grinding nutmeg in ghee, on the forehead, all help to ensure a sound sleep. Older children can be given **San Relax Syrup**, or **Sanbrahmi tablets**. Playing soothing music for the child is good as well. The baby should be properly covered with a sheet or blanket, anti-mosquito measures should be taken, and there should be no direct light falling on the child's eyes.

REDUCED APPETITE OR WORMS

Worms normally cause a reduced appetite, and some children also develop faint white patches on the face if they have worm infestations. In such cases, two pinches of vavding powder in honey, or ½ or one teaspoon of *vidangarishta* in water, may be given to the child. A paste made by rubbing ground ativisha on the tongue reduces worms and increases the appetite. **Santulan Bal Herbal Syrup** is also very helpful.

BED WETTING AT NIGHT

If a child continues to wet the bed two to three times a night without waking up, this is known as bed-wetting. By the age of three, the child should be able to control bowel and bladder urges for a time. Worms or constipation usually causes lack of control, and in such cases, vidangarishta, balachaturbhadra powder, or kruminashak (anti-worm) medicines should be given. **'San Rose'** and **'Shatavari Kalpa'** also give good results.

Another reason for this complaint is local muscle weakness (weak sphincters), and this may be resolved with toilet training, making necessary dietary changes, and the required medication. In some instances, the complaint indicates some other potential disorder in the urinary tract. Children who feel insecure, are fearful of something, or have nightmares, may suffer from bed-wetting. Parents should make sure that the child receives sufficient love and affection, and feels safe. It is helpful if the person who the child feels closest to puts it to bed.

Irrespective of the cause, neither reprimanding the child nor ignoring the problem will help. If the disturbance is not dealt with correctly, and at the appropriate time, the child could enter adulthood with a flawed psychological disposition.

COUGHS, COLDS AND FEVER

At the first sign of a cold or fever, the child should be given $1/8^{th}$ – $1/4^{th}$ teaspoon of Sitopaladi powder with honey. A special mixture, known as Balachaturbhadra, should be prepared for the child. It contains ativisha, kakadshingi, long pepper, and nagarmotha powders, in equal proportions. Two or three doses, each comprising of 2 pinches of this mixture with honey, give significant relief. Balachaturbhadra is also useful in cases of indigestion and loose motions.

Oil and warm fomentation with rui (Calotropis gigantea) leaves, or ajwain seeds is helpful. Apply a few drops of **Santulan Abhyang (Coconut) Oil** on the baby's back and chest. Heat rui leaves on a pan but make sure that they are of a bearable temperature for the baby's sensitive skin. Place the warm leaves on the baby's chest and then on its back. When the leaves reach room temperature, they can be re-heated and applied again. This can be done up to four or five times. Instead of rui leaves one could also use a handful of ajwain seeds tied up in a small, thin cotton cloth. This small bundle can be heated and applied several times like the rui leaves. The ajwain seeds in cotton cloth, heated and held near the baby's nostrils also helps relieve cold. One or two drops of warm diluted ghee put in the nostrils brings relief if the nose is blocked.

If the child has a cough, make the following decoction. One behada, a one inch piece of licorice, one ripe leaf of adulsa, and four cups of water, should be boiled, until the liquid is reduced to one cup. This liquid should be strained and given to the child. A little khadi sakhar (candy sugar) may be added for taste. Children between two to six months of age can be given two to three teaspoons of this water two to three times a day. Five to six teaspoons are advisable for children over six months.

Fever should be under careful observation, especially in children under the age of five. The temperature often shoots up rapidly, and may even cause convulsions, so it is wise to seek medical help the moment the fever begins to increase. In the meantime, measures should be taken to bring down the fever. These include: placing a wet compress on the forehead, cold sponging (wiping the child's body with cool water), padabhyang with **Santulan Padabhyang ghruta**, and feeding the child a solution of sugar and salt in water.

TEETHING

Teething is a very important milestone in the baby's life, and it usually presents no problems for a child who has undergone Garbha Sanskar, and has been provided with correct diet and nourishment. Common complaints associated with teething include loose motions, fever, vomiting and headaches. Drooling, and the need to bite on something (due to irritation of the gums), are also common. A piece of khareek (dry date) or a stick of licorice, are ideal items for baby to chew on. During this time, the gums can also be gently rubbed with a powder of amla and dhayati flowers mixed with honey. This not only relieves teething problems, but also reduces gum irritability. The process is made easier by giving the child four drops of vachadi ghruta in the morning and evening, and by applying a paste (lep) of dantoddbhedagadantak rasa to the gums.

These complaints are usually not very severe, and since they disappear on their own, as soon as the teeth erupt, no specific remedies are required. Expert advice becomes necessary when symptoms are severe enough to interfere with the child's general health. Beware that parents may inadvertently ignore vomiting or loose motions at this time assuming that they are due to teething, when in fact they may be due to more serious causes.

BABY TALK

A child's speech becomes clearer as it grows. Vekhand and hirda, both present in balguti, are known to improve pronunciation. Special remedies are called for, if there are speech and pronunciation defects. In such cases, a powder made from vekhand, licorice, dry ginger and ajwain, in ghee made from cow's milk, is prescribed. Another option is to rub a mixture of jatamansi powder and honey on the tongue. Saraswat powder, saraswatarishta, and other similar medicines, should be used only after consultation with an Ayurvedic physician.

TONSILS

Many children today suffer from tonsil problems, with complaints ranging from a sore or reddened throat, pain during swallowing, talking and drinking, to visibly swollen tonsils on either side of the throat. These complaints are generally caused by excessive consumption of oily or cold foods, cold water, or ice cream. The child needs remedies that will pacify pitta and kapha. It has often been noticed that the complaints persist despite the surgical removal of tonsils. Therefore it is better to focus on increasing the body's resistance rather than surgery.

Simple methods to increase the body's resistance are as follows. The child should be given **Santulan Sitopaladi powder** with honey each morning and evening, gargle with warm water, turmeric, and salt, and be given **San Rose** regularly. An even better option is to take medicines specific to the constitution, on the advice of an expert vaidya.

ANUPAN

The medium in which medicines are given to the child is called ANUPAN. For very young children, breast milk is used to mix the medications. Other options are to prepare chatan (paste put on the tongue) by grinding the herbs in suvarnajal (gold fortified water), honey, or ghee.

Paediatric medicines should be mild, and neither too bitter nor spicy. Powders should be strained (sifted) to obtain finer powder, or a tablet can be crushed into a fine powder, before administering. There are normally several doubts about what dosage should be used for very young children. The medicines described in this chapter, and even the rest of the book, are detailed enough, so that if followed properly, you will automatically end up making the required amount of medicine or dose to be given to either mother or child. However, if you have the measuring facility, Ayurved offers the following simple guidance.

बालस्य प्रथमे मासि देया भेषजरक्तिका । *...शारंगधर संहिता*

Bālasya prathamē māsi dēyā bhēṣajaraktikā
....śāraṅgadhara saṁhitā

Ayurved says that the medicine for a child up to one month, should be 125 milligram (one ratti). After this, the dosage should be increased in accordance with the child's age, digestive power and general health. However, this requires expert supervision.

Premature birth and child care

UNDERSTANDING CHILDBIRTH AND PREMATURE DELIVERY

The birth of a child is a moment of indescribable happiness for its family. It is a great opportunity for the parents and family to shower their love on the child and experience the little miracle they have produced. As human beings we have the capacity to understand that we are part of God's way to keep Nature's Wheel in motion. The human being also understands that the purpose of life goes beyond the mere fulfillment of, and response to, the four natural instincts viz. food, sleep, fear and sex. Man can conceptualize a greater destiny for himself. He has, with great care and effort, developed an intelligence and several other desirable qualities, and created a social fabric such that he will pass on his evolution and culture to a new generation, time and again. Man has conceived all this for himself. Therefore the birth of every child is a great event.

Nowadays, the idea that one should have children only occurs to us after we have spent 25 or 30 years of our lives. In childhood we have the excuse of childhood, and in youth we either focus heavily on studying and preparing for a good career, or while away our time in experimentation or in the sensory pursuits. Either way, we commit errors through our misplaced priorities. And then, when we want to have a child, we realize that we may not be in our peak psychological and physical health. Indulging in sexual activity based only physical attractions at an inappropriate or immature time will cause problems when we really want children. It can cause the unnecessary depletion of seminal fluids or even cause imbalances in the body's vital fluids. It can also lead to actual physical problems during intercourse, and therefore, difficulty in conception. One could have picked up infections, or suffer from ovarian cysts, weak sperm and ova, a blockage of the fallopian tubes or the vas deferens, fibroids in the uterus or swelling of the uterus or ovaries. All these will cause difficulties in conception. While many such diseases or difficulties can be cured through Ayurvedic medicine and therapies, one cannot be one hundred percent sure that conception will definitely be possible afterwards – some things need the help of the Almighty.

If you follow the practices of Ayurvediya Garbha Sanskar for your child from the time of conception (or perhaps even before), without compromise as suggested, then your child is sure to have several good qualities. But any fault or imbalance in the reproductory systems of either parent, or in the process of pregnancy or childbirth will definitely leave some adverse effect on the child.

The birth of a child does not take place only because of the mixing of body fluids. It is the coming together of these physical processes with a specific consciousness, which chooses to take up a suitable body to unfold its own concept about itself. So an inherited fault, or even the soul's own 'programme' to be afflicted thus, could be the cause of a disease or discomfort. Therefore there are cases where both man and woman are medically fit, but they are not able to conceive. It is nearly impossible to pinpoint the causes behind a child being born disabled or handicapped, or why the mother or child had grave and seemingly unexplainable difficulties during pregnancy or childbirth.

There are detailed instructions in the Ayurvedic Garbha Sankar for what and how much a pregnant woman should eat so that neither she nor her growing foetus face any discomfort. These recommendations change for every month of the pregnancy, covering every stage of growth for the foetus. There are also instructions for the kind of energies (deities) the pregnant woman should invoke throughout pregnancy. Besides these, it would be excellent for her and the child if the pregnant woman takes up the chanting of the given 'foetus and womb protecting' mantras (Garbhasanrakshak mantra-stotra). These are available on **Santulan Ayurved's Garbha Sanskar audio CD**. If the pregnant woman has been careful and also followed Garbhsanskar properly, it is expected that her pregnancy will last approximately nine months and nine days. Sometimes though, due to some disease, or the age (usually advanced) of the woman, some past incident of her life, weak reproductive cells or several other such causes, the child is born prematurely.

If a baby is born just after or within six months of pregnancy, its body has not developed fully inside the womb, so its extremely difficult though not impossible to raise such a baby. An eight-month pregnancy is dangerous for both baby and mother and so it is universally advised that all possible efforts should be made to see that the baby is not delivered at this time.

In fact, it is very difficult to raise any baby who has not completed the full term of pregnancy, even though modern science has provided many methods and machines for premature babies. However, experience shows that it is faith and prayer that may prove most important to ensure that a premature baby grows consistently and properly.

CARE FOR THE PREMATURE BABY

A child born before completing 37 weeks in the mother's womb is called a premature baby. Since the child has spent a little less time in the womb, it will not be fully developed and so unable to survive completely independently in the outside world. It is important to take extreme care of the child at this stage.

In the womb, the lungs are the last organs to be developed. When the child is in the womb, it does not need to inhale and exhale, unlike after birth. Among the several transitions a baby has to make once out of the womb, breathing through the lungs is the most important. A premature baby's lungs may not be fully developed, and so it might be necessary to place it in a ventilator to begin with.

The fewer the weeks spent in the womb, the more care needed for the premature baby. A baby born before 24 weeks of pregnancy requires extreme care. A premature baby will be underweight, lack in physical development, have less hair and sometimes even its ears will not have taken shape fully. During childbirth a premature baby may have its arms and legs spread, instead of collected, as happens in full-term babies. In male premature babies it is possible that the testes have not yet separated properly from the main body. It is possible that premature babies may be susceptible to diseases related to the development of the brain, heart, lungs and liver. They could suffer from defects in vision or hearing. They will have low immunity and low energy as well. Therefore they may not grow or develop as fast as other children. Even handling a premature baby at birth is difficult. It is extremely important to keep the baby in the care or supervision of a specialist for the first few weeks or couple of months. It has been seen that a woman who delivers prematurely is often not given as much attention as she needs. It is important that the oil massages, hot fomentation, dhoop, and abdominal belt, as well as all other post-partum care recommended for a woman who has had a normal labour process, should also be administered in case of a premature delivery.

There could be several reasons for premature delivery.

- Weak or deficient sperm or ova
- Deficiencies in the pregnant woman
- Some problems during pregnancy
- Food or action that is detrimental during pregnancy
- Accidents

From the above general understanding we can derive the following specific instances that may lead to a premature delivery

- If the pregnant woman is over 35 or under 18
- If the pregnant woman is either very short, or extremely overweight
- Conceiving again within six months of childbirth (the new foetus will then have chances of being delivered prematurely)
- A previous history of miscarriage or abortion
- Inadequate nourishment during pregnancy
- If the pregnant woman suffers from diabetes or high blood pressure. She could be suffering from these before pregnancy or she may have contracted them during pregnancy.
- Twin or multiple pregnancy
- IVF or IUI artificial pregnancy techniques. In these processes, depending on individual cases, hormones are used to stimulate the ovaries to produce eggs.
- If the pregnant woman has weak or small uterus
- If the pregnant woman has tumors in the uterus
- If the pregnant woman faces extreme psychological stress, fear, disappointment or other such emotionally stressful situations
- If the pregnant woman smokes or chews tobacco or consumes alcohol, or has other such addictions

The obvious conclusion is that one should make maximum effort to ensure these situations do not occur if one wants to conceive. In case a woman is above the age of 35, or has a history of miscarriage or abortions, or a weakened uterus, it would certainly help her to conceive and have a healthy pregnancy if she undergoes Pancha Karma and follows the processes that help to culture her ova, prior to attempting conception.

A premature baby may not be capable of feeding on mother's milk by itself. Breast milk should be extracted and given to the child through special pipes. It is important to remain aware of cleanliness and purity during this process. In the beginning the baby needs only a little breast milk. It is important that unused breast milk also be removed, else it will get stored and cause knots in the breasts or lead to other complications like a decrease in the production of breast milk. Many people start feeding their children milk other than breast milk, because it is much more convenient, but this not good for either mother or baby. Even though modern science has made great advances in the care of premature babies and invented several machines to take care of their needs, they cannot substitute for the kind of development and nourishment possible in the womb. It seems that even after maximum care, the possibility of some deficiency or some weakness in prematurely born children, sometimes revealed much later in life, is quite high.

A child born after full term will weigh around 2.5 to 3 kilos at birth. A premature baby may sometimes weigh less than a kilo. This kind of child requires even more care.

Since a premature baby may be required to be kept under a specialist care for a few weeks, and in some cases, even a few months, it may not be possible to perform all the traditional *Jaatkarma Sanskars*. Only the simpler things like placing gold infused honey on its tongue, rubbing oil into its crown and perhaps applying oil to its body, may be possible. It has been seen that these sanskars definitely help it to recover faster.

CARE OF A PREMATURE CHILD

In the womb, the baby is in a comfortably warm environment. A premature baby cannot be expected to acclimatize to the outside environment as quickly as a child born at full term. A premature baby needs to be placed in an incubator which will provide the necessary warmth and physical security for its survival and transition. In an incubator, a child need not be handled, and it will be safe from environmental disturbances and micro-organisms. The amount of time a premature baby will spend in an incubator depends on its health and its speed towards full recovery. Even after the baby leaves the incubator or comes home, it will probably require more care than other babies.

The baby will require regular check-ups from an expert doctor. Even its eyesight and hearing need regular testing, and you should pay close attention to whether the baby is able to achieve all the growth milestones at the appropriate time.

It is natural that a premature baby will weigh far less than full term babies, and their immune systems will also be weaker. Everyone at home will have to be extremely careful that they do not carry any infections.

- Make sure that your hands are absolutely clean when touching the baby
- The baby's clothes, bed sheets and covers should be absolutely clean
- Use dhoop that gets rid of micro-organisms every morning and evening in the house
- Handle the baby as little as possible
- Do not let guests or outsiders come in contact with the baby
- Do not travel with the baby

A premature baby may have weaker or not yet fully developed lungs, and so may also have low haemoglobin. Balguti will really help to make up for this. A rasayan containing saffron and gold, for example **Santulan Balamrut**, is excellent for the baby. It helps increase the formation of blood and fortifies the immune system.

A premature baby's digestive system is also not fully developed. The diet plan followed for a baby born after nine months in the womb may not be suitable for a premature baby. A prematurely born baby should be introduced to food very cautiously, and the food should be in extremely small quantities. Make sure that the food suits the baby. The possibility of abdominal pain, low appetite and improper clearance of the bowels is much greater. Balguti will help here as well, and so will hot fomentation to the abdomen. **Santulan Baal Herbal Syrup** is extremely useful as well.

It is most important to be aware that a premature baby's growth milestones should not be calculated from the time of its birth, but from the expected date of delivery. E.g. A child that was expected around the 1st of March may be born prematurely around the 1st of January. The child's growth milestones at eight months after birth should reflect six months growth to compensate the duration by which the child was born prematurely. It is also possible that since the child did not receive all the nourishment it was supposed to in the womb, its growth may be slightly slower than normal. It may take up to two years for a premature baby to catch up with the growth levels of other babies. It is important to understand this so that one does not take improper measures in the hope of speeding up the growth of a premature baby.

The therapies and practices suggested in the Ayurvedic Garbha Sanskar to ensure all-round development of the child should certainly be done for a premature baby. These include regularly performing, abhyang (massage), with oil and **Santulan Baby Massage Powder**, dhoop and placing gold infused honey on the baby's tongue. This will help the baby recover faster and fill the developmental and nutritional gaps it has suffered.

Taking care of a premature baby, right from childbirth, is an extremely difficult proposition. For example if any special techniques, like holding the baby's head with forceps and pulling it out during labour, were required, it may have had an adverse effect on the child's brain or further growth. But once such a child begins to grow, it normally catches up with other children, and perhaps some premature babies may have special attributes, which will then begin to reveal themselves. The birth of a child is the greatest among Nature's miracles. One obviously wants that it occurs according to nature's given time and within the correct natural period. One needs to make efforts towards this. Habitually listening to healing music during pregnancy certainly helps with this. The music album called 'Garbhsanskar', mentioned earlier, is ideal for this purpose.

To increase our trust in God and to engender the positive faith that He is always with us is the need of our times.

POST MATURE LABOUR / POST - TERM DELIVERY

Delivery after 42 weeks is known as post-term labour. Such babies have more birth weight, dry, wrinkled skin, and fully-grown nails on fingers and toes. There is also less amniotic fluid at birth, which is of a different colour. The placenta exhibits some changes as well.

6

Appendices

Concepts of Ayurveda

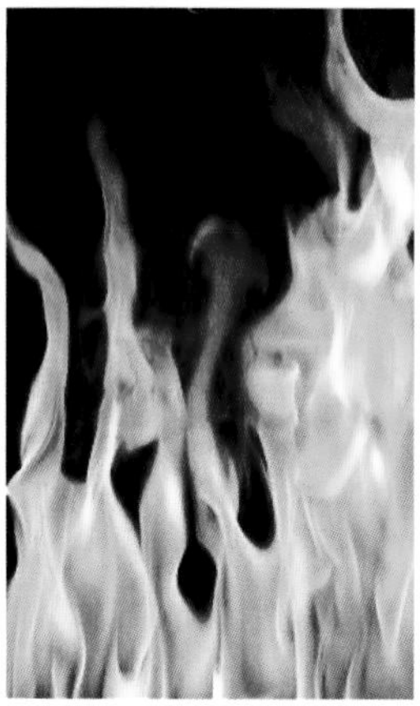

You will have come across several Ayurvedic terms and concepts while going through this book. While it may not have been difficult to understand them in terms of practicing Garbha Sanskar, you may want to know more about them in general. This chapter will take you through some of the basic ideas and principles of Ayurveda in a little more detail.

THE FIVE ELEMENTS

महाभूतानि खं वायुरग्निरापः क्षितिस्तथा ।
शब्दस्पर्शश्च रूपं रसो गन्धश्च तद् गुणाः ॥

... चरक शारीरस्थान

Mahābhūtāni kham vāyuḥ
agnirāpaḥ kṣitistathā
śabda-sparśaśca rūpam
raso gandhaśca tad guṇāḥ

....Caraka śārīrasthāna

This verse explains that every living or non-living substance, is made up of the five basic elements called the *'pancha-mahabhoot'*. These pancha mahabhoot are *Prithvi* (earth element), *aap* or *jala* (water element), *tej* (fire element), *vayu* (air element), and *akash* (space element).

Every substance is comprised of these five basic elements, but in different proportions and combinations. Depending on which mahabhoot dominates that substance, it can be categorized as *jaleeya*, *parthiv*, or *agneya*.

Substances with the Predominance of the Earth Element (*Parthiv dravya*) have the following characteristics - heaviness, high density, imparts *gandhatva* (smell), bulkiness and hardness. They impart stability, strength and compactness. Example: Iron.

Substances with the Predominance of the Water Element (*Jaleeya dravya*) have

Characteristics of panchamahabhoot (5 elements)

Element	Subject	Taste	Characteristics	Action
Prithvi (earth)	smell	sweet, astringent	heavy, dense, slow, bulky and hard	heaviness, stability, conjunction, firmness, hardness, downward action
Aap (water)	taste	sweet, salty, sour, slightly astringent	liquid, lubricating, soft, cooling, slow, slimy, flowing	moisturizing, lubrication, pervasive, softening, adhesive action, refreshing, going downwards
Agni (fire)	form	pungent, salty, slightly sour	dry, sharp, hot, clear. subtle, light, rough	burning, digestion, illuminating, going upwards, transformation
Vayu (air)	touch	astringent, slightly bitter	dry, light, cooling, rough, subtle, clear, quick, easily diffused	drying, cleansing, makes lighter, thinning, provides speed
Aakash (space)	sound	not manifested	soft, light, subtle, easily diffused, clear, smooth	softening, creates vaccuum, makes lighter, creates space

the following characteristics - liquidity, coolness, sluggishness, viscosity and imparts *rasatva* (taste). These substances function to provide lubrication, flow, moisture, refreshment, hydration and adhesiveness. Examples: Milk, water.

Substances with the Predominance of the Fire Element (*Agneya dravya*) have the following characteristics - dryness, sharpness, heat, clarity/ cleanliness, subtlety and imparts *saroopta* (form). These substances function to burn, glow, colour, light and digest. Example: Saffron (Crocus Sativus)

Substances with the Predominance of the Air Element (*Vayaveeya dravya*) have the following characteristics - dryness, clarity/cleanliness, lightness, imparts *sparshaadnyeyta* (touch). Their function is to provide mobility, cleansing Examples: peas, barley (yav Hordeum vulgare).

Substances with the Predominance of the Space Element (*Akasheeya dravya*) have the following characteristics - subtlety, clarity/cleanliness, lightness, imparts *shabdopaadakta* (sound). Their functions are to give hollowness, porosity, lightness. These substances are the best pacifiers of the doshas. Example: Guduchi (Tinospora cordifolia).

THE THREE DOSHAS

Ayurveda recognises that there are three major functioning energies in the body. These energies are the 'ones who function' in the body.

वायुः पित्तं कफश्चोक्तः शारीरो दोषसंग्रहः ।

...चरक सूत्रस्थान

Vāyuḥ pittam kaphaścoktaḥ śārīro doṣasaṅgrahaḥ
....Caraka sūtrasthāna

Vata, pitta and kapha are the three doshas present in our bodies. When balanced, and in their natural state, these bio-energies protect the body and keep it healthy. If, however, they are disturbed or aggravated, they can lead to disease in the body. Since they are independently capable of causing disease, they are known as 'doshas'.

The doshas - vata, pitta and kapha - correspond to the wind, the sun and the moon respectively. Just like all functioning in our world can be traced back to the wind, sun and moon, our bodily functions too depend on the balanced working of the doshas.

VATA DOSHA

In nature, when winds function normally, the biosphere is regulated. Fire burns normally, the clouds bring rain on time, and the moon, stars and planets move in accordance with their planned schedule. But if the wind is aggravated it brings storms, tidal waves, landslides; it uproots trees, and causes earthquakes.

Ayurveda calls the function of wind in our bodies, 'Vata'.

The following shlokas provide more descriptions.

वा गति गन्धनयोरिति । *...सुश्रुत सूत्रस्थान*

Vā gati gandhanayoriti ...Suśruta sūtrasthāna

The above shloka, refers to vata as that which flows constantly and has velocity. The original word 'va' means 'moving speedily' and 'the one having the quality of smell'. Since this function is one of constant movement, and has speed, it is called vata.

वाय्वाकाशधातुभ्यां वायुः । *...अष्टांगसंग्रह*

Vāyvākāśa-dhātubhyām vāyuḥ ....Aṣṭāṅgasaṅgraha

The combination of the air and space elements (vayu and akash) forms vata dosha in the body. It is also known as *anil* or *sameeran*. In the human body, vata starts accumulating in the summer, becomes aggravated during monsoon, and gets pacified in autumn.

Qualities of vata dosha

रुक्षः शीतो लघुः सूक्ष्मश्चलोऽथ विशदः खरः । *...चरक विमानस्थान*

Rukṣḥ śīto laghuḥ sūkṣmaścalo̱ltha viśadaḥ kharaḥ
...Caraka vimānasthāna

Vata is dry, cold, light, subtle, moving, clearing and cleaning, rough, extremely fast, and tremendously energetic.

Vata imparts knowledge of sound and word, and sensation of touch. Vata is the most influential of the three doshas, affecting the other two as well. It has the property of *rajas*.

Vata dosha is not directly evident. It makes its presence felt through its actions. Ayurveda describes vata as having a unique quality called 'Yogavahi'. This means that vata imbibes and assimilates the qualities of the substances it interacts with. In summer the wind is hot, and in winter, it is cool. Similarly, Vata in combination with Pitta, is hot, and in combination with Kapha, is cool.

Vata is also *sukshma* (subtle). The subtle

nature of vata allows it to permeate everywhere. It influences everything in the body, up to the cells and the smallest cavities.

The functions of vata in the human body are as follows

- वायुस्तन्त्रयन्त्रधरः
  vāyustantrayantradharaḥ - The main aim of vata is to 'run' the human body, similar to the energy and forces required to run a machine, and, for this reason, vata is that which carries pran (life energy). Vata is responsible for all the processes of the body.

- प्रवर्तकचेष्टानाम् उच्चावचानाम्
  pravartakaceṣṭānām uccāvacānām - All 'movements' in the body are because of vata. Voluntary actions - moving the limbs, opening and closing of the eyes, walking etc - and involuntary actions - blood circulation, intestinal movements (peristalsis) and menstrual bleeding - are all controlled by vata. Vata is responsible for urges such as bladder and bowel movements (excretion), sneezing, laughing, crying etc. At the cellular level in the body, vata regulates cell division, the formation of new cells and the death of old cells.

- नियन्ता प्रणेता च मनसः
  niyantā praṇetā ca manasaḥ - Vata holds the propensity to motivate and discipline, and to control the mind.

- सर्वेन्द्रियाणां उद्योजकः
  sarvendriyāṇām udyojakaḥ - It regulates the function of the senses and sense organs. Is responsible for bringing about an understanding of the world around us through the sensory and motor organs.

- सर्वधातुव्यूहकरः
  sarvadhātu-vyūhakaraḥ - Vata is the entity that, from the stage of the foetus ownards, helps create and mould our organs and levels of tissue in the body. The development of tissues in the body throughout life is regulated through vata.

- सन्धानकरः शरीरस्य
  sandhānakaraḥ śarīrasya - Vata binds the organs to each other, when and where required.

- प्रवर्तको वाचः
  pravartako vaach - It stimulates speech i.e. helps in the formation, vocalisation and enunciation of words. Vata is essential for proper speech.

- श्रोत्रस्पर्शनयोर्मूलं
  śrotra-sparśanayormūlam - It is instrumental in the formation of the ears and the skin.

- हर्षोत्साहयोर्योनिः
  harṣotsāhayoryoniḥ - A balanced vata generates a sense of well-being and enthusiasm in the body and mind.

- समीरणोऽग्नेः
  samīraṇolgneḥ - Vata activates and boosts digestive 'fire'.

- दोषसंशोषणः
  doṣasamśoṣaṇḥ - It traps and removes imbalances and impurities in the body.

- क्षेप्ता बहिर्मलानां
  keptā bahirmalānām - It removes and excretes all waste products from the body.

- कर्ता गर्भाकृतीनां
  kartā garbhākṛtīnām - Vata causes the formation of the outline (basic structure) of the foetus.

Vata has been attributed the basic characteristics of speed, enthusiasm and inspiration. It even stimulates the working of the other two doshas - kapha and pitta. In the absence of support from vata, kapha and pitta will not be able to function properly. Therefore, all bodily functions are actually carried out by vata.

Acharya Charak says about Vata:

सर्वां हि चेष्टा वातेन स प्राणः प्राणिनां स्मृतः ।
तेनैव रोगा जायन्ते तेन चैवोपरुध्यते ॥ ...*चरक सूत्रस्थान*

Sarvām hi ceṣṭā vātena sa prāṇḥ prāṇinām smṛtaḥ
Tenaiva rogā jāyante tena caivoparudhyate
.....Caraka sūtrasthāna

In its natural, balanced state, vata performs all physical functions, and is therefore known as 'pran' (life energy). If vata is vitiated, however, the consequence may be severe disease or even death.

For this reason, Acharya Sushrut has given vata the name of 'Bhagwan' (He who is beyond our control). He goes on to say the following.

सर्वेषामेव सर्वात्मा सर्वलोकनमस्कृतः ।
स्थित्युत्पत्तिविनाशेषु भूतानामेषकारणम् ॥ ...*सुश्रुत निदानस्थान*

Sarveṣāmeva sarvātmā sarva-loka-namaskṛtaḥ
Sthityutpatti-vināśeṣu bhūtānāmeṣakāraṇam
....Suśruta nidānasthāna

Just like God, vata is present in all living beings. Vata is holy to humans, and is responsible for the formation, stability, and destruction of everything that happens at all levels in the world.

Although vata, pitta and kapha control all bodily functions, vata is the most significant, and the most vital. This should be kept in mind while studying the physiology and workings of the human body and during the diagnosis of a disease, noting symptoms and planning treatment. It is sometimes the case, that even though the superficial symptoms of a disease may be pitta-related, the treatment of an underlying vata imbalance can help to remove the root of the ailment.

पित्तं पङ्गुः कफः पङ्गुः पङ्गवो मलधातवः ।
वायुना यत्र नीयन्ते तत्र गच्छन्ति मेघवत् ॥ ...*शारंगधर संहिता*

Pittam paṅguḥ kaphaḥ
paṅguḥ paṅgavo maladhātavaḥ
Vāyunā yatra nīyante
tatra gacchanti meghavat ....śāraṅgadhara

Even though moisture-bearing clouds carry rain, it is, in actual fact, the wind, that determines where the rain will fall, and in what amount. Although vata cannot carry out the functions of pitta and kapha (e.g. digestion of food is pitta's work and cannot be done by vata), it provides support to pitta and kapha by providing the speed and enthusiasm necessary to carry out their functions at the right time and place. *In the absence of vata, all other dhatus (tissues of the body), waste products, as well as pitta and kapha, will stagnate.*

To help Balance Vata

There are two types of therapies that help balance vata - *snehan* (oleation) and *svedan* (fomentation). Further, snehan is also of two types.

1. External oleation (massage), using oils cultured with vata -pacifying herbs.

2. Internal snehan, which includes both, the consumption of ghee fortified with similar medicines, and basti.

PITTA DOSHA

Just as fire transforms various substances, converting them into new and different forms through its heat, (e.g. butter being turned into ghee. Even milk being fermented into cheese through heat is a transformation through fire), pitta digests the food that is eaten, and converts this into different types of dhatus. Just as the action of the sun or its fire imparts colours to everything around us (e.g. a raw green mango turns yellow when ripe because of the sun's heat and energy), action of pitta imparts natural and specific colours to organs and products in the body, such as the skin, blood and urine. Fire works on substances to separate out their impurities. On gold, it works in this manner to enhance its clarity and purity. In the human body it carries out similar functions where required. E.g. it separates excess kapha dosha and tamasic material from important organs like the heart, purifying it and increasing its efficiency.

The following shlokas will help us understand pitta further.

अग्निरेव शरीरे पित्तान्तर्गतः कुपिताकुपितः शुभाशुभानि करोति ।
... चरक सूत्रस्थान

Agnireva śarīre pittāntargataḥ kupitākupitaḥ śubhāśubhāni karoti ...Caraka sūtrasthāna

Acharya Charak has *compared pitta to the sun or to fire, saying that pitta facilitates the efficient working of the body when in its natural and balanced state, and creates problems for the body when imbalanced.*

तप सन्तापे तेन पित्तम् ।

Tapa santāpe tena pittam

This phrase tells us about the origin of the word 'pitta'. *Tapa means 'heat'. Santapa means 'burning'.*

Consequently, pitta signifies heat, aggression and digestion.

आग्नेयं पित्तम् । *... चरक चिकित्सास्थान*

āgneyam pittam ....Caraka cikitsāsthāna

It is said that *pitta is agneya (fiery) in nature.* Pitta dosha is formed mainly from the element of fire (agni), with the help of the air (vayu) and water element (aap). The synonyms found in the ancient scriptures for pitta are 'tej' (glow) and 'agni' (fire).

Qualities of pitta

सस्नेहमुष्णं तीक्ष्णं च द्रवमम्लं सरं कटु । *...अष्टांगहृदय सूत्रस्थान*

Sasnehamuṣṇam tīkṣṇam ca dravamamlam saram kaṭu ...Aṣṭāṅgahṛdaya sūtrasthāna

Pitta is somewhat oily in nature, hot, sharp, liquid, sour, light, moving (moves from a higher to a lower position), pungent, and with a slightly unpleasant smell.

Functions of pitta in the body

पक्तिउष्मा दर्शनं क्षुधा तृषा रुचिः
प्रभा मेधा प्रज्ञा शौर्यं तनुमार्दवं च ॥ *...अष्टांगहृदय सूत्रस्थान*

Pakti-uṣmā darśanam kṣudhā tṛṣā ruciḥ prabhā medhā prajñā śauryam tanumārdavam ca
....Aṣṭāṅgahṛdaya sūtrasthāna

The prime functions of pitta are, the digestion of food, control of body heat, and the functioning of the eyes. A balanced pitta also activates the sensations of hunger and thirst, imparts taste, lends softness to the body, and a glow to the skin, gives *abha (brilliance), and sharpness to the mind. Qualities such as intelligence, bravery, and boldness, also stem from pitta,* and, it is for these reasons that pitta dominates during youth, providing the urge, determination (fire), aim, and enthusiasm, necessary for work. It enhances our ability to grasp concepts.

Since the main function of pitta is digestion, it is of the utmost importance that it remains balanced and healthy. It is very important that this digestive fire works properly, since digestion of food is the only way for the body to receive energy to function. It is important to pay attention to the kind of food one eats. All of these factors, in addition to a balanced diet, help to maintain a stable pitta. One should always be conscious of keeping pitta in a natural state of equilibrium.

KAPHA DOSHA

The cooling nature, mildness, and mood-elevating properties of the moon, lead to the formation of moisture in nature (*ardhrata*), in the form of strength, humidity, and nourishment. Kapha carries out the same functions in the human body.

सोम एव शरीरे श्लेष्मान्तर्गतः कुपिताकुपितः
शुभाऽशुभानि करोति । ...*चरक सूत्रस्थान*

Soma eva śarīre śleṣmāntargataḥ kupitākupitaḥ
śubhā~śubhāni karoti ....Caraka sūtrasthāna

Acharya Charak says, *that the moon lives in the human body in the form of kapha. When balanced, and in its natural state, kapha brings good health. Out of balance, it can cause imbalance and disease.*

अम्भः पृथिवीभ्यां कफः समुत्पद्यते ।...*अष्टांगसंग्रह*

Ambhaḥ pṛthivībhyām kaphaḥ samutpadyate
....Aṣṭāṅgasaṅgraha

Kapha is formed from the water (jal) and earth (prithvi) elements. Since it functions as a binding agent, kapha is also known as shleshma (one who joins things together).

Qualities of Kapha dosha

गुरुशीतमृदुस्निग्धमधुरस्थिरपिच्छिलाः ।
श्लेष्मणः प्रशमं यान्ति विपरीतगुणैर्गुणाः ॥ ...*चरक सूत्रस्थान*

Guru-śīta-mṛdu-snigdha-
madhura-sthira-picchilāḥ
śleṣmaṇḥ praśamam yānti
viparīta-guṇairguṇāḥ ...Caraka sūtrasthāna

Kapha is heavy, cool, soft, oily and lubricating, stable, gelatinous and slow in nature. In a balanced condition it tastes sweet. When vitiated and imbalanced, it tastes salty.

Based on these characteristics, kapha has the following functions in the human body:

स्नेहो बन्धः स्थिरत्वं च गौरवं वृषता बलम् ।
क्षमाधृतिर्लोभश्च कफकर्मविकारजम् ॥ ...*चरक सूत्रस्थान*

Sneho bandhaḥ sthiratvam ca gauravam vṛṣatā
balam Kṣamā-dhṛtir-lobhaśca kapha-karma-
vikārajam ...Caraka sūtrasthāna

A healthy and balanced kapha lubricates the entire body. It binds body parts together e.g. keeps joints firmly together, and strengthens the origins and insertions of the muscles in the bones etc. Furthermore, it maintains the body's compactness, grounding, strengthens the dhatus and organs, keeping them firm and strong. Kapha strengthens shukra dhatu, and, as a result, improves fertility, and boosts the immune system, thereby increasing

Dhatu	Updhatu	Mala (waste product)	Function
Rasa	breast milk, menstrual blood	Kapha	satisfying
Rakta	tendons, blood vessels	Pitta	giving life
Mamsa	skin, lubricative fluid present in the muscles	Kha-mala (waste products from the ears, eyes, nose, mouth and reproductive organs)	covering, platering the body
Meda	ligaments	sweat	lubrication nourish asthi dhatu,
Asthi	teeth (according to Kashyap)	hair, body hair, nails,	holding, protecting
Majja	-----	lubricating substance for the skin, eyes and stool	nourishment of shukra,
Shukra		----	rejuvenation ofconception

the body's resistance to disease.

It speeds up healing processes in the body and fills up wounds.

On the mental level, healthy kapha brings enthusiasm, tolerance, the ability to forgive, mental stability, knowledge, intellect, the capability of determining right from wrong, and a feeling of satisfaction. Kapha controls lubrication, stability, strength, and nourishment, all of which are important during childhood. It is for this reason that kapha dominates during this phase. In childhood, the dhatus need to be developed and stabilized. They need to grow at appropriate times. This will only happen if kapha is balanced and healthy.

Because of these qualities, kapha is also referred to as *bala*, or strength.

प्राकृतस्तु बलं श्लेष्मा विकृतो मल उच्यते ।
स चैवोजः स्मृतः काये स च पाप्मोपदिश्यते ॥ ...*चरक सूत्रस्थान*

Prākṛtastu balam śleṣmā vikṛto mala ucyate
Sa caivojaḥ smṛtaḥ kāye sa ca pāpmopadiśyate
....Caraka sūtrasthāna

Kapha in its balanced state is considered to be the body's best strength-provider. It is equivalent to Ojas, providing the maximum amount of energy to the body. In an imbalanced and vitiated state, it becomes a waste product, which then has to be excreted from the body.

Balanced kapha plays an important role in maintaining strength, and the body's immune system, thereby increasing resistance to infections. For the maintenance of good health, care should be taken to ensure a proper functioning of kapha.

AGNI (FIRE)

After learning about the three doshas, let us now turn to the concept of Agni as outlined by Ayurveda. Normally, the word 'Agni' , brings to mind the image of a raging fire. Although the nature of agni in the human body is slightly different, the functions of an external fire and the fire in the human body are the same, namely to digest and transform.

In the same way that fire is used to cook food, the agni present in the body digests the ingested food to generate energy. Just as one cannot eat raw wheat, rice, grains or uncooked vegetables, ingested food cannot give strength without first being transformed into energy by agni.

A balanced agni results in regular bowel movements, appropriate appetite, enthusiasm and energy for work, as well as a feeling of lightness in the body.

In describing the qualities of this fire, Acharya Charak says:

आयुर्वर्णो बलं स्वास्थं उत्साहोपचयौ प्रभा ।
ओजस्तेजोग्नयः प्राणाः चोक्ता देहाग्निहेतुकाः ॥

शान्तेऽग्नौ म्रियते युक्ते चिरं जीवत्यनामये ।। ...चरक

āyurvarṇo balam svāstham utsāhopacayau prabhā
Ojastejognayaḥ prāṇāḥ coktā dehāgnihetukāḥ

śānte~gnau mriyate yukte ciram jīvatyanāmaye
...Caraka

Life, complexion, colour, strength, good health, enthusiasm, radiance, lustre, a well-built body, Ojas, and glow all depend on agni. Once it is extinguished, there is no life, and death occurs. Conversely, a healthy agni provides a good, healthy, long, and disease-free life.

The following are the qualities attributed to this digestive fire.

रोगाः सर्वेऽपि मन्दाग्नौ ।

Rogāḥ sarvelpi mandāgnau

This Sanskrit verse means, *that a vitiated and low agni is the root cause of all diseases.*

The agni responsible for the digestion of food is called *Jatharagni*. In addition, the five main elements (mahabhutas) have five *bhutagni* or *panchagni* and the seven dhatus have seven *dhatvagni* bringing the total sub-parts to 13. Of all of these sub-parts, Jatharagni, which influences the state of all the other agni, is the main, and most important. Jatharagni transforms the ingested food into 'ahar ras' (essence), which is subsequently digested by the seven dhatvagnis, to form the seven dhatus. During each transformation into each dhatu, waste products (malas) are also formed and are used or excreted in different ways.

The function attributed to the various agnis correspond to the function of the hormonal system in western medicine. Agni converts food into all the required energies. Agni organizes the natural physiological cycles, and ensures that they occur at the right time and place, and that they are supplied with the energy they require. The concept of agni includes the understanding of the hormone system.

THE SEVEN DHATUS

Rasa - plasma, lymph and all other liquid components and secretions

Rakta - blood
Mansa - flesh
Meda - fat
Asthi - bones
Majja - bone marrow
Shukra - vital fluids

रसासृङ्ङ्मांसमेदोऽस्थिमज्ज्ञाशुक्राणि धातवः । सप्तदूष्याः ।

...वाग्भट सूत्रस्थान

Rasāsṛṅmamāmsamedo~sthimajjāśukrāṇi dhātavaḥ, Saptadūṣyāḥ ....Vāgbhaṭa sūtrasthāna

Dharanaat dhatavah means the basic components that constitute, construct, sustain and nourish the body, are called dhatus. Imbalanced doshas can disturb these dhatus and cause disease, which is why dhatus are also sometimes referred to as *dushya* (that which can be contaminated).

According to Sushrut, the following time is required for food to be transformed into dhatus. It takes one day to convert it to rasa, five days to rakta, 10 days to mansa, 15 days to meda, 20 days to asthi, 25 days to majja and 30 days for the final transformation to shukra dhatu.

Food digested by Jatharagni is subsequently formed into dhatus. Each dhatu is formed from the previous one in the order described above.

The initial conversion is into ahar ras (essence of food). Ayurveda calls this *sthul pachan* (gross break down of food). Ahar ras is an essence comprising of essential food elements, and is *paramsukshma* (extremely subtle). It is capable of nourishing all of the dhatus and up-dhatus (by-products of dhatu transformation).

The transformation occurring after the stage of ahar ras is known as *sukshma pachan* - (subtle transformation into various dhatu levels).

The Seven Dhatus are as follows.

1. RASA DHATU

Rasagni converts the ahar ras into the first dhatu, namely 'rasa dhatu'. The word 'rasa' itself, indicates the nature of this dhatu. It is liquid in nature. It imparts satisfaction, and nourishment in childhood, adulthood and old age, in specific ways. During childhood, it helps quick and appropriate growth of the body. In youth it helps maintain the body and through old age it helps to prevent the tissues of the body from perishing. It lubricates the body, adding to its strength and firmness. The healthier the 'rasa dhatu' the better these functions in the body overall.

The most important function of rasa dhatu is to provide satisfaction by 'reaching' where required. E.g. If you have been out in the scorching sun and you come home and have a glass of fresh juice, you will feel refreshed and satisfied. This is the kind of satisfaction and function the rasa dhatu provides internally.

Location of rasa dhatu: The primary location of rasa dhatu is the heart. From there, it spreads throughout the body together with *vyanvayu*, which is also present in the heart.

Rasa dhatu and dosha: Rasa dhatu is closely related to kapha dosha, as is evident by such functions as providing contentment, lubrication and sustenance.

Symptoms of rasa deficiency: If, for any reason, the quantity of rasadhatu is reduced, the following dhatus (which rasa will nourish) such as blood and muscle become weak and de-vitalised. The face and skin turn rough and dry, the mouth and throat feel dry, the tongue is parched and tiredness and fatigue set in easily. Tolerance to noise, loud talk or even to a baby's cry, becomes low. Even a little activity causes palpitations and breathlessness and the mind feels blank.

Milk and ghee are the best remedies to increase rasa dhatu. Besides these, honey, tender coconut water, sweet lime, pomegranate, apple, grape and other fresh fruit juices, water from soaked *shashti shali lahya* (a special variety of rice which is puffed), also help to nourish rasa dhatu.

Reasons of rasa deficiency: चिन्त्यानां चातिचिन्तनात्

Cintyānām cāticintanāt

Excessive worrying, or unwarranted tension is the main cause for the deficiency of Rasa Dhatu

Diseases of Rasa Dhatu: Imbalances in the three doshas can lead to disturbances in rasa dhatu which can show up as the following symptoms.

1. Lack of appetite
2. Lack of taste; inability to distinguish tastes
3. Nausea
4. Feeling of heaviness in the body
5. Fever
6. Drowsiness
7. Body ache
8. Paleness of the skin
9. Body stiffness
10. Weakness and fragility
11. Klaibya (impotence)
12. Krushangata (excessive weight loss)
13. Premature wrinkling and greying of the hair.

The treatment plan for all the above should not only aim to balance the dosha related to the symptom, but also balance and reinforce rasa dhatu. The remedies for this include rasayans and a diet plan. Since rasa dhatu is the uppermost and first dhatu, it is vital that its balance is maintained so that the subsequent dhatus are not affected. Acharya Sushrut says the following in conclusion.

रसजं पुरुषं विद्यात् रसं रक्षेत्प्रयत्नतः । ...*सुश्रुत सूत्रस्थान*

Rasajam puruṣam vidyāt rasam rakṣet-prayatnataḥ
...Suśruta sūtrasthāna

Since man is dependent on rasa dhatu, it should be kept in balance through appropriate diet, lifestyle, and behavioural disciplines.

2. RAKTA DHATU

The second level of dhatu is rakta (blood), which is formed when rasa dhatu gets digested by *raktagni*. The word rakta means 'red'. As per Ayurvedic understanding, pran or 'life force' is located at ten specific places in the body, and rakta dhatu is one of them. This makes rakta dhatu even more important.

Like rasa, rakta dhatu is also in a fluid/ liquid form. Since, it flows out the moment there is an injury, it is also known as *kshtaj* (from the wound).

Functions of raktadhatu

1. Is responsible for one's complexion and, if healthy, lends a shine and a pleasant glow to the skin.
2. Helps to activate agni to aid the digestion of food.
3. It holds Pran.
4. Enables sensation in the skin through circulation.

The following is a description of healthy (pure) rakta from the *Ashtangahrudaya*.

मधुरं लवणं किंचित् अशीतोष्णमसंहतम् ।
पद्मेन्द्रगोपहेमाविशशलोहितलोहितम् ॥ ...*अष्टांगहृदय सूत्रस्थान*

Madhuram lavaṇam kiñcit aśītoṣṇamasamhatam
Padmendra-gopa-hemāviśaśalohita-lohitam
....Aṣṭāṅgahṛdaya sūtrasthāna

Rakta dhatu is mostly sweet and slightly salty in taste, and at a temperature that is neither too hot nor too cold (since it is at body temperature). It has a bright red colour, like a red lotus, red-hot gold, or gunja (Abrus precatorius) seed.

Rakta can be said to be pure if its stain on a muslin or cotton cloth can be completely washed away with water.

Rakta dhatu and dosha: Rakta is connected to pitta since it is one of the locations of pitta dosha. This is also the reason for Rakta dhatu's sharp smell (the smell of blood). Of the three doshas, pitta is most likely to affect rakta dhatu.

Symptoms of deficiency in rakta dhatu: A deficiency of rakta leads to the following symptoms

1. Weakness in agni and consequently digestion.
2. Excitement in Vata
3. Blood vessels begin to lose their tone
4. Dry and lustreless skin. Cracks in skin.
5. Increased desire for cooling and sour foods.

Diseases of Rakta Dhatu: Several diseases may result if rakta dhatu is disturbed by an imbalance in doshas. *Kushta* (skin ailments), *visarpa* (herpes), *pidka* (rashes, boils, pustules), *raktapitta* (bleeding from different orifices of the body, i.e. mouth, nose, ears, anus etc.), *asrugdar* (excessive vaginal bleeding), *gudmedrasyapaak* (boils, ulcers, and blemishes, around the anal and genital regions, or in the mouth), spleen disorders such as splenomegaly, abcessess, jaundice, facial hyper pigmentation, alopecia, and the formation of itchy lesions on the skin are all results of vitiated rakta dhatu.

Acharya Charak also points out that any chronic disease that does not heal properly or quickly has its origins in rakta dhatu. In Ayurvedic practice, in many cases, the physician has also to consider the treatment of rakta dhatu itself, besides treating the disease.

Clear skin and good complexion depend solely on rakta dhatu. People who wish for skin like this should ensure that their rakta dhatu is balanced and pure. Some important blood purifiers used in Ayurveda are anant (Hemidesmus indicus), manjishtha (Rubia cordifolia) and gokshur (Tribulus terrestris).

Rakta dhatu is a vital component of the human body, besides being an important location for pran. A heavy loss of blood due to injury, accident or in the process of surgery leads to loss of pran and therefore, loss of life. Acharya Sushrut explains further

देहस्य रुधिरं मूलं रुधिरेणैव धार्यते ।
तस्मात् यत्नेन संरक्ष्य रक्तं जीवं इति स्थितिः ॥... *सुश्रुत सूत्रस्थान*

Dehasya rudhiram mūlam
rudhireṇaiva dhāryate
Tasmāt yatnena samrakṣya
raktam jīvam iti sthitiḥ ....Suśruta sūtrasthāna

Rakta is the foundation of the human body, important for its sustenance and functioning. Hence, rakta is synonymous with life, and all efforts should be made to protect and preserve it.

3. MANSA DHATU

Mansa dhatu is formed when *mansagni* digests raktadhatu. This is the third level of tissue, and, like rakta, is also one of the ten locations where pran resides.

Mansa dhatu is important for the determination of the physical structure and build of a person. Its main function is to provide 'fullness' and 'form' to the body. It, also supports physical movements and activities.

Although vata is the force that 'drives' all movements, that movement is achieved through the contraction and relaxation of the muscles (formed out of mansa dhatu).

At a physical level mansa dhatu can be understood as meaning 'muscles', although the complete Ayurvedic point of view on mansa dhatu is not limited to this understanding.

Acharya Sushrut mentions mansa dhatu in the following way.

मांसावयवसंघातः परस्परं विभक्तः पेशी इत्युच्यते ।

...सुश्रुत शारीरस्थान, डल्हण

Māmsāvayava-saṅghātaḥ parasparam vibhaktaḥ peśī ityucyate ...Suśruta śārīrasthāna, ḍalhaṇa

Mansa dhatu can be seen as differentiated into different mansa peshi throughout the body. These mansa peshis correspond to individual muscles as per modern understanding.

Qualities of mansa dhatu

पिच्छिलं घनं श्लक्ष्णमीषद् रक्तमिति मांसस्य स्वरूपम् ।

... चरक विमानस्थान

Picchilam ghanam ślakṣṇamīṣad raktamiti māmsasya svarūpam ....Caraka vimānasthāna

Mansa dhatu is gelatinous, dense, smooth, and mildly reddish in colour.

Acharya Sushrut has described five hundred mansa peshi, which are spread in all parts of the body, around bones, tendons and small and large joints.

Mansa dhatu and dosha: Mansa dhatu is closely associated with kapha, which is evident from the similarities in their main functions - to hold the body together and provide strength.

Symptoms of mansa dhatu deficiency

1. Weight loss, especially noticeable in the hollowing of cheeks and the flattening of buttocks
2. Reduced physical strength
3. Weakness of the senses and sensory organs,
4. Dryness of skin, dryness in the body
5. Pricking pain in the entire body, joint pain
6. Laxity in vessels transporting the blood.

Symptoms of excessive mansa dhatu: Mansa dhatu may increase due to inappropriate diet. It can be seen to have increased at the cheeks, abdomen, buttocks, waist, thighs and neck. Its increse also leads to a feeling of heaviness in the body.

Diseases of Mansa Dhatu: The vitiating of mansa dhatu due to the imbalance of a dosha can lead to any of the following.

Abnormal or disproportionate growth in certain muscles, arbud (tumour-like growth), *galshaluk* (cysts in the throat), *gandamala* (goiter, and swelling of lymph nodes), mumps, gangrene of particular muscle tissue (putimans).

The word dhatu means 'that which holds', and of the seven dhatus, it is mansa dhatu, that specifically holds the body together, and provides physical strength.

The body's stamina, and ability to work long hours or occasionally stretch beyond normal levels of fatigue depends on the health of mansa dhatu. It is imperative to look after mansa dhatu.

4. MEDA DHATU

When mansa dhatu is digested by *medagni*, meda dhatu is formed. It is the fourth level of tissue and corresponds to the body's fatty tissues. It has the greatest propensity, among the dhatus, to increase in volume and size. While a disproportionate increase in meda dhatu is certainly not desirable, it is not prudent to take extreme measures to get rid of excess fat through quick fixes or unnatural methods. One needs a certain amount of meda dhatu, according to individual constitution, that will help in regulating the body's normal functions. An extreme loss of meda dhatu can lead to problems throughout life.

The most important function of meda dhatu is to provide lubrication to the entire body. Like mansa dhatu, it also provides firmness and strength to the body. It helps in the production of sweat, and nourishes the bones.

The location of medadhatu: Meda dhatu is present almost all over the body. It is important to understand that this fatty tissue is what stays in the bones of the fingers, toes, wrists, ankles and other small bones in the body. It is only meda dhatu that can nourish, nurture and lubricate these bones. A deficiency of meda dhatu can cause these bones to become brittle.

Meda dhatu and dosha: Meda dhatu is closely related to kapha, since both of these have similar functions, such as, lubrication, and imparting firmness to the body.

Symptoms of meda dhatu deficiency:

1. Numbness around the lumbar region
2. Weight loss
3. A feeling of hollowness in the joints
4. Unbearable joint pains
5. Tiredness without exertion
6. Reduced activity
7. Dull and lustreless eyes
8. Rough skin and hair
9. Flat or sunken abdomen
10. Splenomegaly.

Symptoms of excess meda dhatu:

1. Fatty deposits around the buttocks, waist, and abdomen.
2. Tiredness after minimal activity.
3. Breathlessness.
4. Oily skin, excessive sweating, and strong body odour.

Diseases of Meda Dhatu: The formation of fatty tumors or lumps, enlargement of the ovaries, hernia, mumps, obesity, adiposity, swelling of the lips, diabetes, and excessive sweating.

Meda dhatu, if deficient or in excess, can cause several problems, and so one should work towards keeping it in balance.

5. ASTHI DHATU

When *asthyagni* digests medadhatu, then *asthi* dhatu, the next level of body tissue, is formed. The word asthi means bones.

आभ्यन्तरगतैः सारैर्यथा तिष्ठन्ति भूरुहाः ।
अस्थिसारैस्तथा देहा ध्रियन्ते देहिनां ध्रुवम् ॥ *...सुश्रुत शारीरस्थान*

ābhyantaragataiḥ sārairyathā tiṣṭhanti bhūruhāḥ
Asthisāraistathā dehā dhriyante dehinām dhruvam
.....Suśruta śārīrasthāna

A tree stands erect due to its firm central core. Similarly, the central structure of the human body is the skeleton.

Asthi dhatu is the core supporting structure of the body. It is hard and firm in nature and gives protection to important organs and *marma* points.

For example, the skull protects the brain, the rib cage protects the heart and lungs, and the vertebral column protects the spinal cord.

Asthi dhatu is the basic framework of the body. It is bound to the muscles by tendons and ligaments, to provide shape, form, and structure to the body. The form of medadhatu and mansadhatu also depends on this framework, and a persons height is entirely dependant on *asthi* dhatu.

The three elements required for the formation of this dhatu are: earth (prithvi), fire (agni), and air (vayu). Although the bones are hard on the outside, internally, because of the presence of vayu mahabhoot, they are sponge-like and porous.

Symptoms of asthi deficiency:

1. Loss of hair
2. Brittle and broken nails
3. Deterioration of the teeth
4. Dry and rough skin
5. Laxity of joints
6. And a pricking type of pain in the bones.

Diseases of Asthi Dhatu: *Adhyasthi* (abnormal bone growth, e.g. heel spur), *adhidanta* (extra teeth), *dantaabhed* (chipped teeth), *asthibhed* (susceptibility to fractures), *asthishool* (pain in the bones), *vivarnata* (skin pigmentation) and *keshalomanashashmashrudosha* (hair, nails, facial and body hair abnormalities) are all asthidoshaj diseases.

Asthi, majja, and shukra diseases, are the most difficult to treat. The medicines and food prescribed should have the capacity to reach these dhatus. Even if a herbal preparation or medicine has the ability to reach these dhatus, the patient's digestive fire must be strong enough to transfer the medicine to the necessary organs.

For these reasons, the treatment and cure of ailments related to asthi, majja and shukra dhatus, require diligent and meticulous efforts, and a lot of time.

6. MAJJA DHATU

The digestion of asthi dhatu by *majjagni* forms this sixth level of body tissue. Majja is an important and essential dhatu, which increases strength and gives nourishment to the body, especially the bones. But its most important function is to form and nourish the last dhatu, namely shukra dhatu.

The location of majja dhatu: Majja dhatu is present in the cavities of large bones as bone marrow.

The entire brain, which resides in the bony cranium, is a part of majjadhatu. So are the eyes, the spinal cord, and nerves, enclosed in the vertebral column. It is, therefore, essential that this dhatu be protected and taken care of.

Majja dhatu and dosha: Majja dhatu is associated with kapha dosha. All dietary substances that contribute to further strengthening and nourishing already health and balanced kapha dosha, also have the ability to strengthen and nourish majja dhatu.

Symptoms of majja deficiency: If majja dhatu is undernourished or if its quantity is less than normal, the following symptoms become evident.

Alpashukrata (deficient shukradhatu - low sperm count and motility, impotence and infertility), *parvbhed* (severe and unbearable joint pain), *asthinistod* (pricking type of pain in the bones), *asthisheeryata* (weak, hollow and brittle bones, nowadays also called Osteoporosis), physical weakness, and various vata-related diseases, such as multiple sclerosis, Parkinson's, and paralysis.

Ayurveda also refers to the core of a fruit's seed as majja, and its function is identical to the functions of majja dhatu in the human body. For example, almonds, which are good for majja dhatu, are found within the kernel of a seed. Apricots (Prunus armeniaca) too have a almond-like fruit inside the kernel of their seeds, which is very healthy for majja dhatu. Other substances, which augment and nourish majjadhatu, are godambi (the kernel of the Semecarpus anacardium), and walnuts. Milk and ghee nourish all of the dhatus, including majja.

Diseases of Majja Dhatu: If majja dhatu is disturbed due to the doshas, the following problems may result.

Tamodarshan (black spots in the vision), *moorcha* (fainting), giddiness, parvbhed (severe and unbearable joint pain), and the formation of ulcers on the bones.

One of the biggest reasons for disturbances in majja dhatu is eating foods that have opposing qualities together (called *viruddha anna* in Ayurveda). Viruddha anna means foods which work against each other, and damage the body in the process. E.g. milk and fruit (milkshakes, fruit salads), honey and hot water (honey should never be heated), salt and milk (salt curdles milk immediately), and many such examples. Ayurveda advises strongly against taking these foods together.

Diseases due to the imbalance of majja dhatu are, as a rule, difficult to treat, and require a long period of recovery. This is because it is difficult for medicines to reach this dhatu and the effects of the medicines are seen only after an extended period of time. Therefore, once such diseases occur, both doctor and patient should be disciplined, meticulous and apply themselves fully to the treatment for an adequate amount of time.

The treatment of majja related problems normally requires an extended Pancha Karma. While basti and virechan bring good results, some specialized therapies such as shiro basti and netratarpan may also be required. Pind svedan - a massage for the full body using a special variety of rice which has been cultured with certain herbs and medicines - is usually quite beneficial in these cases.

7. SHUKRA DHATU

सप्तधातुषु सप्तमो धातुः

Sapta-dhātuṣu saptamo dhātuḥ

Shukragni converts majja dhatu into the seventh and final level of body tissue, shukra dhatu. This is one of the ten locations of pran. Shukra is commonly thought of as semen in males. However, semen (virya) is only one part of shukra dhatu.

Shukra dhatu is present in men, women, and children. It works at many levels. Psycholigically it encourages valour, fearlessness, courage, enthusiasm and steadiness. At the physical level, strength, endurance, the motivation/attraction for the opposite sex and the formation of sperm and ova in males and females respectively, are all functions of shukra dhatu.On the cellular level, it is responsible for cell division and the formation of new cells.

The location of shukra dhatu: Shukradhatu is present in the whole body. The following verse explains:

रस इक्षौ यथा दध्नि सर्पिस्तैलं तिले यथा ।
सर्वत्रानुगतं देहे शुक्रं संस्पर्शने तथा ॥ ...चरक चिकित्सास्थान

Rasa ikṣau yathā dadhni
sarpistailam tile yathā
Sarvatrānugatam dehe śukram
samsparśane tathā ....Caraka cikitsāsthāna

The juice in sugarcane, the oil in sesame seeds, or ghee in the curd made from the cream of milk, are not seen, although they are subtly present in these substances in ample quantities. In the same way, shukra dhatu is present in every cell and particle of the human body.

Shuka dhatu is seen only in the form of semen when discharged during sexual intercourse, or at times, as the result of sexual thoughts.

Shukra dhatu is even present in children but is not evident or manifested. The rose has a wonderful fragrance which is not apparent when it is still a bud; the scent emanates when the flower blooms. Similarly, shukra dhatu, although present from birth, becomes evident only in youth.

Shukra dhatu and dosha: Shukra dhatu is closely related to kapha. A balanced kapha dosha and healthy shukra dhatu are required to ensure a strong immune system.

Symptoms of deficiency of shukra dhatu:

1. Physical weakness and feebleness
2. Frequent dryness of the mouth
3. Lethargy
4. Weakness despite no physical exertion
5. Impotence
6. Reduced or no seminal discharge
7. Decrease in sexual stamina
8. Occasional presence of blood in the semen
9. Pain in the genitals
10. Body ache
11. Pain in both large and small joints
12. Depression, lack of enthusiasm
13. Aggravation of vata and pitta dosha
14. Loss of memory, concentration, imagination, recall capacity, creativity and comprehension.

Excessive sexual activity is the main cause of this deficit, the other causes being masturbation, sexual voyeurism, reading sexually stimulating literature, thinking of sex or any activity that leads to discharge of virya. Excess worrying, excessive physical and mental activity, unwholesome food, chronic illnesses and old age, can also cause deficiency in shukra dhatu.

Once the symptoms become obvious, it is absolutely necessary to find and treat the root cause. Engaging in inappropriate sexual activities, such as masturbation, should be refrained from, even though this may be difficult.

Due to the effects of shukra dhatu, the desire to masturbate may be natural at a certain age, just as wet dreams during sleep are natural. However, virya, which is necessary for the body, should be conserved at any cost. Just as water simply overflows when a water tank is full, only excess (overflowing) virya should be discharged. In practice, this means that priority should be given to virya required for the day-to-day activities. One should at least make sure that virya discharged should not be so much that one experiences lethargy, laziness and a lack of enthusiasm to work.

There are several opposing opinions and on-going debates, regarding this topic, but they arise because only one view is taken into consideration - that the urge is natural. However, if virya is used up for masturbation etc, it will result in very little virya being supplied to the main organs, such as the heart and brain. This deprivation of vital strength means that the daily functions of the body will either not occur properly, or be weak. It is important that we understand all the effects of virya and protect it in accordance with one's own capacity and constitution.

Foods such as milk, ghee, almonds, panchamrut and Ayurvedic rasayans (only if made scientifically and by an authentic Ayurvedic process) like shatavari kalpa, chyavanprash, dhatri rasayan, bruhan modak vajikar kalpa and other appropriate rasayans could be consumed to improve shukra dhatu. Herbs such as amla, gokshur, ashwagandha, kavach, vidari, jyeshthamadh, are also excellent for increasing shukra.

When treating shukra dhatu imbalances, it is important to first cleanse the body with the help of Pancha Karma, before further therapies and medicines. The next step is a nutritious and balanced diet, along with rasayan and medication, to strengthen and nourish shukra dhatu.

Shukra is the final level of tissue in the body. It is the purest constituent of the body. Each previous level of digestion or conversion removes impurities from the digested matter. Shukra is the last, and consequently, purest possible form of this matter - or energy itself. Like rasa and rakta dhatus, shukra dhatu is also in a liquid/ fluid form. When shukra dhatu is healthy, most of the physiological functions of the body occur smoothly. The immune system is dependent on this dhatu, as is the functioning and health of the organs, such as the heart and the brain.

Thus Acharya Charak advises:

आहारस्य परं धाम शुक्रं तद् रक्ष्यमात्मनः ।
क्षयो ह्यस्य बहून् रोगान् मरणं वा नियच्छति ॥ ...*चरक निदानस्थान*

āhārasya param dhāma
śukram tad rakṣyamātmanaḥ
Kṣayo hyasya bahūn rogān
maraṇam vā niyacchati ....Caraka nidānasthāna

Lack or deficiency of shukra can cause serious life threatening diseases, and even death. All who desire good health, should take absolute care of shukra dhatu.

UPADHATU AND MALA

As described earlier, after the first level of digestion, the dhatus are converted from one level into the next - from rasa to rakta to mansa etc. It is for this reason that each level of conversion requires a specific *agni*. The main agni, *Jatharagni*, digests ingested food, which is then divided into two parts, namely *ahar-ras* (essence of food) and *mala* (waste products, for example urine and faeces). The mala (waste products) are excreted in the body's natural cycle, and the ahar-ras is further converted into the dhatus.

This process is repeated when each dhatu is formed. Every *dhatvagni* digests the earlier dhatu to create the next one. At the same time, it forms 2 additional parts, the updhatu (sub-type of that dhatu) and mala (impurity or waste product).

Updhatus do not then get further converted into the next level of dhatu. As we shall see further, they have their own functions. There are seven updhatus, and these are not metabolised further.

Updhatu and mala assist in various bodily functions. Once formed, mala is naturally excreted from the body, but its presence for a stipulated time, in certain organs, is sometimes useful as well.

By-products of Rasa Dhatu : When rasa dhatu is formed, its updhatus in women are *stanya* (breast milk) and *raja* (menstrual fluid).Stanya is formed towards the end of pregnancy and after childbirth. *Raja* accumulates in the uterus from the time of puberty until menopause and is discharged every month in the form of menstrual blood, if conception has not occurred in that monthly cycle.

The reason that menstruation ceases during pregnancy, is that the updhatu being formed of rasa dhatu is engaged in nourishing the foetus and helps in the formation of breast milk. Even when the child is being breast fed there is no menstruation, but as soon as the menstrual cycle recommences, the production of breast milk reduces, and eventually stops.

It is for this reason, substances that nourish and strengthen rasadhatu, such as milk, fruit juice, tender coconut water, and shatavari kalpa, are recommended during pregnancy.

The mala of rasa dhatu is the type of kapha that is present in the mornings, in the form of stickiness and phlegm in the throat and mouth. In small quantities, and in a balanced state, this kapha causes no harm. However, if the stickiness or phlegm persists even after you have cleaned your mouth in the morning, or if it remains throughout the day, it indicates an excess formation of mala. You must administer appropriate remedies to remove this from the body.

By-products of Rakta Dhatu: *Kandara* and *sira*, are the updhatu of raktadhatu. The term kandara refers to strong and firm *snayu* (tendons), and the word *sira* means vessels. Kandara impart the necessary firmness required to shape the muscles, which form from mansa dhatu. The arteries and veins, that transport oxygenated and de-oxygenated blood, are a part of sira.

The waste product formed from rakta dhatu is pitta, which is eliminated through the body with the normal waste products.

By-products of Mansa Dhatu: The updhatu of mansa dhatu, is skin and *vasa* (the lubricating element naturally present in the muscles). The waste products excreted from the ears, eyes, nose, mouth, genitals, are the mala components of mansa dhatu.

By-products of Meda Dhatu: The updhatu of meda dhatu are another type of stronger *snayu* (ligaments). Meda dhatu's mala is perspiration. This is why obese people tend to sweat so much.

By-products of Asthi-Dhatu: Sages such as Acharya Kashyap, consider the teeth to be the updhatu of asthidhatu, and the hair and nails as the mala components. To maintain good health of hair, it is therefore necessary to have good and healthy asthi dhatu.

By-products of Majja Dhatu: Majja dhatu does not have an updhatu. The oiliness in the eyes, skin and the stool, required for lubrication of these functions, is actually the mala from majja dhatu.

By-products of Shukra Dhatu: Shukra Dhatu produces no updhatu or mala. All impurities have already been removed from the material through successive conversions from one dhatu to the next.

Shukra dhatu can be compared to that gold which has been heated several times and is free of any possible impurity. It is the purest and best of all dhatus.

MALA FROM GROSS DIGESTION

Mala are the substances that have to be excreted/

removed from the body. If these waste products remain in the body for any length of time, they can cause a variety of problems. So, they are excreted from various body openings.

Faeces, urine and sweat are the three main forms of mala. In addition, blood which is old and which has served its purpose in the body, impure blood, old and worn-out mansa dhatu and other dhatus that have completed their functions, are mala as well.

Mala will also contain imbalanced Vata, Pitta and Kapha.

PURISH (FAECES)

Most of the nutrients of digested food are absorbed by the small intestine. The remaining substance is passed on to the large intestine where any remaining nutrients are also absorbed, leaving only residue in the form of faeces (called *purish* in Ayurveda). This is then pushed towards the rectum and anus to be removed. This is the mala from the ingested food, and should be excreted in appropriate time, in order to maintain the balance and health of the body.

Faeces is stored in the rectum and anus. Prolonged fasting, eating little food and constipation can cause an imbalance in the quantity of faeces, a disturbance of vata, flatulence, and burping. The accumulated vata, may travel in an upward direction, causing pressure and pain due to the movement of gases in the abdomen and sides of the body.

It is essential that every individual develops the discipline to remove the faeces at a regular time each day. Faeces is, to some extent, also responsible for maintaining the strength of the body. An increased frequency of stool evacuation and a reduced quantity of faeces, may cause a hollow feeling in the abdomen, general weakness and the sapping of strength.

MUTRA (URINE)

Urine is a waste product from the liquid components of the diet. It removes excess moisture and lubrication from all over the body and the blood. The waste produced during the formation of rasa and rakta dhatus is excreted through urine.

If the quantity of urine being released by the body reduces drastically, it can cause pain in the urinary bladder region. On the other hand, excess urine, will result in an increased frequency in urination, leading to an enlarged bladder, and a pricking type of pain in the urinary tract.

The process of urine formation is continuous, and the urine is stored in the bladder before being excreted. The urinary bladder and kidneys taken together (called *basti* in Ayurveda), are one of the three most important marma points in the body (the other two being the heart and the brain).

SVEDA (SWEAT)

Sweat ('sveda' in Ayurveda) is the third important mala, and is a waste product formed from meda dhatu. It is excreted through the skin. The Sushrut Sutrasthan says

शरीरार्द्रता त्वक्सौकुमार्यञ्च । *...सुश्रुत सूत्रस्थान*

śarīrārdratā tvaksaukumāryañca ....Suśruta sūtrasthāna

Sweat has two important functions, namely, to maintain moisture (hydration) in the body, and to keep the skin soft.

If there is a reduction in the production of

sweat, the skin becomes dry, the sense of touch is hampered, and the hair becomes rough and dry. Excessive sweat production, results in itchy skin and an unpleasant body odour. The steam bath is an important Ayurvedic therapy, that uses either a steam chamber, or a hot cloth wrapped around the body, to stimulate sweating. This helps to balance vata and kapha.

Purish, *mutra*, and *sveda* are the three main waste products of the body. If vata-pitta-kapha doshas and the seven dhatus are vitiated, the resultant waste products are also called mala, and this 4th type of mala is also excreted from the body. For example, a vitiated and aggravated pitta will give a yellow tinge to the skin and the whites of the eyes; aggravated kapha causes a feeling of heaviness in the head, and congestion in the chest. When the dhatus are used up, they become waste products, for example when blood becomes impure and vitiated, the skin darkens and this may lead to skin diseases.

It is absolutely necessary to excrete all such waste products from the body, and this is best accomplished through the body-cleansing treatments of Pancha Karma. Pancha Karma therapies have been designed in a way that only such mala - disturbed/used up dhatus and imbalanced dosha components - are removed, while healthy dhatus and balanced doshas are conserved.

E.g. Virechan is designed to clear accumulated imbalanced pitta dosha from the intestines. It does not disturb the normal functioning of the body or cause undue weight loss, or other side effects associated with having several motions.

The following verse puts it concisely

दोषधातुमलं मूलं हि शरीरम् ।

Doṣadhātumalam mūlam hi śarīram

Good health is founded on balanced doshas, a sufficient quantity and excellent quality of dhatus, and a regular excretion of waste products in appropriate amounts.

OJAS

Ayurveda defines ojas as follows:

सर्वधातूनां परं तेजः ओजः ।...*अष्टांगसंग्रह सूत्रस्थान*

सप्तधातू स्नेहः ओजः ।...*सुश्रुत सूत्रस्थान*

Sarvadhātūnām param tejaḥ ojaḥ
....Aṣṭāṅgasaṅgraha sūtrasthāna

Sapta-dhātū snehaḥ ojaḥ ...Suśruta sūtrasthāna

Ojas is the most excellent and exceptionally pure result of all seven transformations. In short, the purest essence of all the dhatus is said to be ojas, and, therefore, it is said to possess supreme power and strength.

This concept in Ayurveda refers to the best possible result of energy transformations in the body. It cannot be physically identified. It is only experienced. It can be seen in somebody else as the glow in their eyes, their aura, their excellent strength and health or their very efficient immune system etc. In short, a person with a lot of ojas will have characteristics like these. We have seen how the dhatus become progressively purer and more nourishing as they go through their tranformations. Ojas is the best, or the essence, of all the seven dhatus. The body is formed from this pure and disease free part of all the dhatus put together. All life and progression depend on this energy.

Acharya Charak describes it further as follows.

ओजसा प्रीणिताः सर्वदेहिनो वर्तयन्ति ।
तदृते सर्वभूतानां जीवितं नावतिष्ठते ॥ ...चरक सूत्रस्थान

Ojaasā prīṇitāḥ sarva-dehino vartayanti
Tadṛte sarva-bhūtānām jīvitam nāvatiṣṭhate
....Caraka sūtrasthāna

All living beings are alive because of good ojas. Life is impossible without it, and if ojas is destroyed, death is a certainty.

Ojas, in its natural and balanced state, is a form of kapha, and shelters pran. According to Charak Samhita, the main characteristics of ojas are: It is sweet, cool, oily or greasy, heavy, soft, spreads easily, and is bright and pleasant.

The functions of Ojas: Ojas is the reason for the existence of the body in the first place. If ojas is extremely deficient, even balanced doshas are unable to function. It imparts psychological satisfaction and fulfillment, and nourishes every organ and cell of the body, stimulating them to function optimally. Ojas controls all physical and mental functions, motor and sense organs, the intellect and the mind. The voice and the colour of the skin also depend on this energy. In general the body's strength, health, and the absence of disease, are all reliant on a healthy ojas.

Types of Ojas: *Par* and *apar* are the two types of ojas. Par is the purest form of ojas, mainly located in the heart, and its quantity is described as being the equivalent of eight drops. This ojas is maintained in its qualitative and quantitative form throughout life, and the definite result of any reduction in par ojas, will be death.

The second type is *apar* ojas. Its qualities are similar to those of balanced kapha. Its quantity in the body is about half *onjal* (one onjal, is the quantity that your hands can hold when cupped). In general, it is apar ojas that reduces when an ojas deficiency occurs, and a major reduction can ultimately cause death.

Reasons for ojas-kshaya

अभिघातात् क्षयात् कोपात् शोकात् ध्यानात् श्रमात् क्षुधः ।
ओजः संक्षीयते ह्येभ्यो धातुग्रहणनिःसृतम् ॥ ...सुश्रुत सूत्रस्थान

Abhighātāt kṣayāt kopāt
śokāt dhyānāt śramāt kṣudhaḥ
Ojaaḥ saṅkṣīyate hyebhyo
dhātu-grahaṇaniḥsṛtam ...Suśruta sūtrasthāna

Mental or physical injuries, any type of dhatu deficiency (a reduced amount of any of the seven dhatus), excess anger, grief, worry, physical or mental stress, or hunger, can all lead to a reduction of ojas.

Symptoms of an ojas deficiency: Strength and stamina are generally low, the sense organs experience a drop in working capacity, the skin loses its glow and becomes dull, the complexion becomes lusterless, the person will experience tiredness and malaise, dryness and roughness over various parts of the body like the skin, eyes, and lips. It also causes instability of thought and mind and too much worrying. There may be bouts of sadness, gloominess, depression and worry, and a lack of enthusiasm about everything. Unnecessary and groundless fear, diminished self-confidence, and constantly falling prey to negative and morose thoughts are more symptoms. This deficiency can lead to death if it is not immediately remedied.

The nourishment of ojas is detailed as follows

मधुरस्निग्धशीतानि लघूनि च हितानि च ।
ओजसो वर्धनान्याहुः ॥...काश्यपसंहिता सूत्रस्थान

Madhura-snigdha-śītāni laghūni ca hitāni ca
Ojaaso vardhanānyāhuḥ ....Kāśyapasaṃhitā sūtrasthāna

Substances which are sweet, oily and lubricating, cooling in nature, and which are easy to digest, nourish ojas. In addition, foods which are consumed in accordance with the constitution, also enhance ojas.

For example, milk, homemade butter with sugar, ghee, panchamrut, rasayans prepared from high energy and high *virya* herbs, as well as herbs which belong to the *jeevaniya* group of herbs, all nourish ojas.

Mental peace, enthusiasm and a happy frame of mind, are all beneficial to ojas. This does not mean simply doing whatever one wants, but indicates a tendency towards genuine satisfaction and peace. If guidelines to bring peace of mind, satisfaction and contentment are followed, this will help nourish ojas. So, following practices such as yoga, pranayam and meditation, as well as listening to healing music, all help to increase ojas. Actions that give peace of mind, such as reading, and engaging in a hobby, also help.

Acharya Charak has described ojas in the following lines

यस्य नाशात् तु नाशोऽस्ति धारि यत् हृदयाश्रितम् ।
यच्छरीररसस्नेहः प्राणा यत्र प्रतिष्ठिताः ।। ...*चरक सूत्रस्थान*

Yasya nāśāt tu nāśo~sti dhāri yat hṛdayāśritam
Yaccharīrara-sasnehaḥ prāṇā yatra pratiṣṭhitāḥ
....Caraka sūtrasthāna

Ojas is that which is the essence of all dhatus, which is stored in the heart, and which, if destroyed, can cause the destruction of the body. Pran resides in ojas and for this reason, ojas should be conserved and protected.

PRAN

अग्निः सोमो वायुः सत्त्वं रजस्तमः पञ्चेन्द्रियाणि भूतात्मेति प्राणाः । ...*सुश्रुत शारीरस्थान*

Agniḥ somo vāyuḥ sattvam rajastamaḥ pañcendriyāṇi bhūtātmeti prāṇāḥ ....Suśruta śārīrasthāna

Pran is the principal energy that allows life to continue. The main activity of Pran comes through the following 12 spheres of action - knows as *Dwadasha* (12) *Pran.* These 12 things sustain life. Pran is identified, and also expresses itself, through them:

1. Agni - Fire - The Catlytic Agent
2. Som - Liquidity. This is represented by kapha, rasa and shukra. It is the carrier of the conceptual pragramme of the person, or the mind.
3. Vayu (as explained earlier)
4. Sattva - to act without expectation
5. Raja - to act with expectation
6. Tama - to expect without action
7. Shrotrendriya (sense of sound)
8. Chakshurendriya (sense of vision)
9. Rasanendriya (sense of taste)
10. Ghranendriya (sense of smell)
11. Sparshanendriya (sense of taste)
12. Bhutatma (jeevatma- soul)

PRANAYATANA (The Locations of Pran)

दशैवायतनान्याहुः प्राणा येषु प्रतिष्ठिताः ।
शंखौमर्मत्रयं कण्ठो रक्तं शुक्रौजसी गुदम् ॥... *चरक सूत्रस्थान*

Daśaivāyatanānyāhuḥ prāṇā yeṣu pratiṣṭhitāḥ
śaṅkhau-marma-trayam kaṇṭho raktam śukraujasī gudam ...Caraka sūtrasthāna

The locations where the pran resides in the body, are known as pranayatan, and are as follows: the heart, urinary bladder along with the kidneys and the head (brain) - are the three most important. Then - the two shankhamarma (temples on either side of the head), the throat, rakta dhatu, shukra dhatu, ojas, and the anus. Any damage, injury, or deformation of these can lead to death.

MERUDANDA

This is actually a synonym for the vertebral column or spine, which is made up of 33 vertebrae, with a flexible and soft inter-vertebral disc between each of these. This disc serves to prevent wear and tear caused by friction between two adjacent vertebrae.

The spinal cord extends from the neck to the sacrum. The cranial and spinal nerves leaving these foramina (openings in the spinal column), spread all over the body. It is because of this unique vertebral column, that we stand erect.

Kundalini Massage

This is a specialised massage for the entire vertebral column and back. A specialised oil for the spine, such as **Santulan Kundalini Oi**l which has been cultured with several herbs is used to massage the entire back.

The kundalini massage helps prevent and treat ailments such as backaches, slipped disc, spondilitis, stiff neck, frozen shoulder and sciatica, as well as in symptoms arising from excessive vertebral degeneration.

This massage should be done by a trained Ayurvedic therapist using **Santulan Kundalini Oil**. Simply applying **Santulan Kundalini Oil** on the back is also beneficial and provides relief.

ARTAV

रसादेव रजः स्त्रीणां मासि मासि त्र्यहं स्त्रवेत् ।
तद् वर्षाद् द्वादशादूर्ध्वं याति पञ्चशतः क्षयम् ॥

मासेन रसः शुक्रं स्त्रीणां चार्तवं भवति ॥...*सुश्रुत सूत्रस्थान*

Rasādeva rajaḥ strīṇām
māsi māsi tryaham stravet
Tad varṣād dvādaśādūrdhva
yāti pañcaśataḥ kṣayam

Māsena rasaḥ śukram
strīṇām cārtavam bhavati ...Suśruta sūtrasthāna

With puberty, usually around the age of twelve, bleeding occurs every month, marking the onset of menstruation (menarche). This is also known as *artav*, *stripushpa*, or *raja*. The bleeding is called artavdarshan (presence of bleeding). *Menstruation ceases around the age of fifty,* heralding the onset of menopause (known as *rajonivrutti*).

The twelve days following the fourth day of menstruation (and after having bathed on the fourth day), are favourable for conception, and during this phase, the woman is called *rutumati.*

PANCHA KARMA

यदीरयेद् बहिर्दोषान् पञ्चधा शोधनं च यत् ।
निरूहो वमनं कायशिरोरेकोऽस्त्रविस्त्रुति ॥...*वाग्भट सूत्रस्थान*

Yadīrayedbahirdoṣān pañcadhā
śodhanam ca yat
Nirūho vamanam kāya-
śiroreko~stravistruti ...Vāgbhaṭa sūtrasthāna

Ayurveda outlines five purification procedures, collectively called Pancha Karma.

These procedures remove excess, vitiated, and aggravated doshas from the body, from both upper and lower openings of the body.

Pancha Karma encompasses the following:

Vaman (to expel kapha dosha), virechan (to remove pitta), shirovirechan (for diseases of head, neck, shoulder, i.e. organs above shoulder level), basti (to balance vata dosha), and raktamokshan (blood-letting - for blood-related disorders).

Before these therapies are administered, the following preparatory procedures, known as *purva karma*, must be completed. They are -

Snehan - Consists of external and internal lubrication by oil massage and the drinking of ghee. This gives softness to the body and lubricates it. It balances vata. It loosens toxins that they can be expelled in the process of Pancha Karma.

Svedan - Liquefies the vitiated doshas to make them fluid, removes the toxins from their original places, brings them into the bloodstream, and transports the doshas to the digestive tract to be expelled.

RASAYANCHIKITSA

लाभोपायो हि शस्तानां रसादीनां रसायनम् ।... *चरक चिकित्सास्थान*

Lābhopāyo hi śastānām rasādīnām rasāyanam
....Caraka cikitsāsthāna

The treatment that leads to the formation of excellent rasa, rakta, and other dhatus, is called rasayan chikitsa. The medicines and herbs required for this treatment, are known as rasayans.

Advantages of rasayanchikitsa: These remedies impart longevity, increase physical strength and tolerance, foster a sound memory, excellent health and youth, lend glow, lustre, an excellent skin colour, strong voice, clear speech, an excellent functioning of the sense organs. Ayurveda explains that these benefits of rasayan chikitsa have several desirable effects that come along with excellent health, including, a greater social life, status and success.

Types of Rasayan Chikitsa
(Medication Therapies)

1. **Kutipraveshika:** A prolonged therapy in which a person lives isolated and without contact in a cottage and consumes rasayans and food as recommended and given (again without contact, for e.g. by sliding the food and medicines through a hatch). 'Kuti' means cottage.

2. **Vatatapik:** Undergoing rasayan chikitsa (a diet of herbal preparations and food) while living a normal daily life. Both Kutipraveshika and Vatatapik therapies have been designed for maintaining health, rejuvenating the body, and achieving a long life. They should be done when one is already healthy.

3. **Naimittik:** Taking herbs and medicines meant to deal with specific diseases and imbalances.

4. **Achar rasayan:** Guidance with regard to appropriate behaviour and the lifestyle to be followed.

GARBHA SANSKAR

शुक्रशोणितजीवसंयोगे तु खलु कुक्षिगते गर्भसंज्ञां भवति ।
... *चरक शारीरस्थान*

śukra-śoṇita-jīva-samyoge tu khalu kukṣi-gate garbhasañjñām bhavati ...Caraka śārīrasthāna

According to Ayurveda, a foetus is not just a physical body, but is formed from the male and female reproductive cells, the *atma* (soul), mind, intellect, the five elements (*panchamahabhoot*), and consciousness (*chetanadhisthan*). From the third month onwards, the foetus can feel happiness and joy. By the fourth to fifth month the consciousness begins to express itself, the mind and body come closer, and are bound together. At this time, the foetus can be influenced by sound and this must be used to help develop the foetus at all three levels - physically, psychologically and spiritually. This culturing (*sanskar*) is the most important part of Garbha Sanskar.

Investigations during pregnancy

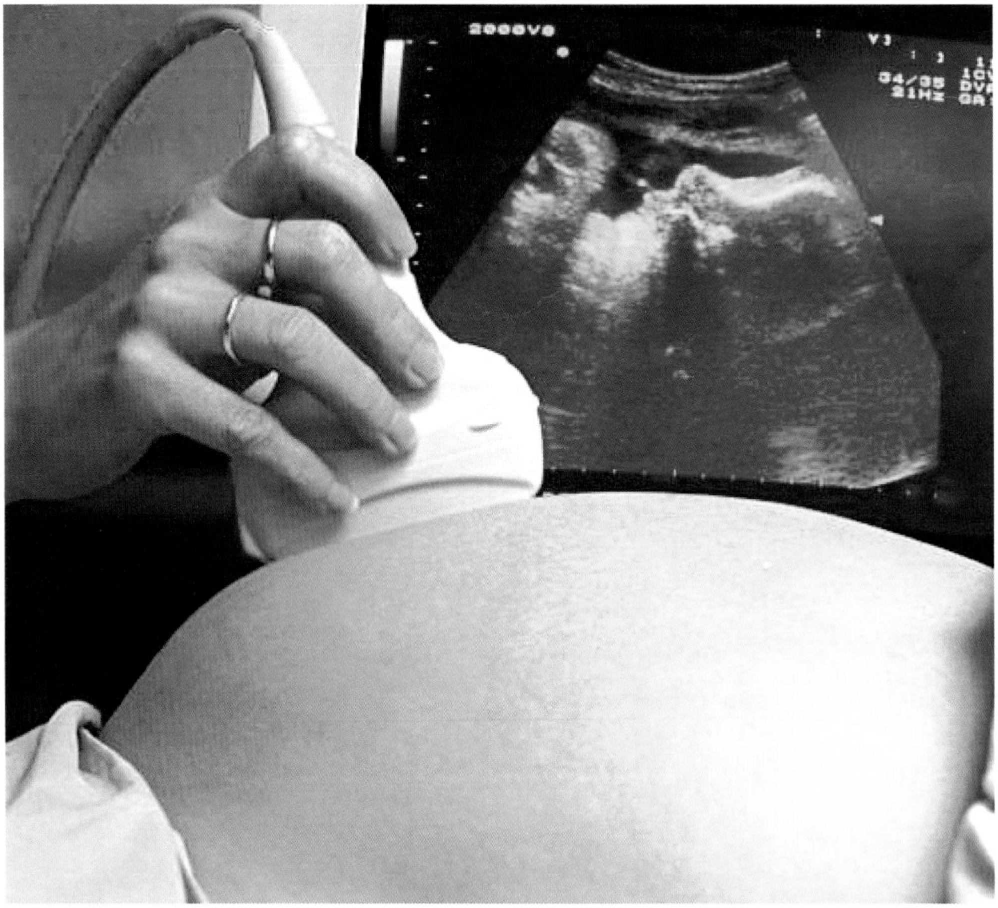

Some investigations are advisable during pregnancy, to ensure the well being of both, the mother and the foetus. However, they need to be done with extreme care so that no harm comes to the mother-to-be and her child. Only very few and necessary tests should be conducted during pregnancy. They are listed here with some information about each.

1. Blood tests

a) **Haemoglobin:** The pregnant woman is susceptible to low haemoglobin since she nourishes both herself and the baby within her. If there are signs of haemoglobin deficiency (anaemia), it is better to focus on correcting her diet, and on the intake of Ayurvedic medicines to normalise the haemoglobin levels, rather than repeating blood tests unnecessarily.

b) **Blood sugar:** There may be some fluctuations in the blood sugar levels during pregnancy, due to changes in carbohydrate metabolism. It is vital that the blood sugar levels be monitored on a regular basis if there is a sudden increase in weight, and an existing family history of either diabetes or idiopathic abortions (miscarriages due to unknown cause). An increase in blood sugar levels at this time may not necessarily mean diabetes. To begin insulin treatment or other medication in such circumstances may harm the foetus. It is better, instead, to control sugar levels by controlling the diet and relying on natural Ayurvedic remedies

c) **HIV and Hepatitis B:** Tests for these conditions are now mandatory, prior to delivery.

d) **Determination of blood group:** It is vital for the pregnant woman to know her blood group in case of an emergency. In the event that her blood group is Rh negative, appropriate measures can be taken early in order to safeguard her health and that of the foetus.

It is advisable that all blood tests be carried out in one sitting to avoid drawing blood from the pregnant woman again and again. If absolutely necessary, only the haemoglobin tests may be repeated.

2. Blood pressure :

In some cases, blood pressure tends to increase towards the end of pregnancy, so this should be checked regularly, particularly during the last trimester. This is all the more necessary if there is swelling in the feet or body, or bouts of giddiness. In most cases, blood pressure returns to normal after delivery.

3. Urine check :

The kidneys (urinary system) of the expectant mother, are under pressure, as they have the dual responsibility of excreting wastes from her body as well as from the foetus. For this reason, it is normal to find traces of albumin or sugar in the urine. If this is the case, no treatment is required. But if these levels, especially albumin, are found to be abnormally high, it could affect the nutrition of the foetus. The following symptoms require that an urgent urine test be carried out - swelling around the eyes, burning urination, itchiness, frequent urge to urinate or white discharge (of watery or yoghurt-like consistency).

Please seek expert medical advice if the levels of albumin are very high or present consistently in urine.

4. Sonography :

Sonography, where sound waves are used as an investigative method, when discovered, was propagated as harmless to mother and child. It is a common practice these days to regularly have sonography tests conducted during pregnancy. But modern science has now discovered that repeating sonography tests could harm the baby's brain.

The investigation may be performed once, during the 4th or 5th month of pregnancy, to check for any physical abnormalities or genetic defects. It should be repeated only if any specific irregularities have been found. Unnecessary repetitions for any other reasons, like checking the growth of the baby, should be avoided.

5. X- Rays :

These are usually avoided during pregnancy. If unavoidable, they should not be taken during the first trimester. Exposure to these harmful rays can cause severe side effects to the foetus, such as genetic mutations, cancer, or growth defects (teratogenesis), to name a few.

General rules for investigations and tests

1. Only those tests which are absolutely necessary for certain diagnostic purposes, should be conducted.
2. Repetition of tests should be kept to a bare minimum.
3. This also applies to blood tests, as the experience of a needle piercing and drawing of blood is not advisable during pregnancy.

Table for calculating delivery date (EDD)

Jan	1	2	3	4	5	6	7	8	9	10	11	12	13	14	15	16	17	18	19	20	21	22	23	24	25	26	27	28	29	30	31	
Oct	8	9	10	11	12	13	14	15	16	17	18	19	20	21	22	23	24	25	26	27	28	29	30	31	1	2	3	4	5	6	7	Nov
Feb.	1	2	3	4	5	6	7	8	9	10	11	12	13	14	15	16	17	18	19	20	21	22	23	24	25	26	27	28				
Nov	8	9	10	11	12	13	14	15	16	17	18	19	20	21	22	23	24	25	26	27	28	29	30	1	2	3	4	5				Dec
Mar	1	2	3	4	5	6	7	8	9	10	11	12	13	14	15	16	17	18	19	20	21	22	23	24	25	26	27	28	29	30	31	
Dec	6	7	8	9	10	11	12	13	14	15	16	17	18	19	20	21	22	23	24	25	26	27	28	29	30	31	1	2	3	4	5	Jan
Apr	1	2	3	4	5	6	7	8	9	10	11	12	13	14	15	16	17	18	19	20	21	22	23	24	25	26	27	28	29	30		
Jan	6	7	8	9	10	11	12	13	14	15	16	17	18	19	20	21	22	23	24	25	26	27	28	29	30	31	1	2	3	4		Feb
May	1	2	3	4	5	6	7	8	9	10	11	12	13	14	15	16	17	18	19	20	21	22	23	24	25	26	27	28	29	30	31	
Feb.	5	6	7	8	9	10	11	12	13	14	15	16	17	18	19	20	21	22	23	24	25	26	27	28	1	2	3	4	5	6	7	Mar
June	1	2	3	4	5	6	7	8	9	10	11	12	13	14	15	16	17	18	19	20	21	22	23	24	25	26	27	28	29	30		
Mar	8	9	10	11	12	13	14	15	16	17	18	19	20	21	22	23	24	25	26	27	28	29	30	31	1	2	3	4	5	6		Apr
July	1	2	3	4	5	6	7	8	9	10	11	12	13	14	15	16	17	18	19	20	21	22	23	24	25	26	27	28	29	30	31	
Apr	7	8	9	10	11	12	13	14	15	16	17	18	19	20	21	22	23	24	25	26	27	28	29	30	1	2	3	4	5	6	7	May
Aug	1	2	3	4	5	6	7	8	9	10	11	12	13	14	15	16	17	18	19	20	21	22	23	24	25	26	27	28	29	30	31	
May	8	9	10	11	12	13	14	15	16	17	18	19	20	21	22	23	24	25	26	27	28	29	30	31	1	2	3	4	5	6	7	
Sept	1	2	3	4	5	6	7	8	9	10	11	12	13	14	15	16	17	18	19	20	21	22	23	24	25	26	27	28	29	30		
June	8	9	10	11	12	13	14	15	16	17	18	19	20	21	22	23	24	25	26	27	28	29	30	1	2	3	4	5	6	7		July
Oct	1	2	3	4	5	6	7	8	9	10	11	12	13	14	15	16	17	18	19	20	21	22	23	24	25	26	27	28	29	30	31	
July	8	9	10	11	12	13	14	15	16	17	18	19	20	21	22	23	24	25	26	27	28	29	30	31	1	2	3	4	5	6	7	Aug
Nov	1	2	3	4	5	6	7	8	9	10	11	12	13	14	15	16	17	18	19	20	21	22	23	24	25	26	27	28	29	30		
Aug	8	9	10	11	12	13	14	15	16	17	18	19	20	21	22	23	24	25	26	27	28	29	30	31	1	2	3	4	5	6		Sept
Dec	1	2	3	4	5	6	7	8	9	10	11	12	13	14	15	16	17	18	19	20	21	22	23	24	25	26	27	28	29	30	31	
Aept	7	8	9	10	11	12	13	14	15	16	17	18	19	20	21	22	23	24	25	26	27	28	29	30	1	2	3	4	5	6	7	Oct

Instructions for the use of the above table

Find the date of your LMP (last menstrual period) in the row of unshaded boxes. The date shown below this is the EDD (expected date of delivery). The actual date could be within the span of eight days on either side of the EDD. According to Ayurvedic literature, the duration of pregnancy is nine months and nine days. Counted in this manner, the EDD falls four to five days before that acquired from the table. Example: If LMP is January 1 then due date is October 8, ± eight days, indicating anytime between 1 to 15 October.

Family Planning

Family planning is a necessity in these modern times. While we have developed several methods of family planning, we need to ensure that neither partner is adversely affected by the methods we choose to employ. Let us take a look at the various methods and their effects.

1. **Spermicidal chemical jellies, foam liquid and creams for females:** These are applied internally (in the vagina) before sexual intercourse. There is a possibility that such chemicals have side effects on the vaginal tissues.
2. **Diaphragm** (a thin coating placed on the cervix): The woman can insert this herself prior to sexual intercourse, but it is tedious, and has to be learned from a medical practitioner. The diaphragm needs to be used in conjunction with the spermicidal products mentioned above, and can produce the same side effects.
3. **Condom for men:** This is the simplest method and least harmful for both the partners. It should be used only during the Rutukal (fertile period), and need not be used at other times. Take care that the condom is intact before you use it.
4. **Loop or copper T:** These devices are implanted in the uterus. Urinary and vaginal infections are common side effects in many women who use this method. It may also lead to excess menstrual bleeding which persists long after the loop or Copper T has been removed. Some women even tend to gain a lot of weight due to these side effects. All in all, an unhealthy method of contraception.
5. **Contraceptive pills:** It has been propagated for many years that these pills do not have any side effects. But in practice, it is obvious that regular use causes weight gain, skin pigmentation, and deterioration of the health in general. Research has proved beyond doubt that the long-term effects of contraceptive pills are severe. Hence, it is advised that contraceptive pills be avoided.
6. **Rhythm techniques:** This involves avoiding sexual intercourse during a specific period of the menstrual cycle. Ovulation is possible from the first day of menstruation onwards until 16 days after. So from the first day of menstruation onwards for 18 days (two days after possible ovulation) sexual intercourse should either be avoided or performed with a condom.
7. **Surgical options**: Minor surgical procedures are carried out to permanently sever the vas deferens (in the male) or the fallopian tubes (in the female), and is normally be done if the couple does not wish to have any more children. The procedure is more common in women. It has been seen that such closing or severing of the tubes, often causes weight gain around the abdomen and buttocks, or irregular menstrual cycles. Severing the vas deferens has certain side effects for the man as well, and consequently, such surgical techniques are not recommended as effective family planning techniques.

After consideration of the above methods, one can surely say that the safest and least harmful techniques are the use of a condom, and having sexual intercourse during the safe period of the monthly cycle. If pregnancy is then desired, it can occur easily and quickly, after these are discontinued.

Balguti

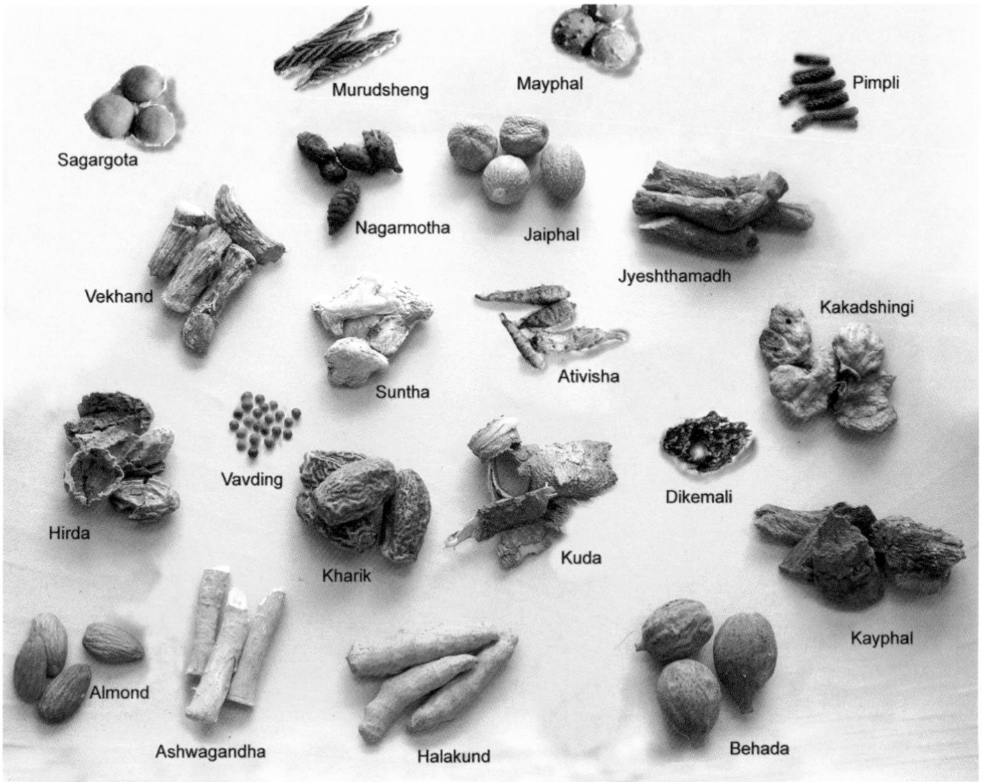

It is a common tradition to give *Balguti* to infants every day. The benefits of Balguti have been described earlier in the book. The herbs that make up balguti, are to be ground in mother's milk or in gold water ('survarnajal' - water boiled and infused with gold), and should be given to the baby once a day. Balguti should be started when the baby is ten days old and continued until the baby is fifteen months old.

DOSAGE

At 10 days Old - Grind each herb on the sahan in a circle the size of a one rupee coin just once or twice, in the clockwise direction. The total quantity of paste generated when you have finished grinding all the herbs like this is the size of the dose to be given to the baby.

At 1 Month Old - Increase the grinding to 2-3 circles per herb.

Increase the number of circles the herb is ground for as the child's age increases.

At 5-6 Months Old - If the baby is healthy, you could give as much paste as is generated from 7-8 circles of grinding.

If the child has any health problems, add more circles of the herb effective for that illness while grinding. Keep doing this until the symptoms of that illness subside.

The different herbs used, and their benefits and relevance to particular diseases, are mentioned below

Murudsheng (Helicteres isora): As the name suggests, Murudsheng helps to reduce cramps (*murda*), and parasitic infestations. The proportion of Murudsheng in the Balguti should be increased, if the baby suffers from cramps and loose motions.

Hirda (Terminalia chebula): This herb stimulates the appetite and liver function, improves the digestion, facilitates the passage of wind, improves bowel movements, and helps eliminate worms. Increse hirda in Balguti if the baby has a tendency towards constipation, or a bloated abdomen due to gases. Hirda is a rejuvenating herb (rasayan), and nourishes the dhatus. It is also beneficial for the eyes.

Pimpli (Piper longum): A medicinal fruit, also known as *long pepper*, is mainly used for problems of the respiratory and digestive systems. It helps prevent frequent and recurrent bouts of coughs and colds, improves the appetite, reduces abdominal pain, and is beneficial in cases of indigestion. If the child suffers from frequent coughs and colds, or loses appetite, then the proportion of pimpli in Balguti should be increased.

Jaiphal (Myristica fragrans) or Nutmeg: It is a commonly available kitchen ingredient. When given in small quantities (in Balguti), it helps the baby to sleep better. It improves memory, recall, and intelligence. Nutmeg also gives consistency to stools, and is mainly used to treat loose motions. You can grind nutmeg for one or two turns more for the above complaints. However, since nutmeg is a strong substance, one should not use more than four or five turns in Balguti. Use in greater quantity

can induce vomiting.

Vekhand (Acorus calamus): This bulb has a strong odour. Vekhand helps to improve comprehension, intelligence, and clarity of speech in children. It also prevents the recurrence of infections, frequent coughs and colds, and parasitic infestations. This should be turned a maximum of five to six times on the stone.

Behada (Terminalia belerica): This is the best herb to pacify imbalanced kapha. Because of its astringent taste and effect, it is very useful in the treatment of loose motions. Increase its dosage in Balguti if the child suffers from colds, coughs, and frequent diarrhoea.

Jyeshthamadha (Glycyrrhiza glabra) or Licorice: Another easily available herb which pacifies vata-pitta, strengthens balanced kapha and reduces constipation. It is commonly used to improve the quality of voice, brings lustre to the skin and is able to nourish all dhatus. It should be added regularly to Balguti. Increase its amount in Balguti, when the baby suffers from difficulty in breathing due to kapha (phlegm / mucus) accumulated in the chest. It can be used as a medicine if the child is suffering from a cough. ¼ teaspoon of ground Jyeshthamadha with three to four drops of honey should be administered to the child 2-3 times a day until the cough subsides. This helps to loosen the sticky mucus. At times it can cause vomiting, but this clears the phlegm, and provides relief to the child.

Nagarmotha (Cyperus rotundus): It is cooling in nature, facilitates the digestive process, and acts as a diuretic. It also improves the baby's intelligence and grasping power, and has anti-helminthic properties (it destroys parasites).

Ativisha (Aconitum heterophyllum): This herb grows in the Himalayas and is frequently used in Ayurvedic medicines. It aids digestive processes and controls fever. It helps to alleviate pain in the abdomen, vomiting, or diarrhoea. Because of its special benefits for children, it is also known as *shishubhaishajjya* (babies' medicine). It should be used in limited quantities, and ground only for a maximum of four or five rounds for daily use. It provides all round nourishment to the baby.

Kakadshingi (Rhus succedanea): Reduces kapha and vata, and is therefore very effective against cough, vomiting, hiccoughing, and fever. It is especially useful during teething.

If the child suffers from cold, cough, vomiting or loose motions, nagarmotha, ativisha, kakadshingi and pimpli can be given together as follows: Grind the herbs together in milk or water. A teaspoon of this paste should be mixed with honey, and rubbed on the tongue of the child. Children over 18 months can be given ¼ teaspoon of the churna (powder), mixed with honey, made from these herbs. Children younger than 18 months should be given only $^1/_8$ teaspoon.

Halkund (turmeric -Curcuma longa): Haldi pacifies and balances kapha-vata, purifies the blood, and improves liver function. It imparts a glow to the complexion, and is beneficial for the health of the skin. It prevents parasitic infestations and skin diseases.

Kayphal (Myrica nagi): Very beneficial for the throat and voice. Kayphal also balances kapha-vata, and is helpful in cases of cold, cough, fever, or throat pain.

Mayphal (Quercus infectoria): It is astringent in taste and is, therefore, useful in cases of loose motions and vomiting. It is also helpful in conditions of kapha (phlegm / mucus) accumulation. Increase Mayphal in Balguti in such cases.

Sagargota (Caesalpinia bonduc): The seed of sagargota helps against worms and parasites in the digestive tract, and is anti pyretic in nature (fever-pacifying). It is especially used in cases of abdominal pain. It can be used everyday in Balguti. Increase its usage in case the baby has fever or abdominal pain.

Kuda (Holarrhena antidysenterica): Kuda is very useful for the digestive system. It works as an excellent appetizer, and ensures the proper digestion of food. It helps to bind stool. Increase its use in case of loose motions.The dosage should be increased whenever there are loose motions, especially if they are accompanied by fever. Another way of effectively administering Kuda is that it can be ground with buttermilk instead of water to form a paste. $^1/_8{}^{th}$ of a teaspoon is enough for one dose.

Dikemali (Gardenia gummifera): This is a type of resin (gum). It prevents parasitic infestation in the digestive tract and is an excellent remedy for all types of teething problems. However, as it has a strong smell, grinding only a small quantity (only two to three turns) for Balguti, so that the child doesn't develop a dislike for the taste.

Vavding (Embelia ribes): This works against

worms and parasites as well and fosters the child's development in general. Ayurvedic literature advises that increasing the dosage of vavding by one grain in balguti every two months, until the child is a year old, can help prevent a variety of complaints. Moreover, vavding aids digestion and purifies the blood. It can be said that it acts as a rasayan for the child.

Ashwagandha (Withania somnifera): It increases strength, nourishes shukra dhatu, and has rejuvenating properties. Its regular intake helps to ensure that the baby gains weight steadily, in a healthy manner, and the baby's immune system improves.

Suntha (Zingiber officinale) or Dry Ginger: It aids the digestive process, facilitates the passage of wind (gases) and the easy passing of stools, improves the voice, relieves and reduces coughs, vomiting, and loose motions. If these complaints are present, the amount of suntha should be increased in Balguti.

Badam (Prunus amygdalus) or Almond: It is nutritious and beneficial for the brain. It also promotes intelligence, and strengthens the dhatus. Almonds should be soaked in water for 8-10 hours, peeled and then eaten. Until the age of two months, ¼ ground almond is recommended; from 6-12 months, ¾ ground almond can be given; one whole almond thereafter. A child of two years old can be given two almonds, and, as the child grows, the quantity may be increased to three to four almonds a day.

Khareek (Phoenix dactylifera) or Dry dates: It pacifies and balances vata-pitta, and is cooling in nature. It imparts adequate lubrication to the body, improves the strength, fortifies the bones and is very nourishing for the child. Rubbing 12-15 turns of khareek in the daily balguti, is recommended. Almond and khareek are both sweet in taste, and cause no harm, even if given in larger quantities. Children like their taste, so they are used to improve the taste of the balguti.

Mrugshrung: It should be ground on the sahan stone, and a small quantity mixed into the balguti. Mrugshrung helps strengthen the bones, teeth, and hair, and fosters their proper growth.

The following list shows the substances to be increased in balguti for specific complaints

- **Cold and cough:** kakadshingi, pimpli, suntha, vekhand, kayphal, behada
- **Cold and cough with fever:** all of the above plus nagarmotha, ativisha
- **Loose motions:** kuda, behada, murudsheng, suntha, nagarmotha, jaiphal.
- **Loose motions with fever:** nagarmotha, ativisha, kuda, behada, murudsheng, suntha, sagargota.
- **Loss of appetite:** pimpli, hirda, suntha, vavding
- **Constipation:** hirda, jyeshthamadha, suntha
- **Abdominal pain:** sagargota, murudsheng, suntha, ativisha
- **Vomiting:** kakadshingi, nagarmotha, ativisha, mayphal
- **Worms:** vavding, dikemali, sagargota, halkund, nagarmotha, murudsheng, hirda
- **Rashes:** halkund, nagarmotha, and vavding.

Sixteen Sanskars

Indian traditions give great importance to *sanskar*. Sanskar means 'culturing'. In keeping with the same Indian tradition, this idea is best explained with examples.

When you add a little curd to a lot of milk, slowly, the entire milk is transformed. The end result is not a mixture or a compound. We say that the milk has been cultured. Similarly a student, for example, a student of music, comes to live with his teacher. He learns not only the craft or skill, but also a manner of being, a way of life and imbibes his teachers habits and positive values. We say that he has been cultured into a musician.

The ancient seers realised that we must follow certain practices so that are able to fulfill the purpose of our lives.

These are called sanskars, and they are used to culture people. The seers have researched the physical actions one must perform on the body and mind and ritualized them into these practises. They contribute to bringing about a desirable positive change in us.

Each person must face many different kinds of changes, from birth until death, and specific sanskars have been advised for each of these, so that the individual is capable of meeting these challenges, physically, mentally, and intellectually.

Ancient Indian science, refers to around 40 sanskars, and 16 of these are considered to be most important. These are described below.

1. Garbhaadhaan sanskar: This sanskar has already been described in great detail in the earlier chapters. It includes the process of preparing for conception, and focuses on ensuring the purity of sperm and ovum, and ensuring that conception occurs at the appropriate time. This is a very important procedure, because it affects the child's overall health and development. The appropriate time of conception, ensures the birth of a healthy, intelligent, and well-endowed child. A person's conception itself is his first sanskar. You will see that several such sanskars have to be done for a person throughout childhood by his or her parents.

2. Punsavan sanskar: This is carried out before the second month of pregnancy ends to ensure that the child to-be-born is full of life energy.

Contrary to common belief, the result of this sanskar is not to ensure that the child is male. The aim is to ensure fertility (for the continuation of nature's cycle) in the newly developing child. This sanskar ensures that the child born will further be able to have children as well.

Both men and women play an equally important role in the formation of a strong social framework, and in ensuring the continuation of our species. By nature, the male is physically stronger than the female, and many atrocities have been committed against women because of this. Some changes in social norms are therefore called for. It is not wrong for a family to want a son, especially if they already have a daughter, and in such situations, Ayurveda has suggested special measures, whereby, either a male or a female child can be conceived.

Punsavan sanskar aims to ensure the proper physical development of the child, so that it remains healthy and free of disease, with sufficient virya and ojas for its entire life, irrespective of its gender. Although, the name may suggest that this sanskar is a religious ceremony, it is, in fact, a completely Ayurvedic treatment.

Ayurveda clearly states that the success of this procedure is dependant on many factors, such as, the time and place, and the karma as well as destiny of the person. Only if these factors are positive can the procedure be successful. There are different ways of performing Punsavan sanskar.

For example: Take the tender shoots of a north or east-facing branch of a banyan tree. Grind them in milk, and use this liquid for *nasya* (as nose drops). This nasya must be done on *pushya nakshatra* (the occurrence of the *pushya* constellation). These drops are put into the left nostril of the mother if a daughter is desired, and in the right nostril if the couple wants a son. A similar procedure can also be done with Durva grass juice.

3. Seemantonnayan sanskar: The commonly performed *dohaale jevan* (satisfying the baby's food wishes) ceremony, is a part of this sanskar. This is to be done in the fourth month of pregnancy, when the woman is normally experiencing *dohaale* (cravings). The ceremony is focussed around satisfying the expectant mother's wishes and desires, and the aim is to ensure the intellectual progress of the child.

4. Jaatkarma sanskar: Includes rubbing gold on the tongue of the baby, immediately after birth, and bathing the newborn with herbal water. The aim is to protect the baby's health, and to stimulate intellectual growth. This has been dealt with in detail in earlier chapters.

Gold is rubbed into honey which carries it all over the body. This culture helps against infection that the baby may have brought from the womb, and reduces the possibility of further infection. Gold also helps the baby face the light and energy of the outside world. If one wants to understand this deeper, then one can imagine the impressions the baby must have received in the dark womb. This sanskar helps remove those impressions.

5. Namkaran sanskar: The naming ceremony performed when the baby is 12 days old. The baby is bathed with fragrant water and herbal powders, and is then given an auspicious and meaningful name.

6. Nishkraman sanskar: This is performed when the baby is four months old, and is taken out of the house for the first time. The baby should be taken to a temple on the same date (tithi) as the day it was born. This clearly also indicates that, unless it is urgent or unavoidable, the baby should not be taken out of the house during the first four months.

7. Annaprashan sanskar: This is performed when the baby is six months old. After this ceremony, fruit juice, mashed rice, and other foods can be gradually introduced into the baby's diet.

8. Karnavedh sanskar: This sanskar involves piercing the earlobes, and is performed on any auspicious day in *Shukla paksha* (first half, or ascending period, of any lunar cycle moving towards the full moon), usually when the baby is six or seven months old. Baby boys will have their right earlobes pierced first and then the left, and baby girls their left earlobes first. This is a therapeutic activity which helps to stimulate the brain.

9. Mundan sanskar: It is performed either when the baby is in its third year of life, or fifth year of life (not before and not in between). In this sanskar the baby's hair is cut for the first time. According to ancient Ayurvedic science, cutting a girl's hair may adversely affect her hormonal balance, so 'mundan' is only done for boys. Hair is associated with the fire of the body and is an indicator of proper growth. This sanskar should be performed only if the baby has good all round development. Therefore one waits for three years to be sure of such development.

10. Upanayan sanskar: Also known as the 'Thread Ceremony'. It is considered to be a second birth for the male child. It can also be done for girl children. The tradition believes that while the physical growth of a human being occurs automatically through the balance between the three doshas, excellent knowledge can be gained only through special effort. This is an initiation into learning and awakening true humanity in the person. While all other development takes place automatically, one has to clearly decide to take this initiation. It is a new birth in terms of the personality of the individual. The child is given 'Dnyana diksha' to awaken his inclination towards knowledge. The child takes a vow of celibacy, which must be adhered to strictly after the upanayan sanskar.

11. Dnyana sanskar: This ritual is performed by the teacher (guru) or the father, when the child is old enough to start learning. In ancient times, there existed the practice of staying in a gurukul to obtain knowledge. The gurukul was pure and sanctified, and located in a peaceful place, where the child could live until the age of twenty-five. Students in the gurukul remained celibate (brahmchari) and acquired knowledge. Ayurveda describes the learning proces in the Ashtang Uttarsthan as follows:

शक्तिमन्तं यथावर्णं विद्यामध्यापयेत् ततः ।
अनुशिष्यात् सदा चैनं धर्माय विनयाय च ॥
यथा नेन्द्रियदुष्टाश्वैः ह्रियते यौवनागमे ॥ ...अष्टांगसंग्रह उत्तरस्थान

śaktimantam yathā-varṇam vidyāmadhyāpayet tataḥ

Anuśiṣyāt sadā cainam dharmāya vinayāya ca

Yathā nendriyaduṣṭāśvaiḥ rhiyate yauvanāgam
.....Aṣṭāṅgasaṅgraha uttarasthāna

When the child is physically, mentally, and intellectually ready to attain knowledge, then an arrangement for his training needs to be made, depending on his capability, potential, likes, and intelligence. The training should include an awareness of duty, humility, truthfulness and good behaviour, all of which will stand him in good stead in his youth. He will learn to control his sensory organs, ensuring that he does not fall prey to sensory impulses. This control will help him fulfill his desires, and ensure his progress.

12. Samavartan sanskar: This refers to the departure from the gurukul at twenty -five years of age, after duly passing all of the required examinations. The student receives the blessing of his guru or teacher, and returns home.

13. Vivah sanskar (Marriage) : It is the beginning of family life or *gruhasthashram*, which binds together a healthy man and a healthy woman, with the aim to bear children. Vivah Sanskar is a vital foundation of our social structure.

14. Vanaprastha sanskar: It entails transferring all of one's worldly responsibilities to the next generation, after having properly discharged all family duties. The person now goes beyond the immediate family, and assumes responsibility for society as an extended social family.

15. Sanyas sanskar: It aims to bring about spiritual progress and helps the person on the path of *moksha*. It is the process that binds a person with the universal family, going beyond that which has been bestowed upon us by our ancestors. It is the journey that unites us with every living being in the whole world. One should try to overcome selfish motives, and work for the benefit of all humanity. This is the beginning of understanding the meaning of 'sva' or self.

16. Antyeshti sanskar: They are the final rites, which are to be performed after death, and consist of consigning a persons physical remains to fire. The aim of this sanskar is to prevent any harm that could be caused to society, in the form of infection or disease, which may come from the corpse. The soul separates from the physical body at death, and this sanskar helps the soul to have a speedy onward journey.

According to Indian science, these 16 most important sanskars are to be carried out at different stages in our lives, and should include all these, like Garbhadhaan (conception and before), Punsavan and Seemantonnyan (during pregnancy), Jaatkarma up to Sanyas (during a person's lifetime), and Antyeshti (after death).

Immunisation

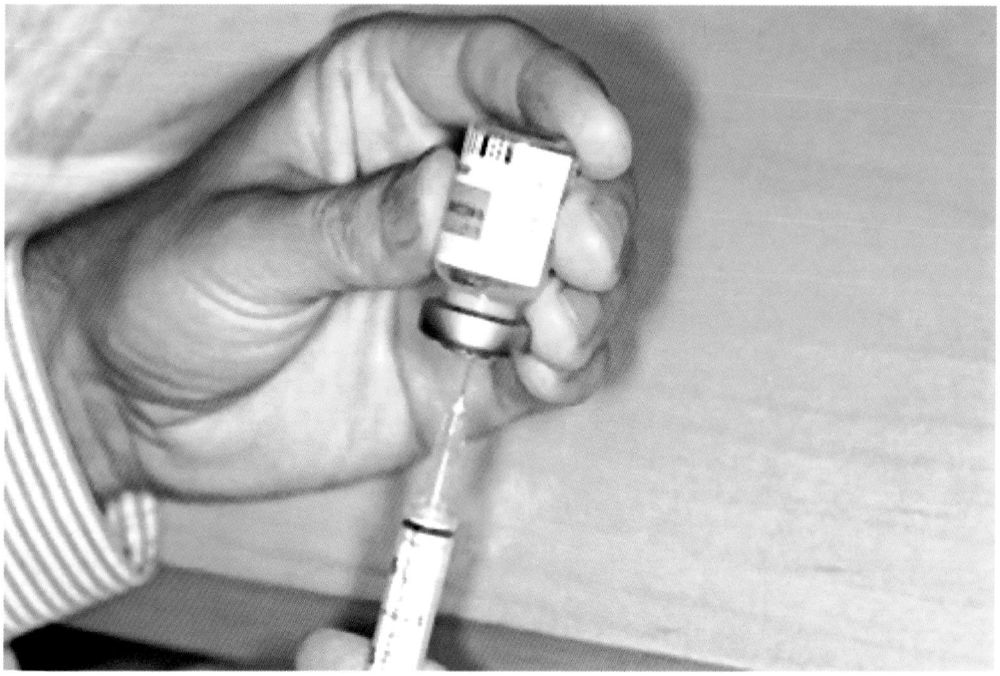

Immunisation is common all over the world now. While it is not specified in Ayurvedic texts, we have included it here so that you understand this process while carrying out all that is required for your baby's health. Inoculation is carried out to prevent infections by certain virulent and dangerous organisms at a young age or later in life.

There are several vaccines for various diseases. They are given through different methods, and have varying schedules of administration. Vaccines basically use dead or weak disease causing microorganisms to stimulate an immune response to that disease in the body. This immunity once developed at a very early age, will serve to protect the person from that disease in future. One can read more about vaccines from expert sources.

In comparison to adults, a newborn has weaker resistance (immunity) to infection, and this must be gradually strengthened through proper diet and lifestyle. A debate is currently in progress as to whether this feeble resistance mechanism should be additionally burdened with vaccination or not. This is a dispute concerning the relative benefits of inoculation.

On one hand immunization protects against infection. On the other hand, the possibility of resulting reactions, for example fever, epileptic seizures, suffering from the disease for which the vaccine was originally given, autism or, in rare cases, even mental retardation, certainly can hamper the child's physical and mental development.

In view of the above, many lay-persons

are justified in harbouring doubts, about whether to agree to inoculation or not.

In addition to taking into account the pros and cons of immunization, the following points should also be considered before a decision is made:

1. What are the chances of the child acquiring the disease against which the vaccination is intended?

2. What are the possible adverse effects of the vaccine?

3. What is the condition of the immune system at the time of vaccination? For example, does the baby have normal weight? Is the baby healthy? Has the baby recently suffered from a cold, cough, fever, loose motions, or any other ailment?

Illness can weaken the immune system, so if the baby is not healthy, any inoculation given at that time can be potentially dangerous, and may actually cause the baby more suffering.

There have been cases where a full-blown polio attack was triggered when the polio vaccine was given to a child suffering from fever.

In view of this, it is better to wait until the baby is healthy again, before giving any vaccines. A 7-8 day deviation from the vaccination schedule is permissible.

Furthermore, combination vaccines such as MMR or DTP could be potentially dangerous. This is because the baby's weak immune system is placed under stress by having to deal with three different types of organisms, and this could have disastrous results, such as being infected by the very disease the baby has been inoculated against. In former times, breast-feeding, appropriate and nutritious diet, herbal smokes (dhoop), and Balguti, were attended to without fail. These measures protected the baby's health adequately, and the chances of infection were low. If you take proper care of the baby's diet, lifestyle and nutrition, the chances of any infection are negligible.

Many people think that it is necessary to inoculate the child with all the commercially available vaccines, but this is not always true. Parents should consult their doctor about which vaccines are necessary for their baby and only then begin to have their child inoculated. There is no need to go along with 'herd mentality', i.e. administering all vaccines to your baby just because everyone else is doing it.

Essential immunisation schedule advised by the Indian Government

BCG*	From birth up to one month of age
DTP** and Polio	When baby is 6 weeks old
DTP and Polio	When baby is 10 weeks old
DTP and Polio	When baby is 14 weeks old
Measles	When baby is 9 months old
DTP and Polio (booster)	When baby is 1.5-2 years old
* Protects against Tuberculosis ** Protects against Diphtheria, Whooping Cough and Tetanus	

Experience speaks...

When the Garbha Sanskar series was published in the 'Family Doctor' a supplement of Sakal newspaper, it received an overwhelming response. Many who have listened to the 'Garbha Sanskar' music album, and have benefited from our advice, have sent us their feedback. Here are some of the experiences they shared.

I personally found Sakal's supplement 'Family Doctor', very informative and useful. Having read information regarding application of 'lep' on a pregnant woman's abdomen, I used it on my daughter during labour pains. She delivered the baby before the expected time, and the pains were bearable. Witnessing the positive results of the 'lep', the doctor in charge used the same lep on two other women, who were benefitted tremendously.

My daughter also listened the 'Garbha Sanskar' CD regularly during her pregnancy.

Here is another experience: a woman was able to deliver her child normally despite her baby passing stools while still inside her abdomen, thus avoiding an emergency surgery.

I thank you from the bottom of my heart. Any amount of thanks would be insufficient.

Mrs Sulabha H. Purohit, Amravati

Firstly, I want to thank you for the CD , 'Garbha Sanskar'. I had liked it the moment I heard it but I am now convinced about its true effectiveness. Since a year, everyone in our family listens to it daily. I began to listen to this music from the fifth month of my pregnancy, and also took Ayurvedic medications. My son, Rishi is now seven months old.

Right from birth, he began to turn on his side, and responded very well when spoken to. He was able to lie on his stomach when he was 1 ½ months old.

His response to music, rhythm, tunes and melodies is excellent right from the beginning. Everyone who has seen him is surprised at his development. He was able to walk around the house when put in a walker when he was 5 months of age; however, I have discontinued it on doctor's advice. He really tries to converse, and I am sure, if he knew words, we would be conversing by now!

I have applied ghee on his anterior fontanelle (talu) regularly for 1 ½ months, and am regularly massaging his soles with ghee. When we recite the "barakhadi" (Marathi alphabet series) to him, he tries to repeat after us. His overall progress is really astonishing. I hope to benefit from your guidance in future.

Thank you once again for the 'Garbha Sanskar' CD.

Mrs Manjusha Deshmukh, Solapur

I am a regular reader of 'Family Doctor', which has benefited me tremendously. I have a six-month-old daughter. I have followed all the suggestions and advice during my pregnancy, according to your 'Garbha Sanskar' articles. My child is healthy, and more importantly, I had no problems during labour. My delivery time lasted only for 2 to 2 ½ hours. I thank respected Dr. Shri Balaji Tambe for the 'Family Doctor' series.

Shubhangi Dole, Kurduwadi

I am a regular reader of 'Family Doctor'. The 'Garbha Sanskar' series has helped me tremendously. As luck would have it, your article on 'Care to be taken in the ninth month', coincided with ninth month of my pregnancy. The same was true, for the article on 'Care of the newborn child'. I was able to have a normal delivery only because I have followed all your advice in great detail. My son is four months old now.

Mrs Hema Jagdish Konge, Ahmednagar

I have regularly heard 'Garbha Sanskar' during my pregnancy, and I experienced serenity and contentment. Often I slept soundly after listening to the music. The baby within me also used to move less whenever I listened to it, and I experienced that it would become calm just by listening to the music. My son is now one and a half years old. He is very sharp, bright and has very good comprehension. He is not fussy about food. All physical and mental milestones like crawling, teething, walking, talking occurred on time and without any problems.

Mrs Reena Maheshwari, Solapur

I have been reading the 'Garbha Sanskar' series on 'e-sakal' regularly, and I am sure, it will help many couples. I would like to share my experience from 15 years ago, and I am still benefiting from it.

At that time, my husband and I were planning for a second child. We were fortunate enough to get your guidance. According to your advice, both of us took Ayurvedic treatments and medicines prior to conceiving. We meditated using Santulan Aumkar Meditation. I listened to healing music (swasthya sangeet) before conception and throughout my pregnancy. I did not require any other medications, except the Ayurvedic medicines prescribed by you. I religiously applied 'Kundalini oil' on my back, and used other oils like 'Femisan oil' regularly. I delivered my child at the appropriate time without any untoward problems.

My son had bright glowing eyes, and was able to focus his gaze from birth itself. He would sleep for 7-8 hours at a stretch, when he was 15 days old, and I never had to get up at night because of him. I had no complaints of his crying or irritability. He has shown excellent progress and understanding. He loves to hear your 'bhajans' especially 'Hanuman chalisa'. My son is now 15 years old and has always stood first in academics. His knowledge and understanding of music is exceptional. He composes music for all school music competitions, and is proficient with the keyboards and Saxophone. His drawing and elocution is also noteworthy. In short his overall development and progress is remarkable.

The credit for all this goes to 'Garbha Sanskar'. It is impossible to put in words the benefits we are seeing today, for measures taken years ago.

Mrs Sadhana Talele, New Zealand

■ ■ ■

I regularly read the 'Family Doctor' supplement every Friday. I have followed all the advice given in the 'Garbha Sanskar' after I became pregnant, especially the diet and exercise regimes. This helped me to deliver the baby in only one hour. My 4-month-old daughter is very healthy today.

Mrs Chaya Temkar, Ahmednagar

■ ■ ■

I listened to 'Garbha Sanskar' album from the fourth month onwards during my second pregnancy. My son is now nine months old. He is completely healthy and has a very happy disposition.

Mrs Archana Joshi, Pune.

■ ■ ■

I was impressed by the concept of 'Garbha Sanskar' right from the beginning. So, I commenced taking your medications before conception.

I began listening to 'Garbha Sanskar' music from the day I conceived, and I listened to it for the entire nine months of my pregnancy every morning and evening, in spite of having a regular full time job. Listening to this music kept me fresh throughout the day, and helped me sleep soundly at night. I also took your prescribed medicines regularly.

I have got positive results from these measures taken. Despite being a little overweight, I was able to have a normal unproblematic delivery, by using your 'lep'. My son is healthy. He listens to your 'Ramraksha' stotra every night.

Since his birth I have been giving my son gold and balguti daily. He has a calm nature and generally does not get irritable. If he cries, then listening to the 'Garbha Sanskar' or 'Shiva' CDs made by you calms him down immediately.

My son is 1 ¼ years old today. He is very intelligent and has a very good comprehension and understanding.

In 6 months I have reduced the weight gained during pregnancy. I had feared a weight gain in this time since I was already overweight. The surprising thing is my weight now is less than my pre-conception weight. Inspite of having delivered recently, I have no complaints of tiredness, hair loss, or back ache. I am grateful to you, Dr. Malavika and Dr. Bhagyashree for your guidance.

Mrs Sangeeta Bhor, Lonavala

■ ■ ■

After discovering the benefits of following a holistic way of living, my life has changed for the better. Once my husband and I decided to have an addition to our family, I wanted to make sure that I kept things as natural as possible, without any artificial interventions. I followed almost all the things I possibly could, mentioned in the Garbhasanskar book.

I was very careful about my diet, because of which my weight gain was ideal. I would have people comment that I didn't look pregnant even in my seventh month…I did not suffer from the usual complaints women have during their pregnancy, like high blood pressure, varicose veins, etc.

I listened to the Garbhasanskar music every day. Every time the baby got uncomfortable for any reason, I would play this music and I felt that instantly he was settling back and feel at ease. Even today whenever I feel that my baby is uneasy I play him this music and he's back being his peaceful self after listening to Dr. Balaji's voice.

The birthing of my baby was one of the most fun and memorable experiences of my life. It was beautiful. Nothing like the horror stories of what others made it out to be. I was able to do all of this without an epidural, chemicals, or man made drugs.

I gave birth to a healthy, happy and alert baby. He started to support his head after only a few weeks out of the womb. He would sleep for around six hours during the night at only two months old. He asks for food and attention with minimal crying.

I can't thank Dr. Balaji enough. His guidance and insight carried me while on this journey. Any women, planning on embarking on this miracle would only benefit by reading this book. It may become your best friend.

Gargi, America

When we decided to plan a family we were aware of the Garbhasanskar concept. The book gave concise guidelines about the care to be taken before and after conception. With the expert advice from Dr. Shri Balaji Tambe and Dr Bhagyashree we did Pancha Karma, followed by appropriate diet restrictions, strengthening rasayans (tonics) and supporting medicines.

The detailed information specified regarding the monthly diet and dietary restrictions helped in maintaining excellent health during pregnancy. My blood pressure and weight were ideal throughout pregnancy. The regular Yoga and listening to the Garbhasanskar CD in addition to the other Santulan Healing Music assisted me in staying active and pleasant. I was able to work full-time right until the end of pregnancy.

The book provided excellent knowledge on the various aspects of labour and tips on how to cope in all the phases, thus helping me to mentally prepare for the birth. With the help of Balant Lep and Kundalini Oil applied during labour I was able to give birth to our son naturally without resorting to any pain-relief

After birth we gave our son gold with honey every day. He was holding and turning his head from the minute he was born. He is very strong, alert and bright. His is accomplishing his physical growth and mental development goals earlier than babies of his age. He is a very happy baby and responds positively to Santulan Healing Music.

The after-delivery care specified for new mothers proved to be very effective in regaining strength and ensuring sufficient breast-milk formation. The book answers the countless questions a new mother may have about the baby's care and her health. Having those answers at one's fingertips is very comforting hence giving confidence to the new mother to enjoy the beautiful phase of motherhood in her life.

Our faith in the Garbhsanskar process never wavered in spite of the sometimes contradicting advice from other experts.

We hope that the Garbhasanskar concept reaches out to all couples and they also embrace and enjoy parenthood to the fullest.

There are no words to express our gratitude towards Dr. Shri Balaji Tambe for his blessings and invaluable advice.

Dipika Sharma, New Zealand

The experiences of a doctor and a mother

In the year 2000, I tied the knot with Mr. Sunil Tambe. For a young girl, a fresh graduate in Ayurvedic Medicine, it was fortunate to be accepted as a member of Dr. Shri Balaji's and Smt Veena's unique family. The fact that my father-in-law practised Ayurved, was not unknown to me, but what was pleasantly surprising was, that even my mother-in-law and brother-in-law, Mr. Sanjay, and his wife Dr Sujata (settled in Germany), believed in and followed the Ayurvedic and Vedic principles in their lives in great detail. As a part of this family, I experienced a new life, a life where the modern times are lived through an ancient science, and through the practice of all Indian customs and traditions, irrespective of where one was located.

When my husband and I thought of extending our family, we were provided with invaluable guidance by my parents-in-law. I was extremely happy to note that Ayurved had researched and outlined norms in detail about this miraculous process.

So both of us, my husband and I, underwent Pancha Karma, besides taking Ayurvedic medicines, Rasayans, etc. I regularly listened to musical compositions by my father-in-law, especially the Feminine Balance album. Members of our family practice the reading of certain scriptures and the chanting of certain mantras. This became my routine as well, which I followed twice a day.

Soon enough, I had the opportunity to deliver the happy news of my pregnancy to my family. I then followed all suggested measures, including daily exercises, diet, intake of medicines and herbal preparations, oil application and so on. At every stage of my pregnancy, I adhered to the prescribed guidelines, strictly following the do's and don'ts.

I also listened to the Garbh Sanskar CD, and felt my baby listening intently and calming down. I meditated daily, recited different mantras (stotras) and Aumkar. This, combined with yoga, helped to develop my baby's aura. I never felt burdened with the diet plan, or other lifestyle changes that I followed.

After delivery, I did not suffer from common complaints (like back ache, hair loss, weight gain), as I followed the post delivery regime mentioned in this book.

Furthermore, my baby stopped crying whenever the 'Garbhasanskar' CD was played at home. I regularly gave my child 'Santulan Balamrut', balguti, Brahmaleen Ghruta (ghee), abhyang massage and smoke therapy using Santulan Tenderness Dhoop. I followed all of this for all my three daughters. It has shown visible results in their progress.

My daughters, Tanushree, Tanishka, and Sushmita, are very understanding, obedient and cooperative. Their creative capacities, good memory, and ability to grasp things were evident from a very early age. They are not stubborn or cranky. Drawing, music and singing come naturally to them. Their ability to understand musical notes is astonishing. In all their cases, I had a sense of their affinity to music since the time they were in the womb. I never had to force or scold them, to believe in or have faith in God, and to respect teachers and elders, etc. As mothers, if our children are like this, their progress will always satisfy us, make us happy and serve to inspire us.

Every woman will have a happy and fulfilling child bearing experience if she follows the guidance offered in this book. I am sure that all those who make the efforts prescribed here will give birth to healthy and creative children.

By Dr. Mrs Malvika Tambe, Karla

Special Recipes

PANCHAMRUT

As the name suggests, this preparation is like an *amrut* or elixir. It prevents disease, slows down the process of aging, increases enthusiasm, immunity, memory, and resistance to infection. If taken daily before breakfast, panchamrut is extremely beneficial.

A couple should take panchamrut for at least two months before they want to conceive, and once the woman conceives, she can continue to take panchamrut throughout pregnancy. If taken during this period, it benefits the foetus, and if continued after delivery, it ensures proper formation of breast milk, and consequently, optimum development of the child. In addition, it helps maintain the health and energy levels of the mother. Once the baby has been weaned, it can be given a spoonful everyday. A 2½ -3 year old child should eat a whole serving as described below.

Serves : 1 person

Ingredients and their properties are as follows:

- **One teaspoon sugar:** for strength, good for the heart and brain.
- **One teaspoon honey:** strengthens the heart and eyes, balances all three doshas.
- **One teaspoon curd (not yoghurt):** beneficial for shukra dhatu, balances vata dosha.
- **Two teaspoons pure Ayurvedic ghee:** improves intelligence, strengthens digestive fire (agni), balances vata and pitta dosha, and strengthens kapha dosha.
- **Seven to eight teaspoons lukewarm milk:** strengthens mind and body, increases the life energy (ojas), and nourishes all the dhatus.

The ingredients should be added in the above given sequence.

'Amrutshatakara' (a sugar-based preparation containing shatavari (asparagus racemosus), saffron, and gold can be used instead of normal sugar to increase the benefits of panchamrut. The use of a silver cup to make panchamrut is recommended.

SEMOLINA KHEER

Semolina (rava) made from wheat is very nutritious. Prepared in the form of kheer (like porridge), with milk and saffron, it strengthens shukra dhatu. Ayurveda recommends that the pregnant woman should eat kheer in the 8th month of pregnancy, and semolina kheer is the best kind of kheer for this purpose. It can be eaten 3-4 times a week. It is also beneficial if eaten occasionally in the other months of pregnancy, and after delivery.

Kheer is also well-suited to be the baby's first solid food (*annaprashan sanskar*) and can be continued thereafter as it is nutritious for children. Children usually like its taste.

Serves: 4-5 persons

Preparation time: 30 minutes

Ingredients

Fine semolina	50 g.
Ghee	10 g.
Sugar	125 g.
Saffron powder	a pinch
Milk	1 lit.

1. In a thick bottomed pot, roast semolina in ghee on a low flame, until golden brown
2. Add milk and boil it. Milk should already be slightly heated before adding. Add sugar and saffron and boil once again. Almond slivers can

be added for more nutrition and taste.

Vermicelli (wheat noodles) and rice kheer can be prepared similarly.

NARAYAN SHEERA

This delicious preparation is beneficial for health in general. It can be eaten for breakfast, or as a sweet with the mid-day meal. It is satisfies the stomach and the mind. It improves physical strength, memory, immunity and the abilities of the brain. Narayan sheera can be eaten by everyone all year round. It is especially beneficial during pregnancy, after delivery and for children as well.

Serves: 4-5 persons

Preparation time: 30 minutes

Ingredients

Semolina	125 g.
Ghee	125 g.
Sugar	125 g.
Milk	½ lit.
Almonds	25 g.
Cardamom powder	½ tsp.
Raisins	25 g.
Saffron powder	¼ tsp.
Banana (sliced)	1

1. In a thick bottomed pot, heat ghee and fry the almonds and raisins in it. Remove them once fried.
2. In the same ghee, cook semolina on a low flame until it is well roasted.
3. Slowly, add the (pre-heated) milk. Milk will cause the semolina to puff up. Mix well, cover the pot and allow it to cook for 5 minutes. Keep stirring occasionally so that it does not stick to the bottom of the pan. If required place a griddle below it to prevent it from sticking and burning.
4. Add the sugar, saffron powder, raisins, cardamom powder and almonds. Stir well, cover the pot, and allow it to cook until the sugar has been absorbed into the mixture. Add the sliced banana, and cover for two minutes, then turn off the flame. It is now ready to serve.

MUNG DAL SHEERA

Mung dal is a rich source of easily digestible proteins which are readily absorbed by the body. This dish, which is made with milk and ghee, imparts strength, and nourishes all dhatus, especially bones, muscles, and ligaments. It is extremely beneficial to the health of the mother and child, during pregnancy and lactation. A diluted version of the sheera, may be given to babies when they are a year old.

Serves: 4-5 persons

Preparation time: 45 minutes

Ingredients

Mung dal	100 g.
Ghee	60 g.
Milk	400 ml.
Sugar	100 g.
Cardamom powder	0.75 g. (½ tsp.)

1. Wash the mung dal and soak it in water for about 1½ hours. Drain the water and grind the mung in a mixer.
2. In a thick bottomed pot, heat the ghee and roast the ground mung dal on a low flame until it is golden brown and emits an aroma.

(Approximately fifteen to twenty minutes). Keep stirring constantly. Add the hot milk, stir well, and cover for five minutes

4. Add the sugar and cardamom powder, mix well and cook on a low flame for a few minutes.
5. Cover the pot, and allow it to simmer until done. Serve hot.

CARROT AND MUNG DAL SALAD

Carrots are rich in Vitamin A and mung dal is rich in proteins. Since both are easy to digest, this salad is excellent during pregnancy and after delivery. Children can be given this salad from the age of 2 or 2 ½ when they start having entire meals.

Serves: 4-5 persons

Preparation time: 30 minutes

Ingredients

Carrots	125 g.
Mung dal	20 g.
Chopped coriander	4 g.
Lemon juice	6 g. (1 tsp.)
Cumin seeds	3 g. (1 tsp.)
Grated Coconut fresh or dry	3 g. (1 tsp)
Salt	3 g. (½ tsp.)
Sugar	6 g. (1 tsp.)
Asafoetida (hing)	0.7 g. (¼ tsp.)
Dry red chilli	1 piece
Ghee	2 tsp.

1. Wash and soak the mung dal for 3-4 hours in water. Then drain it.
2. Wash, peel, and grate the carrots.
3. Mix the grated carrots, soaked mung dal, chopped coriander and coconut.
4. Heat the ghee in a small pan, add cumin seeds, asafoetida, and red chilli (the procedure is known as *fodni*), and add to the carrot-mung dal mixture.
5. Add salt, sugar, lemon juice, and mix well. The preparation is ready to be served.

SPINACH, BOTTLE GOURD (DUDHI) AND MUNG DAL SOUP

Spinach is a rich source of iron, which makes this soup especially beneficial during pregnancy and after delivery. Bottle gourd (dudhi) is very healthy, nutritious, and balances all three doshas. Mung dal is rich in proteins. The soup may also be given to the baby at the age of 8-10 months, but it must be well pureed, and homogeneous, to make it easily digestible.

Serves: 5-6 persons.

Preparation time: 40 minutes.

Ingredients

Bottle gourd (dudhi)	150 g.
Spinach	50 g.
Mung dal	50 g.
Hot water	1¼ lit.
Grated ginger	9 g. (1½ tsp.)
Salt	9 g. (1½ tsp.)
Sugar	3 g. (½ tsp.)
Ghee	2 tsp.
Asafoetida (hing)	1.5 g. (½ tsp.)
Cumin seeds	3 g. (1 tsp.)

Turmeric powder	0.5 g. (¼ tsp.)
Grated Coconut fresh or dry	9 g. (3 tsp.)
Dry or green chilli (optional)	1
Chopped coriander	3 g (1½ tsp.)

1. Wash, peel, and chop the bottle gourd into very small pieces. Clean, wash, and chop the spinach.
2. Wash the mung dal.
3. In a thick bottomed pot, roast the cumin seeds, hing (asafoetida), turmeric, coconut, and chilli, in ghee, for a short time, and then add the chopped vegetables and mung dal. Mix well.
4. Add the hot water, salt, sugar, and ginger. Allow to boil, until the mung dal, bottle gourd, and spinach are cooked.
5. Puree coarsely, add chopped coriander, and turn off the flame.

Omit the chilli if necessary.

When soups are mentioned, tomato soup is usually the first that comes to mind. However, the basic method as given above may be used to prepare nutritious and appetizing soups from any other vegetables that are available.

KULITH SOUP

Kulith is a bean that is easy to digest and pacifies vata and kapha. This tasty and nutritious soup enhances digestive fire (jatharagni), supports the proper functioning of the urinary system and is good for the health in general. The special quality of kulith is that it helps the uterine muscles constrict. Therefore, it is recommended in Ayurvedic literature to be taken regularly by the new mother after delivery, especially during the first 45 days post-partum.

Serves: 4-5 persons.

Preparation time: 30 minutes.

Ingredients

Kulith flour	50 g.
Ghee	3 tsp.
Cumin seeds	3 g. (1 tsp.)
Asafoetida	1.5 g. (½ tsp.)
Turmeric	1.5 g. (¾ tsp.)
Grated Coconut dry or fresh	9 g. (3 tsp.)
Chilli paste	1.5 g. (¼ tsp.)
Water	1 lit.
Salt	9 g. (1½ tsp.)
Kokam (Garcinia purpurea)	2-3 pieces
Chopped coriander	3 g. (1½ tsp.)

1. In a thick-bottomed vessel, roast cumin, hing (asafoetida), turmeric, coconut, and chilli, in ghee for some time.
2. To this, add hot water, salt and kokam. Wait for it to boil and then put it on simmer.
3. Add kulith flour in a slow sprinkling action ensuring that no clumps are formed. Let it cook for 5-6 minutes stirring to keep consistent.
4. Add finely chopped coriander, and the soup is ready to serve.

MINT (PUDINA) CHUTNEY

All the ingredients used here are appetizing, and boost the process of digestion. This chutney is very useful in case of nausea and lack of appetite during pregnancy. It is also good for preventing indigestion post-partum.

Serves: 4-5 persons

Preparation time: 10 minutes

Ingredients

Pudina (mint)	10 g.
Coriander	15 g.
Fresh Grated Coconut	10 g.
Green chilli	7 g.
Lemon juice	2 tsp.
Salt	6 g. (1 tsp.)
Sugar	5 g. (1 tsp.)

1. Clean and wash the mint and coriander leaves.
2. Grind all the above-mentioned ingredients (except the lemon juice) in a mixer until they turn to a paste. A little water may be added if necessary.
3. Add the lemon juice, mix well and serve.

MIXED VEGETABLE THEPLA

Bottle gourd (dudhi) and carrots, used for these *theplas*, are very nutritious, and contain a range of important vitamins. Wheat flour, the only flour used in this recipe, adds to the nutritive value, and asafoetida, ginger, turmeric and coriander enhance taste and make the theplas easier to digest. They can be made quickly, and should ideally be eaten when hot.

Theplas can be included in the child's diet once it has started eating entire meals. Children may often refuse to eat certain highly nurtritious vegetables. These can be added to thepla. They are good during pregnancy as well, to add variety to the expectant mother's diet.

Makes: 7-8 theplas

Preparation time: 45 minutes.

Ingredients

Grated bottle gourd	100 g.
Grated carrot	100 g.
Wheat flour	250 g.
Chopped Coriander	6 g. (3 tsp.)
Grated ginger	3 g. (½ tsp.)
Chilli powder	1 g. (½ tsp.)
Asafoetida	1.5 g. (½ tsp.)
Turmeric	1 g. (½ tsp.)
Salt	9 g. (1 ½ tsp.)
Sugar	9 g. (1½ tsp.)
Curd	2-3 tsp.
Ghee	As required

1. Mix all the ingredients together except the wheat flour.
2. Gradually add the flour and knead to form a slightly firm dough, adding water if necessary. Divide the dough into 7-8 equal sized balls.
3. Flatten each ball with a rolling pin into a circular shape (make it as thin as required), and roast on a gridle (tava) or a flat non-stick pan, adding a little ghee aound and on it while roasting until golden brown on both sides.

Serve it hot with pickle, chutney, curd, jam or homemade butter.

Note: Other vegetables like spinach, fenugreek leaves or grated zucchini may be added for variety and as per one's taste.

SUPARI (FOR THE MOTHER AFTER DELIVERY)

Ajwain (Carum copticum) aids the digestive process and prevents flatulence. Sesame helps to purify the uterus and reduce vata present there. Balantshep is a lactogogue (improves the production of breast milk) and helps to prevent colic and abdominal pain in the infant. All the other ingredients enhance taste and aid digestion as well. The mother should eat this mixture (approx 1 teaspoon), after her meals. It should be chewed really well before ingesting.

Makes: 300 g. approximately.

Preparation time: 30 minutes.

Ingredients

Ajwain	50 g.
Sesame seeds	50 g.
Fennel seeds	50 g.
Balantshep	25 g.
Dry grated coconut	50 g.
Dhania dal	50 g.
Jyeshthamadh powder	25 g.
Clove powder	2.5 g.
Black salt	5g. approximately
Lemon	1

1. Mix the lemon juice and black salt.
2. The lemon juice and black salt need to be mixed with the sesame, ajwain, fennel seeds and balantshep, but separately. Put a fourth of the lemon and black salt into each of these. Each should be mixed thoroughly.
3. Roast each of the above mixtures separately in a pan over a low flame. Each of these mixtures will require a different amount of time to roast. You will know that a mixture is roasted properly when it releases its aroma.
4. When cool, add the dhania dal and jyeshthamadha powder to the fennel seeds and balantshep. Grind this mixture in a mixer, but only a little, since it should not be made into a fine powder. Crush the roasted grated coconut by hand to make a coarse powder.
5. Mix everything together thoroughly and store in an airtight container.

SUNTHA GOLI (GINGER BALLS)

Ginger is beneficial for general health and particularly post-delivery. It not only aids digestion, but also helps in purification of the uterus, and has vata pacifying properties.

Makes: 20 balls approximately

Preparation time: 15 minutes

Ingredients

Suntha (dry ginger) powder	20 g.
Ayurvedic ghee	approx 20 g.
Grated jaggery	30 g.

1. Add jaggery to the suntha churna and mix well.
2. Add the liquid ghee to the above mixture and make small balls, the size of betel nuts. Store in an airtight container.

Recommended: one ladu every morning on an empty stomach.

DINK LADU

High quality dink (a special gum resin - gum

acacia), fried in ghee, is excellent for strengthening bones, joints, and the spine. Kharik (dry date) powder balances all three doshas and nourishes bones and muscles. Other ingredients such as almonds, cashew nuts and pistachios provide strength. They increase life energy (ojas) and virya. Suntha, pimpli and saffron make the above mentioned ingredients easy to digest and assist the process of absorbing the other ingredients.

Dink ladus ensure that the nutritional requirements of calcium and iron are met. They also help in increasing stamina and maintaining the weight and figure. For these reasons, having one a day is a must after childbirth, and it is beneficial if eaten during pregnancy as well.

Makes: 30-35 ladus.

Preparation time: 1 hour.

Ingredients

Dink	200 g.
Kharik powder	200 g.
Dry grated coconut	100 g.
Khus khus (poppy seeds)	100 g.
Cashew nuts	50 g.
Almonds	50 g.
Pistachios	50 g.
Charoli	50 g.
Jaggery	300 g.
Sugar	200 g.
Suntha powder	25 g.
Pimpli powder	25 g.
Nutmeg powder	6 g. (2 tsp.)
Saffron powder	½ g. (teaspoon)
Milk	25-30 ml . (¼ cup approx.)
Ghee for frying	as required

1. Carefully crush the larger pieces of dink in a mortar and pestle to make them smaller. (Else large pieces remain uncooked in the centre and very small pieces burn during frying).
2. Coarsely grind the almonds, pistachios, cashew nuts and charoli in a mixer.
3. Roast the khus khus in an iron-frying vessel (kadhai). Allow it to cool, then grind it roughly in a mixer or a mortar and pestle.
4. Roast the dry coconut on a low flame. Crush with the hands after cooling.
5. Heat the ghee in a kadhai and fry the dink pieces, a few at a time until they expand. When cool enough, crush them lightly with the hands.
6. In the same kadhai, fry the date powder in the remaining ghee.
7. In a large plate or bowl, add the fried dink, date powder, ground almonds, pistachios, cashew nuts, and charoli, coconut, khus khus, suntha, pimpli and nutmeg (jaiphal) churna, and mix thoroughly.
8. Combine the jaggery, sugar and milk, and heat in a thick-bottomed pan on a low flame. Once the jaggery melts and forms bubbles, remove the mixture from the flame. Add saffron powder and mix well.
9. Add the above mixture slowly to this syrup and roll into balls (laddus) while still warm.

METHI LADU

Methi (fenugreek) seeds are extremely helpful in purifying the uterus after delivery, and in restoring it to normalcy. They also help to lose excess weight after delivery, and purify the breast milk.

Fenugreek seeds are normally very bitter and dry. To counter this effect, the seeds are soaked in ghee for a number of days. This process has been described in the recipe below. This methi ladu contains several other nutritious ingredients, such as dink, almonds, khus khus, and godambi. The preparation is extremely helpful for women just after delivery.

Makes: 25-30 ladus.

Preparation time: about 1 hour

Ingredients

Methi (fenugreek) seed powder	75 g.
Ghee	100 g.
Ghee for frying	as required
Wheat flour	150 g.
Powdered sugar	400 g.
Dink	25 g.
Khus Khus	50 g.
Almonds	25 g.
Cashewnuts	25 g.
Charoli	25 g.
Pistachios	25 g.
Godambi	25 g.

1. Soak the methi powder in freshly made ghee (made from homemade butter). Leave it in the ghee for 8 days. Stir well at least once a day.
2. Grind almonds, cashew nuts, godambi, charoli and pistachios coarsely in a mixer.
3. In an iron frying pan (kadhai) roast the khus khus. Allow it to cool and grind coarsely in a mixer or mortar and pestle.
4. Carefully crush larger pieces of dink in a mortar and pestle to make them smaller. Large pieces remain uncooked in the centre and very small pieces burn during frying. Heat the ghee in the kadhai and fry the dink pieces a few at a time, until they expand. When cool enough to handle, crush them lightly with your fingers.
5. Roast the wheat flour in the remaining ghee till it is golden brown in colour.
6. In a large plate, mix the hot roasted wheat flour, fried dink, ground almonds, cashew nuts, godambi, charoli pistachios and khus khus. Add the methi powder and ghee mixture to this. Add powdered sugar and roll into ladus while warm.

AHLEEV LADU

Ahleev (Garden Cress - Lepidium sativum) and fresh coconut improve the quality of breast milk. Since all the ingredients are extremely nutritious for both mother and child, these ladus are a must while the child is being breast-fed.

Makes: 25-30 ladus

Preparation time: 40 minutes

Ingredients

Ahleev	25 g.
Jaggery	300 g.
Almonds	50 g.
Pistachios	50 g.
Cashew nut	50 g.
Nutmeg powder	1 flat tsp.
Fresh grated coconut	100 g.
Coconut water or coconut milk	as required

1. Soak the ahleev properly in coconut water or coconut milk for 3-4 hours. This will puff up the ahleev.
2. Grind the almonds, cashew nuts, and pistachios coarsely in a mixer.
3. Mix the puffed up ahleev, grated jaggery and grated fresh coconut in a thick-bottomed pan

and heat over a low flame.

4. When the mixture is almost cooked (when it turns soft), add the coarsely ground dry fruits and nutmeg powder. Mix thoroughly and roll into ladus when cool enough to handle.

The other essential ingredients contained in dink, ahleev, and methi laddus, are almonds, cashew nuts and pistachios. These should definitely be included in a new mother's diet. Eating the ladus described above, ensures that the new mother are health and nourished while nursing.

Scientific names of medicinal plants

Ahleev	Lepidium sativum
Aamsool, Kokam	Garcinia purpurea
Adulsa	Adhatoda vasika
Agaru	Aquilaria agallocha
Almond - Badam	Prunus amygdalus
Aloe	Aloe vera
Ambat Chuka	Rumex vesicarius
Amla	Emblica officinalis
Anantmool	Hemidesmus indicus
Ashok	Saraca indica
Ashwagandha	Withania somnifera
Ativisha	Aconitum heterophyllum
Bajri	Sorghum vulgare
Bala	Sida cordifolia
Balantshop	Peucedanum graveolens
Banyan - Vad	Ficus bengalensis
Beet root	Beta vulgaris
Behada	Terminalia belerica
Bhagar	Panicum milliaceum
Bhojpatra	Betula bhojapattra
Black gram - Udid	Phaseolus roxburghii
Black Pepper - Mire	Piper nigrum
Black Raisins - Manuka	Vitis vinifera
Bor	Zizyphus jujuba
Brahmi	Herpestis monniera
Cabbage	Brassica oleracea
Cardamom	Elettaria cardamomum
Carrot	Daucus carotaBhendi
Chakwat	Chenopodium album
Charoli	Buchanania latifolia
Chavalai	Amarantus polygamus
Chavya	Piper chaba
Chawli	Vigna catiang

Chick pea - Harbara	Cicer arietinum
Chiku	Achras sapota
Chitrak	Plumbago zeylanica
Cinnamon	Cinnamomum cassia
Daruhalad	Berberis aristata
Deodar	Cedrus deodara
Dhane	Coriandrum sativum
Dhayati	Woodfordia floribunda
Dikemali	Gardenia gummifera
Dink	Acacia arabica
Dodka - Ridged luffa	Luffa acutangula
Dudhi - Bottle gourd	Lagenaria vulgaris
Durva	Cynodon dactylon
Fenugreek - Methi	Trigonella foenum-graeceum
Gawar - Cluster beans	Cyamopsis psoralioides
Ghosali - Smooth luffa	Luffa aegyptiaca
Gokshur	Tribulus terrestris
Gorakhmundi	Sphaeranthus hirtus
Green gram - Moong	Phaseolus mungo
Guava - Peru	Psidium guyava
Guduchi	Tinospora cordifolia
Guggul	Balsamodendron mukul
Gunja	Abrus precatorius
Hirda	Terminalia chebula
Jai	Jasminum grandiflorum
Jambhul	Eugenia jambolana
Jav / Yav	Hordeum vulgare
Jwari	Sorghum vulgare
Jyeshthamadh	Glycyrrhiza glabra
Kadechirait	Gentiana kurroo
Kakadshingi	Rhus succedanea
Kakoli	Zizyphus napica
Kala bol	Aloe vera
Kalalavi	Gloriosa superba
Kankol	Cubeba officinalis

Karela - Bitter gourd	Momordica charantia
Kavach	Mucuna pruriens
Kavath (Kapittha)	Feronia elephantum
Kayphal	Myrica nagi
Khareek, Khajur	Phoenix dactylifera
Kohala	Benincasa cerifera
Kshirkakoli	Gymnema lactiferum
Kuda, Kutaj	Holarrhena antidysenterica
Kulith	Dolichos biflorus
Kushth	Saussurea lappa
Lady finger - Bhendi	Abelmoschus esculentus
Lajalu	Mimosa pudica
Linseed - Atasi	Linum usitatissimum
Lodhra	Symplocos racemosa
Lotus - Kamal	Nelumbium speciosum
Madan	Randia dumetorum
Manjishtha	Rubia cordifolia
Masoor	Lens esculenta
Math	Amaranthus gangeticus
Matki	Phaseolus aconitifolius
Mayphal	Quercus infectoria
Murudsheng	Helicteres isora
Musali	Asparagus adscendens
Mustard	Brassica sp.
Nachani	Eleusine coracana
Nagarmotha	Cyperus rotundus
Nagkeshar	Mesua ferrea
Nutmeg (Jaiphal)	Myristica fragrans
Onion	Allium cepa
Ova	Carum copticum
Padmakashtha	Prunus malus
Padval	Trichosanthes anguina
Pawata	Dolichos lablab
Pear	Pyrus communis
Pimpal	Ficus religiosa

Pimpli	Piper longum
Pittapapada	Fumaria officinalis
Pomegranate - Dadim	Punica granatum
Poppy seeds - Khus khus	Papaver somniferum
Potato	Solanum tuberosum
Pumpkin	Cucurbita maxima
Rajgira	Amarantus paniculatus
Rajma	Phaseolus vulgaris
Raktachandan	Pterocarpus santalinus
Ratale - Sweet potato	Ipomoea batatas
Renuka	Piper aurantiacum
Rui	Calatropis gigantea
Saffron	Crocus sativus
Sagargota	Caesalpinia bonduc
Sago - Sabudana	Sagus laevus
Sandalwood	Santalum album
Sesame - Til	Sesamum indicum
Shatavari	Asparagus racemosus
Shigada	Trapa bispinosa
Shilajit	Asphaltum
Shirish	Acacia speciosa
Soya-bean	Soja hispida
Spinach	Spinacia oleracea
Sunth	Zingiber officinale
Suran	Amorphophallus campanulatus
Tamalpatra	Cinnamomum iners
Tandulja	Amarantus oleraceus
Tondali	Cephalandra indica
Turmeric - Halad	Curcuma longa
Umbar	Ficus glomerata
Vanshalochan	Bambusa arundinacea
Vavding	Embelia ribes
Vekhand	Acorus calamus
Vidari	Ipomoea digitata

Santulan products for Garbha Sanskar

Santulan Feminine Balance Asav: It is important for women to maintain their femininity and achieve optimal hormonal balance. This asav, made from ingredients such as ashok, kumari, dhayati, and lodhra, helps to regulate the menstrual cycle. It alleviates the following symptoms.

1. Excess blood flow or clots during menstruation.
2. Pain during menstruation
3. Black or mucoid discharges

Regular intake helps prevent pre-menstrual symptoms such as pain in the breasts, irritability, and general swelling in the body. In addition, it helps purify and strengthen the entire female reproductive system.

Santulan Prashant Powder: This medicine is made from gokshur, punanarva, and other ingredients which nourish shukra and increase virya. Prashant, ideally to be taken by both partners before conception, ensures healthy sperm and ova. In women, it additionally strengthens the ovaries and uterus.

Santulan Femisan Oil : It contains herbs such as dhayati, daruhalad and ashok. It is an easy and effective medicine for women. It helps to balance female hormones.

Directions for use: Soak a small swab of cotton with approximately 7-8 drops of Femisan oil. Place this inside the vagina at bedtime and leave it overnight. It will usually fall out by itself during urination in the morning, or can alternatively be removed carefully by hand.

Ideally, the use of Femisan oil should be started at 12 or 13 years of age (at the onset of menstruation), and should be used as often as possible, upto old age. The only time when it is not recommended, is during the days of menstruation.

Using Femisan oil like this during the ninth month of pregnancy provides lubrication in the passage for easy and normal childbirth.

Post-partum, the oil can be used again, once vaginal discharge ceases after childbirth. Here, it works to restore the uterus to normalcy and strengthens the reproductive system.

Santulan Shakti Dhoop: Dhoop has several uses. It is often used in temples and houses to neutralise potentially harmful microorganisms. This dhoop is a specific mixture of herbs made according to traditional Ayurvedic formulae. It contains herbs such as dhayati, balantshep, and vavding, which are specifically beneficial for women. The therapy should be administered to the vagina. It benefits the female reproductive organs, helping to restore the uterus and vagina to their normal status after delivery. It is effective in cases of urinary and vaginal infections, white discharge, burning sensation or itching in the vagina, and similar complaints.

It is recommended that all women take dhoop regularly, at least once or twice a week, and more often, in cases of uterine or urinary problems.

Directions: Put 2-3 pinches of dhoop mixture onto a small pan with some pieces of burning charcoal. Sit or stand around the pan in such a way that the smoke rising from the pan reaches the vaginal region. Wrap a sheet around the lower part of the body during the therapy so that the smoke remains contained inside. Sit like this for at least five mins. Make sure to keep adding more mixture to the charcoal as it is consumed.

It can be continued from delivery until menstruation resumes to help restore the uterus to its normal size.

Santulan Purusham Oil: This special oil for men, infused with herbs, such as ashwagandha, kushtha, and mustaa, helps maintain the health of the male reproductive system.

Directions for use: After bathing, gently apply 2-3 drops of the oil on the genital organs. **Santulan Purusham Oil** is helpful in conditions such as urinary and genital infections, defects in the vas deferens, impotence, premature ejaculation, wet dreams, as well as in complaints encountered due to diabetes etc. To help maintain overall health, it should be applied at least twice or thrice a week.

Vitasan Tablets: For problems specific to men, such as low sperm count, weak sperm motility, or premature ejaculation, Ayurveda has suggested many medicines. This medicine should be used after consulting an expert vaidya.

Santulan Uricool Powder: This special medication is beneficial for urinary disorders, pain, or swelling due to infection and to achieve a proper passage of urine.

Santulan Urix Powder: This is beneficial for problems such as a burning sensation or pain during urination, itching, and various urinary problems. In such instances, Urix should be taken with lemon juice, and in combination with **Santulan Uricool**.

Marrosan: It is made from the highest quality dink (specified since several qualities are available), almonds, godambi, and musali, which nourish the dhatus. This preparation increases virya and strengthens shukra dhatu. Since Marrosan strengthens and nourishes the sperm and ova, as well as helps fertilization, it is recommended that couples wishing to have a child should take it for at least two months before planning conception. Ideally, pregnant women should take Marrosan throughout pregnancy, and for at least three months after delivery. It helps the foetus to grow well, and helps prevent post-partum backaches and osteoporosis.

Santulan Dhatri Rasayan: It is made from herbs such as amla, raisins, and kushmanda, which have cooling properties. This formulation is especially effective in improving brain function *(medhya)*. It also helps improve the quality of rakta dhatu (blood) and increase physical strength.

Santulan Chyavanprash: Made from ingredients like amla, ashwagandha and vidarikand, it nourishes the dhatus and increases virya. This mixture helps the ovum achieve proper maturity in women, when taken prior to pregnancy, and supports the development of the foetus when taken during pregnancy.

Santulan Suryaprash: This preparation is similar to Chyavanprash, and enhanced due to the addition of edible gold.

Santulan Ashokadi Ghruta: This is in the form of ghee and contains herbs such as ashok, shatavari and cumin, which purify and nourish the uterus. Ashokadi ghruta facilitates proper ovulation and assists fertilization. Since it strengthens the uterus, it helps to avoid complications arising from the uterus throughout pregnancy. Women with a previous history of miscarriages will find that it strengthens the uterus for future pregnancies. It is recommended that this tonic be taken for two to three months before conception.

San Rose: It is basically *gulkand* (a jam made from the petals of the Indian rose) enhanced with praval bhasma, suvarnamakshik bhasma, abhrak bhasma etc. San Rose is the best of all rasayans for women. It strengthens bones, improves physical strength, boosts haemoglobin levels, stops hair loss, prevents weakness, and nourishes rakta dhatu. When taken regularly during pregnancy, it helps the baby achieve good skin and complexion, and prevents skin diseases. San Rose can be taken before conception, during pregnancy, and post-delivery.

Shatavari

a) Santulan Shatavari Kalpa b) Shatanant c) Shatadaam d) ShatavariSan, e) Shatavari Churna: All these different preparations of the shatavari herb offer different benefits in addition to the basic benefits of shatavari. Shatavari kalpa is beneficial to female health in general, and especially during pregnancy and lactation. One should regularly take two teaspoons of Shatavari Kalpa in a cup of hot milk. Shatavari helps maintain hormonal balance, supports the physical and intellectual development of the foetus, helps the nursing mother to produce a sufficient quantity of milk, and helps maintain her figure. The Shatavari used in **Santulan Shatavari Kalpa** is of a very high quality, and its efficiency is enhanced by the addition of herbs, such as ashwagandha, gokshur, keshar, cardamom and cinnamon. Shatanant kalpa contains anant along with shatavari which improves complexion and balances pitta. Shatadaam kalpa contains almonds, which help improve brain function. **Shatavari San** tablets or shatavari churna also provide some of the above mentioned benefits.

Santulan Amrutshatakara: One teaspoon taken daily, with milk or in Panchamrut, is extremely beneficial for the overall health. This health food contains ingredients, such as, shatavari, saffron and *suvarnavarkha* (edible gold in a film-like form), which nourish shukra dhatu as well as purify and increase rakta dhatu. It also improves immunity and boosts energy.

When taken regularly during pregnancy, Amrutshatakara ensures the proper formation and development of the various organs of the foetus, especially the brain and heart. It also improves intelligence, memory and grasping power. Since it nourishes rakta dhatu it helps give the baby healthy and glowing skin. Saffron, especially, is known to help ensure that the process of labour is normal, and occurs on time, by helping to balance vata dosha. It helps the uterus return to its normal state thereafter. When taken regularly by nursing mothers, it ensures timely growth and development of the baby as well as helps to make the child bright and intelligent.

Santulan Pittashanti Tablets: It is made from praval bhasma, motibhasma, guduchi satva, and other ingredients, which are cooling in nature. This medication in tablet form, helps reduce acidity and heat in the body, and neutralises pitta, thus relieving headaches and migraines. It is also a rich source of natural calcium. Thus, it is recommended, before, during, and after pregnancy, for its bone-strengthening properties for both, mother and baby.

Santulan Calcisan: Santulan Calcisan tablets contain natural calcium, and are thus ideally suited to cater to increased calcium requirements during pregnancy, without causing an increase in body heat or other side effects normally seen due to the intake of calcium supplements. The calcium in Calcisan is easily absorbed and assimilated by the body, making this preparation useful in cases of osteoporosis.

Santulan Rudhira & Lohit Plus Tablets (they are almost alternatives for one another)**:** Rudhira contains valuable ingredients, such as, suvarnamakshik bhasma, mandur bhasma, and *tapyadi loha*, and helps the blood have balanced constituents and boosts haemoglobin levels. Lohit Plus is a good supplier of iron as it contains natural and easily digestible iron, which strengthens rakta dhatu. The regular intake of Lohit Plus, will help maintain physical strength, especially in women.

Santulan Brahmaleen Ghruta & Sanbrahmi Tablets: They are made from brahmi and other herbs, that improve memory, intelligence, and the health of the brain. Brahmaleen ghruta is good for all adults, especially those over forty. When taken during pregnancy, it benefits both mother and child. Sanbrahmi tablets, which are convenient to take, also provide some of the above benefits.

AnantSan & ManjishthaSan Tablets: They impart a healthy skin to the growing foetus. **Anantsan** tablets ensure that the baby's skin becomes clear, radiant, and glowing. It improves the colour and complexion of skin. **Manjishthasan** has the same properties with the added benefits of being useful in preventing skin diseases as well, and helping reduce hereditary skin disorders.

Jeevansan: It is very useful as a general tonic for all types of physical weakness. It supports the proper nourishment of the foetus, and helps to maintain adequate quantities of amniotic fluid.

Gulkand special: Gulkand mixed with praval, reduces excess heat in the body, ensures proper bowel movements, and neutralises dryness and irritation of the eyes. It is, therefore, recommended that Gulkand be taken during pregnancy and after delivery.

Sanpitta syrup & Dadimavaleh: Though both these medicines are quite diiferent from each other, they have very similar effects. **Sanpitta Syrup** is useful against morning sickness, nausea and lack of appetite, all of which are common in the first trimester of pregnancy. **Dadimavaleh**, in addition to the above benefits, helps to reduce acidity.

Santulan Annayog Tablets: The main ingredients of these tablets are various natural salts and lemon juice. The intake of these tablets supports the digestive process, and prevents minor complaints, such as, acidity and flatulence.

Santulan Padabhyang Ghruta: This helps reduce complaints associated with increase in body heat, such as a burning sensation in the eyes, on the palms, or feet. This ghee is to be applied on the soles of the feet, and then using the outside of a bowl made of a special combination of metals (kansa), the ghee is massaged on to the sole. Padabhyang is also recommended for diabetes, especially in cases where the nerves of the feet are affected, and immunity is impaired. It helps improve general health if used during pregnancy and after delivery.

Santulan Suhrud Oil: During lactation, it is important that a mother produces adequate breast milk for her baby. Problems such as dry skin, and improper breast development, could hamper breastfeeding. Suhrud is a sesame-based oil, which has been infused with herbs such as *gorakhmundi* (Sphaeranthus hirtus), dhayati (Woodfordia floribunda) and *kaasis* (an Ayurvedic product containing iron). Used regularly, it maintains the health of the breasts, especially during pregnancy and after delivery. It also helps the breasts remain firm and prevents sagging.

Santulan Rose Beauty Oil: This is coconut oil

infused with skin-nourishing ingredients, such as sandalwood, rose, saffron, and others. **Santulan Rose Beauty Oil** helps prevent stretch marks if applied to the abdomen during pregnancy. It also helps loose skin become firm after delivery and reduces the formation of scar tissue after a caesarian section. If either mother or baby has abdominal pain, gently massaging **Santulan Rose Beauty Oil** on to the abdomen with relieve the discomfort.

Santulan Kundalini Oil: Based on the traditional recipe of *chandanbalalakshadi* oil, this oil strengthens the spine, back muscles, and general structure of the back. It should be used to massage the back and pelvic region of the mother-to-be after the third month of pregnancy. This helps the joints of the pelvis remain flexible. Thus, it facilitates the process of labour, and prevents backache and lumbar pain after delivery.

Santulan Abhyang Oil: Based on the traditional recipe of *narayan* oil, this oil is additionally infused with various vata-pacifying herbs. When gently massaged onto the skin, it gets absorbed fully. Therefore, even if used in small quantities, it penetrates to the cellular level to remove toxic substances. **Santulan Abhyang Oil** provides lubrication, helps maintain flexibility, and increases physical strength. Its regular use balances vata dosha, increases the capacity to work, and lends to clear glowing skin. Since it helps the body eliminate toxins, it consequently helps the immune system and leads to increased enthusiasm.

There are two types of **Santulan Abhyang Oil**: Abhyang (S) (Sesame oil base) can be used by mothers; and Abhyang (C) (Coconut oil base) can be used for children. Abhyang (S) is ideally suited to balance vata after delivery. Regular use maintains the physical structure, prevents the accumulation of excess fat or removes that which is already present. The expectant mother should start using this oil occasionally from the third month of pregnancy, and regularly in the last trimester. After delivery, a full body massage with this oil is recommended for an entire year. It should be applied in combination with smoke therapy (dhoop/ dhuri), for the first three months after delivery. Abhyang (C) is mild, cooling in nature, and nourishing. This renders it ideal for the soft and sensitive skin of babies. Cultured with mild nutritive herbs such as shatavari, bala and sariva, this oil protects the delicate skin, and promotes the baby's general development.

Santulan Balant Lep: This mixture helps to ensure a natural, easy, and quick labour, and is used only at that time. It should be applied around the umbilicus as soon as contractions begin at regular intervals. In addition, **Santulan Balant Lep** helps prevent complications during labour.

Lactosan Tablets (lactogogue): It helps increase the quantity of breast milk being produced and helps ensure that breast milk production continues for as long as required.

San Massage Powder: This is a herbal massage powder containing valuable herbs, such as nagarmotha, turmeric, anantmool, and sandalwood. It balances vata (which increaseds after delivery), helps reduce excessive fatty tissue and stretch marks, and tightens loose skin. It can be used instead of soap while bathing. It may also be used from the third month of pregnancy, as a preventative measure against stretch marks.

Santulan Baby Massage Powder: This is a special massage powder for baby's delicate and tender skin. Made from anantmool, rose petals, sandalwood and several other fragrant herbs, it should be mixed with cream or milk, and used for the baby's bath, instead of soap. Using **Santulan Baby Massage Powder** allows you to avoid the chemicals present in commercial soap. It lends a glow to the skin, clears the complexion, and prevents rashes and allergies.

Santulan Tenderness Dhoop: This mixture is to be used as in smoke therapy for children. It contains germicidal and fragrant herbs such as ajwain, jataamanvsi, and guggul. Regular use helps prevent coughs, colds, fever, and other commonly occurring infections. So, it is recommended that the herbal smoke treatment be given to babies regularly, after bathing. This dhoop strengthens the respiratory system, helps prevent infantile asthma, whooping cough, and other serious respiratory diseases. Additionally, some of the ingredients are also beneficial for development of the entire body. In administering the dhoop, take care that the child does not feel uncomfortable.

San Anjan (black): This is a kajal, made using traditional Ayurvedic techniques.
Method of preparation: A ghee lamp is lit, and the soot produced is collected and mixed ghee that has been processed with triphala, daruhalad, and other ingredients, which are beneficial for the eyes and vision of the baby in particular. The kajal, carefully applied, with a clean finger, in the baby's eyes, helps keep the eyes healthy, bright, and glowing. A small spot is traditionally applied to the baby's cheek to ward off negativity.

Santulan Chaitanya kalpa: This herbal granulate, comprises of a mixture of herbs, such as ashwagandha, kavachbeej, vidari, and dry ginger, which nourish all seven dhatus. **Santulan Chaitanya Kalpa** increases muscle strength, strengthens bones, improves the intellect, grasping power, and all other brain functions. Therefore it is an excellent food supplement for growing children.

Santulan Balamrut: Made from handpicked precious ingredients, like keshar, suvarnavarkha, vekhand, shatavari, gulvel, and candy sugar. This mixture is a nectar for the baby. Dip a clean, honey-coated finger in this powder. The amount of the medicine that sticks to the finger is the ideal dose for a new-born baby. The dose may be increased in small amounts after the first six months as the baby keeps growing. It should be given to the child once a day. Besides enhancing the baby's complexion, **Santulan Balamrut** nourishes the brain of the child, and improves intelligence, memory, grasping power, and comprehension. It also boosts immunity, so that common illnesses, such as coughs, colds, and fever do not occur. It helps the child become intelligent, bright, and healthy.

Santulan Bal Herbal syrup: Made from vidang, suntha, pimpli, and shrungi, this syrup acts on the baby's digestive system. It improves the digestion and appetite, prevents parasitic infestations, and ensures proper weight gain. It is sweet in taste, and generally liked by children.

Other Santulan medicines

Ayurvedic preparations, meant for use prior to conception: Santulan Feminine Balance Asav, Santulan Prashant, Santulan Femisan Oil, Santulan Shakti dhoop, Santulan Uricool, Santulan Urix, Marrosan, Santulan Dhatri Rasayan, Santulan Chyavanprash / Santulan Suryaprash, Santulan Ashokadi Ghruta, San Rose, Santulan Shatavari Kalpa / Shatanant / Shatadaam / Shatavarisan/ Shatavari churna, Santulan Amrutshatakara, Santulan Suhrud Oil, Santulan Purusham Oil, Vitasan.

Ayurvedic preparations to be used during pregnancy: Marrosan, Santulan Dhatri rasayan, Santulan Chyavanprash/ Suryaprash, San Rose, Santulan Shatavari kalpa / Shatanant / Shatadaam/ Shatavarisan / Shatavari Churna, Santulan Amrutshatakara, Santulan Pittashanti, Calcisan, Santulan Rudhira & Lohit Plus, Brahmaleen ghrut / San Brahmi, Anantsan/ Manjishthasan, Jeevansan, Gulkand special, Sanpitta Syrup / Dadimavaleh, Annayog, Santulan Padabhyang Ghrut, Santulan Suhrud Oil, Santulan Rose Beauty oil, Santulan Kundalini Oil, Santulan Abhyang (S) Oil, San Masage Powder.

Ayurvedic preparations for used during delivery: Femisan Oil, Santulan Shakti Dhoop, Marrosan, Santulan Shatavari Kalpa / Shatanant / Shatadaam/ Shatavarisan / Shatavari Churna, Santulan Amrutshatakara, Santulan Feminine Balance asav, Santulan Amrutshatakara, Santulan Pittashanti, Calcisan, Santulan Rudhira & Lohit Plus, Gulkand special, Annayog, Santulan Padabhyang Ghrut, Santulan Suhrud Oil, Santulan Rose Beauty Oil, Santulan Kundalini Oil, Santulan Abhyang (S) Oil, Lactosan, San Massage Powder.

Ayurvedic preparations suitable for infants: Santulan Abhyang (C) Oil, Santulan Baby Massage Powder, Santulan Tenderness Dhoop, San Anjan (black), Santulan Chaitanya Kalpa, Santulan Balamrut, Santulan Bal Herbal Syrup.

Reference Books

- Kashyap Samhita
- Bhaishajya Ratnavali
- Charak Samhita
- Charak Shareersthan
- Rasayogasagar
- Sushrut Samhita
- Sushrut Shareersthan
- Santulan Kriya Yog
- Ashtanghrudaya
- Hathayog Pradeepika
- Ashtangasangraha
- Text book of Obstretics: D.C. Dutta
- Yogaratnakar
- Shaw's textbook of Gynaecology
- Bhavprakash
- Dorlands medical dictionary
- Sharangdhar Samhita
- Gray's Anatomy
- Text book of Pediatrics: O. P. Ghai

Glossary

Abhimanyu – An important character in the Mahabharata. Son of Arjuna and Subhadra. He learned how to break into the feared chakravyuha from Shri Krishna, while still in his mother's womb. The chakravyuha was a supposedly impregnable battle formation. Abhimanyu had not learned how to break out how to break out. He was a supreme warrior. In the Mahabharata War, the Kauravas had to resort to bending the rules of combat to vanquish him after he had broken into the chakravyuha and averted certain defeat for the Pandavas (the heroes of the epic).

Abhyanga – Literally translated as massage, normally with the help of medicated oil. In 'abhyanga' one does not just rub oil onto the surface of the body. It implies a specific practice of massage through which the oil is administered so that it reaches as deep into the body as possible, sometimes as far as the bones.

Acharya – A teacher who has complete mastery over his subject.

Agni – The Fire Element. One of the Five Universal Elemental Forms that constitute all matter in the universe. See also Pancha-Mahabhoot and Chapter on Ayurvedic Concepts. Agni is not what is normally understood to be fire. It is the principal agency for transformation.

Ahar-ras – The ingested part of the food is in the form of a juice which is capable of nourishing all the seven dhatus. This juice is called ahar-ras.

Akash Tattva – One of the Five Universal Elemental Forms that constitute all matter in the universe. See also Pancha-Mahabhoot and Chapter on Ayurvedic Concepts. It does literally mean sky. It means the 'element' or principle of space.

Amavasya – The last day of the waning moon when it cannot be seen from the Earth.

Anahat Chakra – The fourth major energy vortex (chakra) in the body situated near the heart. It is the seat of the element of air (movement) and this is easily conceived looking at the function of the heart. It is associated with love and compassion.

Apanavata – It is one of the sub-types of vata doshas that rules the lower abdominal region of the body and is responsible for driving the natural delivery of a child, among other important functions.

Ashram – A normal person gets tired of trying to achieve his illusory goals and objects of possession. An ashram is a place where one can enjoy rest and recuperation from this process and learn to become quiet.

Ashtanga Sanghraha – One of the central treatises of Ayurveda, authored by Acharya Vagabhatta that deals with subjects across the eight branches of Ayurveda. Ashtanga = Eight-part

Ashtangahruday Shareersthan – The entire Ashtangahruday is one of the central treatises of Ayurveda, written by Acharya Vagabhatta. A section of the Ashtangahruday that deals mainly with anatomy is called the Shareersthan. The Ashtangahruday deals with all the eight branches of Ayurveda. It is a unique piece of medical work that profoundly captures the essence of the subject in the form of verse rather than prose.

Aum – The First and Universal sound from which the entire Universe emerges.

Ayurveda – A complete medical system. An upa-veda (sub section) of the Atharva Veda.

Basti – An oil based medical preparation administered through an enema. It is one of the most effective therapies to help pacify vata dosha.

Bhakri – One of the many ways in which Indians make bread. It is made of millets. Often two or more types of millet flour or grains are mixed to make bhakri. Since it is cooked directly over a fire, it is very light and easy to digest.

Bhastrika –These are special cleansing exhalation techniques. They clean the respiratory tract and purify the channels of energy in the body. They also provide all the benefits of Pranayam. They are often practiced in conjunction with specific poses which provide even more benefit in the exercise.

Brahmacharya – A pattern of behavior and attitude that helps direct the energies of the body to the two main organs (seats of consciousness) – the brain and the heart. Mistakenly assumed to mean celibacy, although the protection and preservation of the body's seminal and vital fluids is part of the practice.

Brahmacharya-ashram – referring to the first major phase of life, as propounded by the ancient systems of thought, where the person prepares to become a useful part of society and a responsible adult, through learning, studies and discipline.

Brahmaghosh – The aural effect of vedic mantras being chanted in unison by many people to create resonance in the atmosphere.

Chakra – A centre for interaction and redistribution of different types of bio-energy.

Chakravyuha – Literally translated as 'the Circular Strategy'. In the Mahahbarata it refers to the seemingly impregnable battle formation created by Drona, commander of the Kaurava army. While Arjuna was distracted and led away, his son Abhimanyu, was the only other Pandava warrior who knew how to break into it, but not how to break out. He bravely gave up his life to save the day for the Pandavas.

Chapati - Thinly rolled bread of coarse grained wheat flour cooked on a pan.

Charak Sharirsthan – Part of the medical canon of the Seer Charak that deals with anatomy and reproduction

Charak Sutrastana – A Sutrasthana text generally deals with the basic principles of Ayurveda. The Charak Sutrasthana has been written by Acharya Charak.

Chetana – Consciousness

Dhatu – They loosely correspond to the tissues of the body as understood by western medicine. They are the result of each transformation of energy in the body, beginning from ingested food and going up to the creation of life energy. Please see chapter on Ayurvedic Concepts for more details.

Dhoop – A method to administer herbal smoke to a physical area or a specific part of the body (or the entire body). Traditionally, a pot or pan is filled with dried cow dung or charcoal. This is lit, and the required dry herbal mixture is sprinkled on top of it. This herb is administered to the desired area in the form of smoke particles for a very penetrating effect. The use of the dhoop depends on the kind of herb used. The revival of therapeutic dhoop formulations for specific health purposes has been a one of Dr. Shri Balaji Tambe's well-known innovations. Nowadays, very easy to use and attractive, candle-based dhoop pots, and even electric dhoop pots are available.

Dosha – vata,pitta and kapha – The three major functioning forces in the human body. When one or more of these 'doshas' is out of equilibrium, it brings disease. The root of all discomforts can be traced back to the imbalance of the doshas. Please see chapter on Ayurvedic Concepts for more details.

Fodni - In Indian cooking, the cooking medium (oil, ghee) is heated with spices in the pan. The spices begin to pop and release their essence into the medium. This is called fodni. Vegetables can now be added to the medium to be cooked.

Fomentation – A therapeutic technique of exposing the body or a part of the body to heat. It can be done in several ways, like steam from hot water, hot water bags or hot sand bags. Often, herbal additions to the water or the hot mixture are used for specific results.

Fulka - extremely thin rolled bread made from coarse

grained wheat flour that is cooked on a pan and then puffed on an open flame.

Garbha Sanskar – Ayurveda has researched and developed a very sophisticated and detailed procedure that takes care of conception, pregnancy and early development of a child. The process described in this book has been further distilled to make it suitable for modern times without compromising on any of the benefits.

Garbhadhaan – The first important sanskar of life.

Garbhopanishad – Ancient knowledge about pregnancy.

Ghee – Pure Ayurvedic ghee is made in the following manner. Pure, unprocessed (at most only pasteurized) milk is boiled and then allowed to settle until its cream rises to the top. Collect this cream. Culture the cream with Indian household curd (not yoghurt). Allow the cream to convert to curd. Churn this curd in a pot with alternating clockwise and anti-clockwise movements until it results in an extract that easily rises to the surface. This extract is butter. Separate out the butter and heat it in a pan until its water content completely evaporates. The resultant substance is ghee. Throughout this book, this is what we mean by ghee. If there are any compromises in the process, the resultant substance is not to be accepted as ghee.

Ghruta – The Sanskrit word for ghee.

Grihast-ashram – referring to the second major phase of life, where a person engages in society, gets married and performs all the social, natural and economic obligations of human life.

Gotra – The pedigree of a human being. Shows the original connection of the genetic thread of the family.

Guna – Tendencies that pervade/motivate all action in the universe.

Guru – A teaches deals with subjects that will be useful merely to earn a living. The guru helps one develop one's personality, and a broader outlook to life identified by one's vocation. The Sadguru offers the practical process to experience that 'oneness' which ultimately allows one to be in permamnent bliss and freedom. 'Guru' is also the name given to the planet Jupiter who is considered the Master and Guide of the Gods.

Hanuman Chalisa – 40 verses in praise of Hanuman, the ultimate devotee of Shri Ram, and a mighty and powerful God, son of Vayu.

Jala Tattva – The Water Element. One of the Five Universal Elemental Forms that constitute all matter in the universe. See also Pancha-Mahabhoot and Chapter on Ayurvedic Concepts.

HCG Tests – This is a pregnancy detection kit. It is in the form of a strip to be inserted in a urine sample, or a card, on which a few drop of urine must be placed. The test delivers the result in about three mins. HCG stands for Human Chorionic Gonadotrophin, which is a hormone secreted during pregnancy, made by the embryo, soon after conception takes place. The test strip or card contains anti HCG globulin for detection of the hormone.

Jatee Sutreeya – A chapter from the collected works of the Seer Charak, that deals with conception, pregnancy, childbirth and childcare.

Jeevaniya group of herbs – This is the name given to a category of herbs that are extremely potent and are able to attract life force positively for the patient. They are useful in the rejuvenation of the human body.

Lep – A viscous paste, usually made out of herbs. It is normally thick since it should be able to stay at the applied location on the body for a while.

Kadha – A decoction, normally made of herbs or food products in water or some other liquid carrier like milk or ghee.

Kalpa – A sugar-based medical preparation. Sugar is cooked with an herbal decoction resulting in a granular powder.

Karma – Action

Kartikeya – He is the child of Shiva and Parvati, created to destroy the demon Tarkasur. In Ayurvedic tradtion, prayers are offered to Kartikeya for the protection of the new born child and mother.

Kashyap Samhita – One of the oldest texts of Ayurveda. It deals with gynaecological issues, child bearing and infant care. It has been written by the seer Kashyap.

Kaushalya – Wife of Dashratha, mother of Shri Rama

Khichadi – A simple dish consisting of rice and pulses cooked together until they are softened and easy to digest.

Krishnaleela – The stories of the naughty child Krishna.

Kriya Yog – A set of actions or postures synchronized with breath and mental attitude as part of the practice of Yoga.

Kundalini Massage – A Kundalini massage is a special massage using Santulan Kundalini Oil that works on Kundalini Energy and the spinal cord.

Lactational amenorrhea –The period after child birth when the baby is breast-feeding and the mother's menstrual periods have not re-started.

Madhavnidan – The collected works of the Seer Madhav describing diagnostic procedures for all diseases.

Mahabharata – It can be understood as 'The Great Play of Energy'. It is one of two Indian epics that have iconic and spiritual status in Indian culture. Part history and part universal metaphor for the eternal struggle of mankind, it is a mammoth work of art consisting over a hundred thousand intricately composed verses in Sanskrit. It contains within it the 722 verses of the Shrimad Bhagawad Geeta, the Supreme Song of the Lord, which is the essence and epitome of Indian culture and values. The Mahabharata continues to influence almost every sphere of life in India, from politics to art, from spirituality to social sciences, to this day.

Mantra – A combination of sounds having phonetic values that stimulate specific brain and nervous system activity.

Marma – A marma is an important cross-section on the meridians, which are passages of bio-energy in the body.

Moodhagarbha – The various undesirable positions that a foetus can accidently get into in the womb. These positions can cause various problems and bring difficulties during childbirth.

Muladhar Chakra – The first major energy vortex (chakra) in the body situated at the base of the spine. It is associated with a person's basic existence. After long practice one may be able to visualize it as a golden-yellow square at the base of the spine, and one may become aware of the Cosmic smell. It corresponds to the element of Earth in the body.

Netratarpan - Walls made of dough are built around the eyes and medicated oil or ghee is poured in over the eyes and kept for a while. Very helpful in various eye problems.

Ojas – When sukra dhatu (virya) becomes active, it turns into action, function and light. This is called Ojas.

Padabhyanga – Pada = foot, Abhyanga = massage. This is a foot massage done either with a special medicated ghee or Shatadhauta Ghruta, being rubbed onto the soles of the feet with the outside of a bowl made of 'kansa' (a specific metal amalgam). It is an extremely effective therapy to help remove excess heat from the body and provide strength to the nervous system.

Panchamrut – Can literally be translated as 'the Five Nectars'. It consists of ghee, honey, sugar, curd and milk in specific proportions. See chapter on Special Recipes for details.

Panchakarma – Literally translated as Five Actions. The five major cleansing and rejuvenating actions of Ayurvedic therapy. Please see chapter on Ayurvedic Concepts for more details.

Pancha-mahabhoot – Literally translated as the Five Great Elements (Sources). The five universally recognized elemental forms of matter that make up the entire world viz Earth, Water, Fire, Air (Wind) and Space. Ayurveda, and all ancient Indian science, recognizes that everything in the material world is made up of various combinations of these elements interacting – coming together and moving apart. The dominance and interplay of these elements lends all matter, living and non-living, the unique qualities and 'nature' that they display.

Panchatattva Beejamantra – It refers to the root sounds associated with the various Chakras in the body, that also correspond to the five elements present in Nature. The sound Lam is associated with the 1st chakra and corresponds to the Earth Element. Vam – 2nd chakra, Water Element, Ram – 3rd chakra, Fire Element, Yam – 4th chakra, Air Element, Ham - Ksham – Fifth and Sixth Chakras (chanted together), Space Element. Aum is the seventh and final, denoting pure energy or light.

Paratha - Rolled flat bread of coarse-grained wheat flour cooked on a pan with oil or ghee.

Payas – A sweet, medical rice preparation.

Payasdaan – Refers to when payas was given to Dashrath by Lord Agni after he performed the Putrakameshthi Yadnya.

Prajapati – The knowledge of creation and art of living a healthy was conceived and ultimately made available to the masses through Prajapati.

Prakriti – The constitution or composition of a person's body in relation to Vata, Pitta and Kapha.

Pran – The finest, most subtle, and conscious life-energy that is spread all over the universe. It uses the vehicle of air and oxygen.

Pranayam – A breathing discipline to attract pran.

Pre–eclampsia – High blood pressure induced due to pregnancy is called pre-eclampsia. It is indicated by large amounts of protein present in the pregnant woman's urine.

Prithvi – The Earth Element. One of the Five Universal Elemental Forms that constitute all matter in the universe. See also Pancha-Mahabhoot and Chapter on Ayurvedic Concepts.

Pushya – Nakshatra – One of the 27 constellations of Indian astrology.

Putrakameshti Yadnya – A 'yadnya' is a transformative process that is normally used to evolve matter into higher forms of result-oriented products or energies. The Putrakameshti Yadnya is supposed to help a couple produce ideal progeny.

Raga – A melody with a specific use of notes. It has a minimum of 5 notes while ascending and 5 notes while descending. It offers a change of colour of the mind i.e. a change in mood.

Raj-Kshaya – Scanty menstrual flow.

Rakta dhatu – The result of the second level of energy transformation in the body, beginning from the digestion of food. 'Rakta dhatu' loosely corresponds to 'blood'. Each level of transformation results in a dhatu (dhatus loosely correspond to tissues as understood by western medicine). Please see chapter on Ayurvedic Concepts for more details.

Ramayana – One of two Indian epics that has iconic and spiritual status in Indian culture, it is the story of Shri Rama as an incarnation of the Lord. It occurred about 10,000 years ago. Shri Rama collected the tribes of the land and brought them together, and defeated the traitorous Ravan. Rama is understood as 'Consciousness', Ravan as the 'Ego' and Sita as 'Material' in the philosophy developed and explained in the Shri Rama Vishwapanchayatan by Dr. Shri Balaji Tambe.

Rasayan – a preparation made from sevral herbal and medicinal products that helps rejuvenate the whole body, or a specific process in the body. It is extremely important that rasayans are made exactly according to scientific Ayurvedic processes.

Sahasradhar Chakra – The uppermost energy vortex (chakra) in the body at the crown centre of the head. It is pure energy or pure light.

Saindhav – Salt obtained from rocks that have their origin in the sea.

Shashti Shali Lahya – also called 'Shashti Shashti Shali Lahya'. Puffed rice. It can be eaten by itself, with milk or in various other forms like chiwda. Only a particular strain of rice, called 'Sixty Day Rice', is used to make Shashti Shali Lahya

Sanskar – Ancient Indian traditional systems were built around natural phenomena that occurred both within the body and in the external environment. Though they are seen as traditional or religious rituals today, they have a deep therapeutic value. Their effects over thousands of years have shaped life in the Indian subcontinent. This effect, along with the adherence to these traditions in the present day, are both called Sanskar.

Santulan Ayurveda – The registered brand name for the Ayurvedic teaching, products and lifestyle practiced at the Atmasantulana Village and designed by Dr. Shri Balaji Tambe.

Satsang – Literally translated as 'to be with Truth' or 'study in person. Discussions about gaining true spiritual knowledge done in person (being present) are called 'Satsang'.

Sattvik, Rajasik, Tamasik – These are the three major tendencies that pervade/motivate all action in the universe.

Sattvik – that which acts without expectation of result

Rajasik – that which acts with expectation of result

Tamasik – that which expects a result without action

Sharangdhar Sanhita – The collected medical works of the Seer Sharangdhar that deal with pharmacology. 'Sanhita' means 'collected works'.

Shatadhauta Ghruta – Ghee – Literally, it means, 'Ghee that has been washed a hundred times.' Pure ghee is put into a copper or 'kansa' (a particular metal amalgam) pot. Water is mixed with the ghee. This mixture is then stirred against the sides of the pot in a circular motion (the hands make one hundred circles while stirring). This is called one 'wash'. The water is drained and fresh water is added, and the process repeated one hundred times. The resulting ghee is called Shatadhauta Ghruta.

Shivcharitra – the biography and character sketch of the great Maratha warrior-king Shivaji.

Shloka – Verses made with Sanskrit poetic rules.

Shiro basti – Special medicated oil is poured into a well (formed of dough) on the head. The oil is then required to stay there for a specific time. Very helpful in brain and nervous disorders.

Shirodhara – An Ayurvedic therapy in which a small and steady stream of medicated oil is dripped on to the forehead for a specific period of time. This therapy is extremely effective in all cases of mental or stress related disorders.

Shri Adi Shankaracharya – The great ancient Seer who re-invigorated the Vedic way of life. He has authored hundreds of stotras in Sanskrit that have great therapeutic value and that are still in use for the purpose of healing many disorders. Shri Adi Shankaracharya travelled the length and breadth of the Indian subcontinent in a herculean effort to raise socio-religious practices to their original higher aim of self-knowledge through a natural way of life.

Shri Krishna – The avatar of the Lord Himself, and the centrifugal force of the Mahabharata, who delivered the Shrimad Bhagawad Geeta to Mankind.

Shri Rama – The avatar of the Lord Himself, Ideal Son, King, Brother, Husband, Friend and Devotee – Best among all Men.

Shri Rama Vishwapanchayatan – The understanding and decoding of the Ramayana for day-to-day life developed and written by Dr. Shri Balaji Tambe.

Sita – Wife of Shri Rama, daughter of King Janaka. She was found in the Earth while ploughing the fields.

Subhadra – Sister of Shri Krishna, wife of Arjuna, mother of Abhimanyu.

Supari – Supari is the Indian name for the betel nut, which, in many places in India is the main ingredient in a digestive mixture and mouth freshener. But 'supari' has now become the generic name for mouth freshener mixtures. The supari mentioned in this book (see Special Recipes) contains no betel nut.

Sushrut Samhita – One of the oldest literatures in Ayurveda written by Acharya Sushrut. The Sushrut Samhita deals with the subject of surgery.

Sushrut Sharirsthan – An part of the medical canon of the Seer Sushrut that deals with anatomy.

Swadhishthan Chakra – The second major energy vortex (chakra) in the body situated in the lower abdomen, a little to the left of the spinal cord. It is associated with a person's sensibilities. After long practice one may be able to visualize it as a It is represented as a silver crescent. It corresponds to the element of Water in the body.

Tantra – Literally translated as a 'technique' or 'mechanism' - a scientific technique, normally used to deal with the plane beyond the physical plane.

Thalassemia – Is a condition in which the body produces an abnormal form of haemoglobin. In thalassemia the body's red blood cells are destroyed in excess, leading to anemia and other problems. Thalassemia is almost always an inherited disorder.

Triphala – A mixture of three fruits - amla, hirda and behada. It is a preparation that helps to balance all three doshas.

Uttar-basti – Basti administered through the vagina into the uterus. Please see 'Basti' for more details.

Uttar-dhoop – Dhoop administered to the genital area. Please see 'dhoop' for more details.

Vagbhat, Acharya – He is one of the authors of ancient Ayurvedic literature. He has written the Ashtangahruday and Ashtangasangraha. These treatises cover subjects across all eight branches of Ayurveda.

Vaidya – An Ayurvedic physician.

Valkal – The bark of a tree used as a dress for covering the body.

Vaman – One of the Pancha Karma (five cleansing actions of Ayurvedic therapy) techniques. It enables toxins collected due to kapha dosha to leave the body with emetics. It is one of the most effective therapies to help pacify kapha dosha.

Vastu Shastra – The Indian science of architecture and space design.

Vayu – The Air (Wind) Element. One of the Five Universal Elemental Forms that constitute all matter in the universe. See also Pancha-Mahabhoot and Chapter on Ayurvedic Concepts.

Vedas – It is the science of life. While they are generally referred to as the four Vedas, three are principal. These are the Rig, Yajur and Sama. The Atharva is the fourth.

Veena – A kind of string instrument that is considered very evolved and whose sounds are supposed to have penetrating properties. It is the musical instrument held by the Goddess Saraswati and Narada, the Sage responsible for mass communication and media. The character of Sage Narada brings information to all three levels of beings – humans, demons and gods. He has access to all private areas and can appear and disappear at will, bringing the latest news to all quarters. Since he brings current news, he is said to be devoted to the 'present'.

Veera Rasa – The mood of the mind that allows the entire body to have energy and protect oneself and others.

Virechan – One of the Pancha Karma (five cleansing actions of Ayurvedic therapy) techniques. It is a medical laxative that helps enables toxins collected dur to pitta dosha to leave the body. It is one of the most effective therapies to help pacify pitta and vata doshas.

Virya – It is generally understood as seminal fluid, but actually it is life energy in liquid form, and the seventh level of transformation of digested food.

Vyanavayu – The most powerful of the pancha-pran (five life forces). It has a seat in the heart and is responsible for circulation all over the body, particularly in the narrow peripheries (fingers, toes etc.)

Yoganidra – A deep relaxation technique that takes the mind towards the inner self and consciousness. It has been designed to help de-stress and refresh the body and mind, and to help develop creativity.

Yogasana – Special postures prescribed by Hathayoga, a science developed by the Seer Patanjali.

Music published by Dr. Shri Balaji Tambe

Holistic Healing for Body, Mind and Soul

Santulan (Om) Meditation

A daily prayer compilation, that consists of meditation and the chanting of Aum. Good for physical and mental health and spiritual practice. Brings a sense of joy, well being, prosperity and peace in day-to-day life. Includes Datta Bavani for astral healing.

Learn to Meditate

A guided audio CD for learning Santulan Om Meditation. 'SOM'.

Yoga Nidra I

For Meditation and Peace. Healing music for spiritual practice. It helps purify the subtle bodies and brings mental peace.

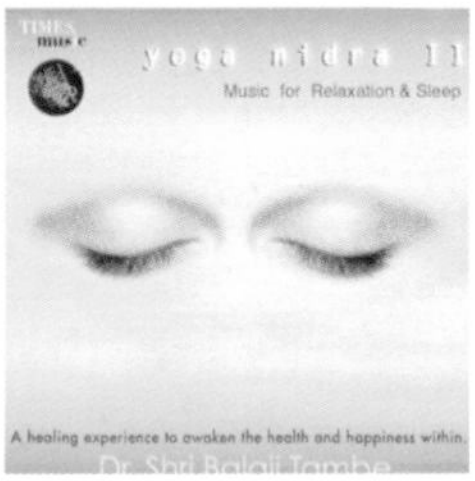

Yoga Nidra II

For Relaxation and Sleep. Healing music for that relieves stress. It brings deep sleep, cleanses the effect of negative dreams and helps bring success in day-to-day life.

Stree Santulan (Feminine Balance)

Healing music for women. It helps with gynecological problems like irregular menstrual cycles and hormonal imbalance. It brings peace of mind. Includes selected compositions and Vedic mantras, based on scientific studies.

Garbha Sanskar

Wellness music for pregnancy. Compositions that encourage the proper growth and development of the foetus. Helps the child to develop good memory and intelligence. Gives a sense of protection to the foetus and the expectant mother.

The Healing Sounds of Mahashakti Durga

Helps to remove, and protect one from, all negative energies. Includes the Tripurasundari-stotram and the Mahishasuramardini-stotram.

The Healing Sounds of Shri Dattatreya

Helps recovery from diseases, removes suffering. Helps to receive Lord Shri Dattatreya's Grace. Includes stotras written by H. H. Shri Vasudevananda Saraswati (Tembe Swami).

Spirit of Harmony

Helps to reduce stress, calms the mind and is good for relaxation. It leads to sound sleep and creates a joyful atmosphere. Recommended for patients of hypertension, diabetes and heart diseases.

Samruddhi

The Healing Sounds of Shri Mahalakshmi.

Promotes prosperity at all levels. Includes Shri Lakshmi-stotram, Annapurna-strotram and Shri Mahalakshmyashtakam etc.

Dawn to Dusk

Healing Music for the whole day in different ragas. Includes mantras, stotras and bhajans.

Shiva

The Healing Sounds of Lord Shiva.

Brings a sense of protection and encourages the listener towards Liberation. Includes Shivatandava-stotram, Shivastuti, Shivashtakam, Shivapanchaksharatotram etc.

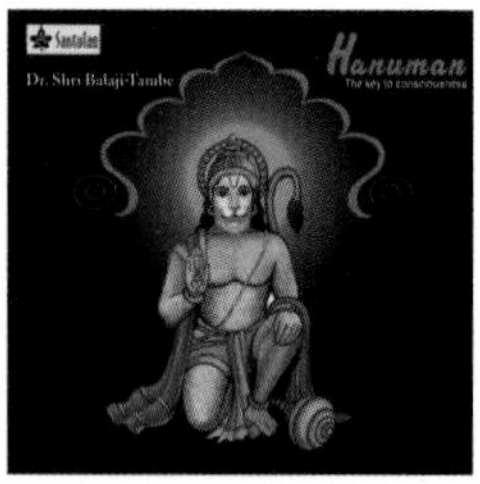

Hanuman

Helps conquer fears and protects one from negative energies. Includes Shri Ramaraksha and the Hanuman Chalisa. Recommended for people suffering from allergies, skin conditions and patients of any heart and lung diseases.

Vitality

Live Performances of Healing Music from Dr. Shri Balaji Tambe's European concert tour. Includes bhajans like Mara Mana Madiriya Maahya, He Pinjare Ki & Shiradiwale Sain Piya.

Devotion

Live Peformances of Healing Music by Dr. Shri Balaji Tambe, presented at the annual Gurupournima seminar in Karla. Includes bhajans/stotras like Datta Dayeche, Re Mana Laga, Guru Ghara Aavya, Shiva-panchakshrastotram.

Aumkar Ganesh

For an energising start to your day. Includes Atharvashisha, Mayureshpratahsmaran, He Dayanidhe

Maha Arti

Eleven of the most popular and effective Artis and daily shlokas. A must for every house during any celebration. Includes Jay Jagdish Hare, Sukhakarta Dukhharta, Gayatri Mantra and Mantrapushpanjali.

Devi Chants

Authentic mantras from the Tantric Tradition. Secret sounds to evoke Mahashakti - the Supreme Energy to bring Protection, Prosperity and Spiritual progress. Includes Shrisuktam, Devi Stotram and Devisuktam

Many more cassettes and CD albums from Dr. Shri Balaji Tambe are also available.

Books published by Dr. Shri Balaji Tambe

Ayurvediya Garbhasanskar

Marathi

Gujarati

Santulan Kriya Yog

(Also in Marathi as Santulan Kriyayog)

Simple and extremely effective daily yoga exercises designed by Dr. Shri Balaji Tambe using some of the secret high energy techniques favoured by Yoga Masters. These exercises have specially been designed so that everyone, from children to the aged, and even those with serious illnesses, can practice these everyday. The book contains detailed instructions for yogasanas as well advice for specific ailments, and daily yoga regimen.

Peacock Feathers I

(Also in Marathi as 'Shri Geeta Yog Shodh Brahmavidyecha Parts 1,2 and 3)

Peacock Feathers is an ongoing series of 18 books on the Shrimad Bhagawad Geeta, one book for each chapter. Dr. Shri Balaji Tambe brings to bear his unique and insightful perspective on the Geeta in this detailed, beginner level commentary. The first book, on the first chapter, talks about Arjun's basic conflict, which is our own – his inability to decide how to act.

Peacock Feathers II

The 2nd of 18 books on the Shrimad Bhagawad Geeta, based on the second chapter. Dr. Shri Balaji Tambe continues his discerning and intuitive commentary on the Geeta.

Ayurvedic Home Remedies

(Also in Marathi as Ayurvedic Gharguti Upchar)

Ayurveda has a host of remedies for several ailments right out of your kitchen cabinet. Simple, effective and natural, these remedies have no side effects and can be administered without medical consultation.

Shri Ram Vishwapanchayatan

(Marathi) [Also in Gujarati as Aatma Ramayan]

Decoding the characters and message of the Ramayan so that we can apply its lessons to modern life. Dr. Shri Balaji Tambe uncovers the nature of action and evolution hidden in the Ramayan. Perhaps the one commentary on the Ramayan that can actually be applied and experienced.

Chakra Sudarshan

(Marathi)

The chakra system in the human body works from the physical to the subtlest levels of existence. Dr. Shri Balaji Tambe has demystified the chakras and explained how and why they work. He has also developed a system whereby one can work on the chakra system in simple ways as part of daily life to realize their benefits to the maximum.

Ayurved Uvach Parts 1 and 2

(Marathi)

Ayurveda like it is taught at school, but simplified even further for the common person. You do not need any prior knowledge of medicine to understand this engaging introduction to basic Ayurvedic principles.

Mantra Jeevanacha

Collections of Dr Shri Balaji Tambe's writings from the weekly 'Family Doctor' supplement of Sakal, Maharashtra's leading Marathi newspaper. In this book Dr Shri Balaji Tambe deals with lifestyle issues in his inimitable way, bringing to the fore how simple practices and habits can dramatically improve your life.

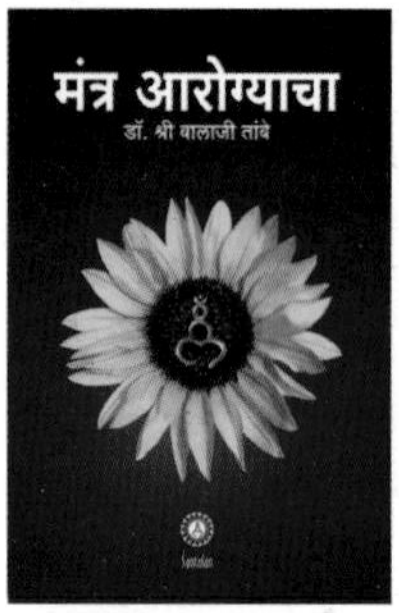

Mantra Aarogyacha

Collected from Dr Shri Balaji Tambe's medical writings in 'Family Doctor', a weekly supplement of Maharashtra's leading Marathi newspaper, Sakal. In this book Dr Shri Balaji Tambe focuses on several serious illnesses, and in his lucid and often humorous manner explains in great detail how one should prevent or deal with such potentially life threatening situations and lead a normal life in spite of them.